Para mi amigo
José MacGaheran

Con mis recuerdos —

Bertita Leonarz de Harding

ROYAL PURPLE

ROYAL PURPLE

THE STORY OF

ALEXANDER AND DRAGA

OF SERBIA

By

BERTITA HARDING

Author of *Phantom Crown*

"History is an Art and
should be written with
imagination."
—*Anatole France*

THE BOBBS-MERRILL COMPANY

PUBLISHERS

INDIANAPOLIS   NEW YORK

To my gentle father

— Don EMILIO LEONARZ —

CONTENTS

CONTENTS — *Continued*

ROYAL PURPLE

PART ONE
SASHA

ROYAL PURPLE

CHAPTER I

Nursery Nights

THE child awoke. His small black eyes pierced the darkness and he knew he was alone. There should have been a faint strip of light under the door, near the foot of his bed, but he could not find it. His mother slept behind that door, yet he had always felt that she didn't really sleep—she just lived beyond the narrow strip of light watching over his safety, protecting him against bad dreams or the violent temper of his father.

Why was there no light behind that door?

Then, suddenly, he remembered. She was gone. Quite swiftly she had stepped out of his life. . . . She was not dead, though. He recalled her wet eyes, swollen and red with tears, as she had kissed him. "Good-by, my Sasha! I am going to a strange country for a little while, but you will grow up and come to see me." He had sobbed aloud at these words, for it seemed to him that waiting to grow up would last forever and he couldn't go that long without seeing her again. But his father had frowned darkly and picked up the child in his strong arms. "Goodby, Natalia," he had said to Sasha's mother; "this is the end."

Since then there was no light under that door, and waking up in the night became agony. The room, so cheerful in the daytime with its nursery pictures and

13

bright painted walls, changed into a terrifying place. Ugly menacing figures lurked in the shadows and the white curtain at the window billowed in great animated waves until it actually breathed.

If only he could find the way to Anya's room without waking his father! Once in the warm comforting arms of his nurse, he would be safe; Papa never scolded Anya, for the old woman had held even him on her knees long before Sasha was born.

It was queer to think of Papa as a little boy. Yet Anya was there to prove it. She had wiped his nose and changed his linen and—when Papa was very small—she had given him milk. The milk came out of Anya. Sasha was intrigued and almost jealous, for only recently he too had wanted to try Anya's milk but the old woman had shrieked with ribald laughter: "Not at my time and age! Go mind your porridge, my lamb——"

All the same, Anya loved him. Oh, he knew Anya loved him. And in these empty days since Mama was gone he needed that love. He needed someone to shield him against those horrible noises across the corridor, the fearsome snorting of a dragon whose breath was flame— though Sasha knew it was only his father snoring because, he had been told, Papa ate too much at night and that was bad for him. Strange, how Papa liked doing things that were bad for him and bad for everyone else. He cuffed the servants and spat on the white carpet in Mama's lovely boudoir. Yet if Sasha spat only into the fish pond Papa cuffed Sasha.

The child brooded in the dark. He sat up among the bedclothes and listened. It was always a good plan to hold your ears shut. He was about to do so when he

discovered that there was nothing to be heard. Not a
sound—no dragon, no horrible snorting—just stillness.
Utter stillness. But this was worse; this was indeed
calamity! Where were they? Where had everybody
gone? Why didn't Papa snore?

It was forbidden to cry out for Anya. Grown-ups
never allowed a small boy to be a coward. He must not
call. He must not cry. He must not—must not——

"Anya!"

The name burst from him in a great choking sob. He
stood at the foot of his bed clutching the brass frame.
Under the long nightshirt his chubby body shook violently. Had someone heard him? Were they coming? He
would be punished for this, but that didn't matter. He
couldn't help himself, he just couldn't stand the loneliness,
the blackness of his room, the silence——

From the corridor came a muffled voice and the sound
of rapid steps. Almost instinctively the child's eager
form shrank back. Papa! But no, the steps were light
and soft; tender, lovable steps, steps that Sasha wanted
now to hug—Anya's steps. The door opened and in
the pale light of a candle stub there appeared the disheveled figure of a wrinkled matron. With wild strands of
gray hair escaping from her sleeping bonnet and the loose
bands of a faded bed-jacket trailing behind her, the creature looked not unlike a witch out of Sasha's own story
books. But the child saw only Anya, beloved Anya. He
flew into her arms. She sat down on the bed, placing the
candle on a near-by mantel, and held the boy against her
withered breast.

"There, my angel," she said, and her words quieted
him, "my little cub—can dreams be as bad as all that?"

"I didn't dream," he protested, for the admission of bad dreams (to grown-ups who miraculously did not seem to have them) humiliated him.

The old nurse looked startled. "But if it wasn't a dream, Sashino, then why did you scream for Anya?"

"Was it loud?" he asked, appalled.

She nodded her head emphatically. "So loud, it woke the Russian Ambassador across the square."

He became frightened again and stared in horror toward the open door. "It was because I couldn't hear Papa——" He began to blubber.

It seemed then as if the old nurse held him more closely. "Well, there's nothing wrong with that, is there? Papa is probably fast asleep, and that's exactly what silly boys should be doing instead of disturbing the peace at this hour of night."

"But I always *hear* Papa sleep," insisted the child in a cautious whisper, "and now—listen—he makes no noises at all!"

Placing fat little hands on her bony cheeks he turned Anya's face toward the gloomy corridor, anxiously proving his point. But the nurse remained evasive. She possessed that irritating quality all adult people had in common. She changed the subject, thereby dismissing, as everyone did, some of Sasha's most important ideas.

"Now, my princelet," she murmured in a noncommittal tone, "back to bed with you, and no more pranks. Do you hear?"

He knew she would leave him as he was always being left, after some ineffectual punching of pillows and tugging at coverlets—as if a crease in the blanket ever mattered to anyone. Grown-ups did contrive to be bothersome.

"No, no, Anya," he pleaded desperately, "don't go away."

"But Anya can't sit here without so much as a cloak about her chilly shoulders."

The child thought fast and strenuously. "I know," he exclaimed, "you get into bed with me; then you won't be cold." He was delighted with the scheme and felt certain that she could not resist. But Anya's face grew solemn.

"No," she said in an almost awed tone, "Anya must go back where she belongs."

Panic returned and tightened his throat. "Then take me with you," he begged, hugging her thin neck. "And Anya," (he hoped that flattery might go farther than pleading), "I'll sleep at once if you sing *Stjenka Rasin*——"

The old nurse shrugged her shoulders helplessly and picked up the candle. With the child clinging to her she shuffled clumsily from the room. In the dim corridor all was still. Even now there came no sound from Papa's room. Anya was walking fast, and as she walked her dry lips softly formed the words of the ancient Slav tune:

> *"Over the steppes rode Stjenka Rasin,*
> *Up the wild river he plied his barge. . . ."*

Sasha's big round head bobbed happily against her starched bonnet. He did not think much of Anya's singing but he felt that his ruse had worked. She was taking him to her own room in the cozily peopled servants' wing.

She was bearing him to safety, away from that which was always with him—fear.

They sped along, and as they sped, it seemed that the old woman's voice grew a trifle louder, the rhythm of her song more pronounced. Anya's chamber was not far from the nursery, but by the time the domestic quarters were reached the ballad of *Stjenka Rasin* had mounted to a high quaver. And now they crossed a little stoop at the top of which a door could be barely distinguished. With the toe of her beaded slipper Anya gave a muffled shove to the oak panel. The door swung back lazily, admitting the nurse and her small burden. Sasha's eyes were already heavy with sleep, so he spoke only half-consciously to a fat Croatian girl who rose from her cot as the two entered.

"Anya brought me," he made a vague attempt at explaining this extraordinary visit, "and you go back to sleep, Nushka."

The girl looked thoroughly alarmed. Turning to the older woman, she took the candle from her hand and hurriedly covered it with a shade.

"*Bog* (God)——" she faltered, "the child! Anya, how could you? I heard you shouting all the way—what if someone——?"

"And who is there to stop me, I should like to ask?"

Defiantly the nurse threw back her head the while she drew up a low rocking chair and sat down. She held the boy on her lap, bedding his head against the lean angle of her arm. The child's eyes had closed in peaceful slumber.

"Who is there to stop me?" Anya repeated. "After the *Gospodar* (Master) himself is gone—nobody!"

Curiosity burned in the younger woman's eyes. "Has he crossed the border, do you suppose?"

Anya's mouth twitched fiercely. "If he knows what's good for him he has. 'Tis treachery, I admit, to talk ill of them we serve—but the way that man treated his wife, no human being ought to turn a hand for him, that's my opinion. And to think that I held him in my arms before ever he could walk!"

Nushka was astonished at this flow of words from her usually taciturn companion. She threw out a little bait, hoping to hear more. "I notice people saying that those two might make up, now he's followed her into exile. It wouldn't surprise me if they did."

"Not if I know Natalia Kesko. She may be stupid, but I don't believe she'd be a glutton for any more of his abuse. As it is, if she had any backbone she wouldn't be moping around foreign parts right now. . . . Letting him take the baby, while she runs off screaming that her husband beat her! . . . We were all on her side. She should have stayed and had *him* driven out of town, if I do say it, that's what she should have done." Anya was forced to pause for breath. "The Police, the Army, the Church—everybody would have helped her. But no, there was no spirit in her. She crawled before that tyrant Milan and even gave up her little son——"

Vehemently the old nurse clutched the sleeping bundle on her knees. Her legs had grown numb and she surveyed the room speculatively with a view to greater comfort. Yet, to put the boy on a servant bed would never do. He was heavy, and very likely her brittle shanks would never be the same, but she decided to remain in the rocker, watching over his sleep until morning.

The girl they called Nushka stretched huge arms before stumbling toward her cot. "Well," she mumbled drowsily, "now the Army's done it. When the Army doesn't want a man, he's through!" She turned suddenly to stare at the recumbent child. Her face jerked with that eloquence of gesture which peasants alone command. "Does he—with all that racket earlier in the evening—does the little whelp know?"

The other shook her head. "Of course not," she snapped. "His Nibs was in such a hurry there could be no time for so much as a 'by your leave' to anybody."

Nushka sank down on the edge of the cot, methodically propelling her vast frame under the rumpled bedclothes. "It's a shame," she mused with sincerity. "The poor kid doesn't realize what's ahead of him. A bunch of old men'll take him in hand, I suppose, and when they've done educating him till he hasn't any sense left they'll give him his chance at the throne. A fine chance—if there are any Black Georges around! And in this country there's a *Cerny* George under every pepper tree." She belched unexpectedly and suffered a change of thought. "Won't have so much to do around the place now, will we? That old rascal's habits—well, he wasn't exactly what you'd want to call a lily, not by a long shot he wasn't." She chuckled significantly to herself and drew the quilted coverlet up to her chin. In a few moments the room resounded indecorously with the deep puffs of her breathing.

In the citron glow of a dying candle Anya sat rocking the child. Softly she crooned the ancient folk song, moving slowly to and fro. Once she stopped and gazed for a long time at the round head that rested upon her breast. Her lips parted into a proud smile, her eyes shone.

"Ziveo, Alexander Obrenovitch!" she breathed with a strange passion. "Hail Alexander, son of the Obrenos!"

The child lay peacefully in her lap. The ghost of a smile played also on his pouting lips. Gently she rocked him to and fro, to and fro, trembling a little with excitement. For, since midnight—when his father and the royal boon companions had evacuated the palace—this unsuspecting boy was king over the Serbian people. In Anya's eyes, at least. That there might be some difficulty in obtaining from the fugitive a formal renunciation of his rights she could not guess. That there might be, in other quarters, a rival for her beloved Sasha's claims she would not admit.

What of that Karageorgevitch rabble? (They were called *Cerny* Georges by Nushka, but Anya had been born near the capital and scorned provincial dialects.) What of those hawk-faced sons of the Black Georges? She laughed at them. For in her arms she held at this moment, sacred and predestined, the anointed head of the nation!

CHAPTER II

PAST AND PRESENT

DESPITE the old nurse's sanguine prognostications, almost four years elapsed before King Milan penned his formal abdication. In the futile hope that he might yet be recalled, the canny monarch lingered near the Croat border, temporizing and procrastinating until even the international press dismissed him for more trenchant news items. At Potsdam the Emperor Frederick III was dying of cancer of the larynx while a young Wilhelm II preened for the office of German Kaiser. In the little hunting lodge at Mayerling, Marie Vetsera and Austria's Crown Prince, the Archduke Rudolf, kept a rendezvous with death. In short, the year 1889 was well along before the truculent Obreno signed the obnoxious document of his renunciation. He did so only after somebody had the bright idea of cutting off the royal allowance, thus forcing the monarch to come to terms.

Long before this the *Skupchina* (Serbian House of Parliament) had regarded Milan's departure as a *de facto* abdication and settled the problem of state control. On an early morning in 1886 the legislative body had held a mass meeting which would decide two vital issues. Would the country, after its dismal experience with royalty, revert to an earlier feudal system in which brigand chieftains vied with one another for supremacy the while they exhausted the nation's resources? Or would Serbia, like Rumania, Bulgaria, Greece, be forced one day to exile her robber barons and implore some English or German dynasty to provide her with a nominal sovereign who, transplanted from his own soil, could never become the father of a Balkan people? No, on one point the wrangling patriots agreed. Let Stirbys, Mavro-Cordatos (Black Hearts), Cantacuzenes give way to Hohenzollern candidates at Bucharest; let Coburg cousins don the purple in Sofia, Danish princes rule at Athens. But Serbia, the only Balkan race with a legitimate dynasty of its own, would remain too proud for that. Serbia still had valiant *haidukes* (a curious blend of hero-bandits) who could force a choice to be made among them. Borrowed masters from western Europe? Not while this small realm cherished the heritage of its great history.

And what a history! Few are the nations that can flaunt a more dramatic past. As far back as the year 638 A. D. a nomad tribe of Slavic huntsmen (who called themselves *Srbs)* had wandered from the east across Carpathian mountain peaks and settled in the valley of the lower Danube. Here they dwelt as a freedom-loving patriarchal society until the time of one Stepan Nemanya, who rose from their midst to proclaim them a federation of states—under himself as Tsar. This step marked the beginning, in 1159, of the Rascian dynasty under which Serbia pushed her way into the front rank among semi-Byzantine nations. There followed years of growth and prosperity culminating, during the thirteenth and fourteenth centuries, in a veritable golden age. The glorious young Tsar Dushan held sway not only in the fertile Sava River basin, but over Macedon, Bulgaria, *Cernagora* (Montenegro) and northern Greece.

Slavdom's splendor aroused the envy of the Turk. Soon

after Dushan's death Ottoman raiders fell upon the mourning land. Sultan Murad (Amurath I) descended with his Janizaries as far as the plain of Kossovo where the new Tsar Lazar confronted him. All Europe trembled before the terrible Moslem. Volunteers arrived in droves from Bosnia, Herzegovina, Croatia, Slavonia, Slovenia, Dalmatia, Italy, Germany, France, to aid the Serbian Emperor in his darkest hour. Apart from the allies, Tsar Lazar sacrificed one hundred thousand men in battle. The slaughter lasted twelve days with their nights, during which the entire Serbian nobility perished. Lazar himself fell captive and was beheaded, whereupon his son-in-law, Milosh Obilitch, galloped at dawn into the Turkish camp to kill the Sultan in his tent. But individual feats of heroism could not stem the hordes that poured across the Hellespont, thrice outnumbering their victims. By the end of 1389 the whole Balkan Peninsula lay crushed under the Scimitar.

For centuries Serbia remained a tributary *pashalik* of the Ottoman empire, forming a stronghold for the Crescent in its march across Central Europe. It was a long historic Calvary, punctuated by the fall of Constantinople into the hands of Sultan Mohammed II (called the "Conqueror"), the siege of Vienna and Budapest by Suleyman (the "Magnificent"), and the Venetian exploits of Selim II. Again and again the Western world produced a champion to defy the Infidel: Prince Eugene of Savoy . . . Hungary's Hunyadi János . . . Lepanto's Don John of Austria. . . .

But for Serbia nothing changed. The Moslem dagger was planted in her entrails, ready, if anything, to strike more deeply still.

And then, in 1804—after interminable years—the astounding thing came to pass. From the mountain fastnesses to the south of Belgrade there emerged, not one, but two ardent liberators who vowed that it was their mission to put ancient Serbia back on her feet. A double Messiah! Then the prayers of well-nigh four centuries had been answered, the *pyesmé* (song-poems) lamenting the immortal disaster of Kossovo had not been handed down in vain. For, if national consciousness could survive under so grim a yoke, the spirit of a beaten race must rise again and live. Hail to the saviors, whoever they might be!

As it happened, they were a pair of swineherds at cross-purposes with each other. Both intended to make a eunuch of the Sultan, but neither wanted collaboration in the matter. Each planned to redeem Tsar Dushan's gilded throne and hoped to seat himself upon it, even if to do so he must cut the other's throat.

Quite apart from any similarity in their tactics, the absolute parallel of their professions—which in the vassal Serbia of that day enjoyed immense prestige—qualified both aspirants for a spectacular career. They were tired of agriculture and had taken up banditry on a large (and, since they robbed Turks) patriotic scale. In their respective communities they were looked upon as *haidukes*.

By far the more swaggering of the brace was George, son of Peter, from the village of Tapolja near Belgrade. Swarthy of countenance, baneful in his wrath, he was referred to in the Ottoman tongue as *Kara* (the Black One). A scourge to Moslems, he was likewise no ray of sunshine to his family, having slaughtered a father and an elder brother who, by reason of priority, stood in his way.

Milosh, son of the Obreno clan, possessed a less lurid record. Although a raw mountaineer, he claimed to have descended from that Prince Obilitch who had avenged the decapitated Tsar Lazar. Serbian titles being long extinct, no one could disprove these doubtful pretensions. At any rate, Milosh Obrenovitch stuck to his story. What was more, he drew a moral from it and, though slightly inverting the order, caused history to repeat itself. On a hot summer day, when the affair between him and the Black George Petrovitch had reached a crucial point, the latter goaded his rival to fight it out. Milosh, slow and clumsy, was not in favor of single combat, but he had no choice. He was nervous, nay, craven. And so, before the signal for battle had been given, he advanced blindly upon the challenger and—spurred on by panic—put his knife through the Black One's gullet. Having up to this time killed nothing but pigs, the experience somewhat upset him. But not for long. Drunk with triumph, he hit upon an extraordinary idea. Mounting his horse, he rode off to the Golden Horn, with the gory head stuffed into a saddle bag as a present for the Sultan. This visit to a common enemy, who had inspired the duel in the first place, he was forever after unable to explain.

Thoughtfulness is seldom left unrewarded. The Grand Vizier of the Sublime Porte took charge of the souvenir (which needed embalming) and in turn presented the bearer with an oriental grant. Milosh Obrenovitch was made *Voyvode* or governor of the province of Serbia, both office and title being hereditary.

A second and a third Milosh followed in the footsteps

of this ancestor before revenge struck from the camp of
the Karageorgevitch. The Obrenos were calling themselves princes by now, although they continued to take
orders from the Bosporus. It was Milosh III, united in
childless wedlock to the Hungarian Countess Julia
(known in her Viennese youth as "Juppy") Hunyadi,
who expiated the ancient feud. He was assassinated on
June 10, 1868, and succeeded by the son of his brother
Jefrenn.

The Crimean War had meanwhile driven the Turks
from the Danube Valley. Prince Milosh IV saw himself
consequently in control of a compact and independent little country, too small for dreams of empire, yet decidedly
monarchical in scope. He resolved to clarify his position
before the rest of the world. In 1882, after Latinizing
his name, he ascended Dushan's throne as *Kralj* (King)
Milan I of Serbia.

And now a strange metamorphosis took place. Under
the dazzling spell of ermine and crown, the erstwhile
simple-minded, sturdy mountain lord degenerated rapidly
into a knave. He gorged shamefully at banquet tables and
displayed other appetites which made his palace, the
Konak, unsafe for the Queen's ladies. He strutted over-
bearingly the while he picked his teeth in the presence of
Paris and Downing Street diplomats, deriding their gov-
ernments in sound expletives and committing numberless
blunders of equally boorish nature. The climax was
finally reached when, armed with a pair of shoe trees, he
stormed after a foolish and intimidated wife, driving her
in screams from the royal apartments. A king who
ejected his consort under such scandalous circumstances
proved intolerable even to the operatic Balkans. Scenes

which drew applause behind musical comedy footlights
were, after all, impractical in a realistic world. And so,
after several hectic years during which Milan juggled the
scepter, maltreated his retinue, and generally mismanaged
the tiny realm, his subjects flatly dismissed him.

The operation was performed with neat dispatch. General Cincar-Marko, President of the Ministry which had
placed the crown on the unworthy Milan's brow, promptly
undid the damage. His Majesty was given a depressing
alternative—banishment into exile, or a peremptory court-
martial. The tempestuous monarch chose that which
undoubtedly benefited his health. He departed by a convenient train (the very next, to be exact) for one of the
less frequented saline resorts in Austria.

In his disreputable wake there remained the acute question of legal succession. According to monarchic principle the infant Crown Prince, Alexander, automatically
assumed his father's title. But there were those in the
Skupchina who condemned the whole Obrenovitch experiment and recanted from all precepts which supported this
mistaken cause.

"Gentlemen," the conservative Cincar-Marko pleaded
from the speaker's rostrum, "we shall be the laughing-
stock of Europe if our laws do not prevail in this, our
first dynastic crisis. Simply because one member of the
Obreno house proved poor material for kingship we cannot overthrow the Constitution and risk a similar fiasco
with candidates from the opposition! Young Prince Alexander comes to a rightful inheritance which none may
challenge. On the contrary, true Serbians should rejoice
that in this unformed child it will be our privilege to
develop the very qualities men most revere in the head of

a nation. Qualities which, I assure you, we cannot hope
to find embodied by unscrupulous adult applicants."

There was a moment of spontaneous applause cut short
by a sudden protest from an upper balcony where sat the
junior army officers' corps.

"If, as our Minister-President says, we are not yet done
with the admirable Obrenos, I suggest that the Queen be
recalled and welcomed by a handkerchief committee
charged to wipe away her wifely tears!"

The speaker, fiery and daring though he appeared to be,
was a pale young man with a short black mustache. He
glared savagely from his vantage point down to the trib-
une below, apparently indifferent to the commotion
aroused by his brash act. General Cincar-Marko calmly
returned the officer's stare.

"You take liberties, Captain Dmitriyevitch, at a time
when jokes are out of place."

The man in the balcony bristled and broke into a
hoarse laugh. Jokes! Who was joking? "If an under-
sized boy is to rule over Serbia," he countered obstinately,
"we might as well submit to the whims of hysterical
females——"

There was chuckling among the listeners, and here and
there a half-uttered exclamation of, "Bravo, Dragutin
Dmitri!" or, "That Officers' Corps is a firebrand!"

Cincar-Marko lashed his pointed beard with angry
strokes. "A queen," he replied icily, "does not, to my
knowledge, exist. Milan himself divorced Natalia Kesko
before his own abdication. Captain Dmitriyevitch seems
unaware of the incongruity in his proposal."

"Correction sustained," the voice from the gallery
mocked again. "And so it will behoove us to spend

the next half-dozen years playing soldiers with little Sasha!"

Enraged, the General smashed his gavel against the paneled rostrum. "You will oblige this assembly by leaving at once," he thundered. "Report at headquarters before noon to answer charges of *lèse-majesté*. The dignity of King Alexander the First of Serbia will be upheld by"—he paused briefly, in search of a vital idea—"by—a council of regents!"

The words struck with authority. There stirred through the audience an unmistakable murmur of response, as if any plan that seemed half-way practicable would meet with instant approbation. Aware that iron was malleable only while hot, the speaker pursued his advantage.

"Gentlemen," he raised his voice to greater eloquence, "I exhort you to vote for the Regency which may guide our ship of state until the coming of age of its legal helmsman!"

At this a cordon of guardsmen rose in disgust and followed their defiant comrade, Dragutin, from the gallery. It was obvious that the Army would not unanimously accept the new arrangement, but from the civil body as well as the diplomatic coterie came shouts of enthusiastic encomium. A regency? Nothing wrong with that. In fact, it smacked faintly of democracy and the modern psychology of government one was beginning to hear about. The implication was altogether appealing: a princeling, to be educated from the start according to specifications laid down by his own future subjects. The true monarchic ideal. . . .

For the fulfillment of so satisfactory a scheme it was essential that a group of able men be appointed to replace

the royal parents who, at best, represented a narrow
Boyar point of view. For here was a brilliant, absolutely
Utopian venture, an example that would go down in history, a lesson for the rest of mankind on the hazardous
subject of kingmaking. Serbia—insignificant, troubled,
repressed Serbia, with all her bravado, her courage, her
ambition—yes, Serbia had been chosen to show the civ-
ilized world a workable formula of government. . . .

There was a long impressive silence after the orator had
closed his dramatic address. The entire assembly needed
time to absorb fully this powerful, grandiose vision. But
now the storm broke. Cheers rose to the dark rafters of
the medieval meeting house where, for centuries past, the
Sultan's Ameers had ruled with iron fist. It was a veritable uproar of acclaim; *Ziveos* rang out for Cincar-
Marko and the boy King alike, while partisans of the
Black Georges crept sullenly away. Particular elation
reigned among those who were singled out to count bal-
lots. It was all very exciting, what with Arcadian happiness looming so near. A divine spark had descended upon
this forgotten Danube country from which there ema-
nated a radiance that would some day encircle the globe.
Had not obscure Judea given birth to Christendom?
Ziveo! Belgrade would become the cradle of a great
political science.

In this fever of idealism, which has ever prompted man
to create gods after his own image, the small Alexander's
future was carved out and Serbia launched upon her second experiment in royal rule. Although there remained
sundry minor dissensions to be disposed of, an election of
sorts took place. By oral vote the temporary Regency was
formed. Its members were: a metropolitan of the Greek

Orthodox Church, two military officers of indeterminate
rank, and Cincar-Marko whose brain had evolved the
whole plan. By periodic conferences and careful reports
to the *Skupchina* the business of state was to be handled.
Meanwhile, Parliament must select the educators for the
little King. Special governors, teachers, gymnasts—out-
standing figures in every field of pedagogy—would be
summoned to pass in review. Their culling might take
weeks, even months. In due course of time appropriate
changes would have to be made. For he must be given
the best of opportunities, this unsuspecting lad Alexander.
The very name was an omen. Serbia might well become
another Macedon! Did not this child foreshadow a rein-
carnation of that other Alexander, called the Great? . . .

Late that afternoon the battle of words had ended. It
had been a joyous battle, for its issue lay close to every
patriot's heart. Until final appointments could be per-
fected a group of schoolmasters—whose selection entailed no small amount of argument—had been listed for
duty at the palace on the following day. All persons pre-
viously concerned with the small King's welfare were to
be discharged; those who had served at the *Konak* for ten
or more years would receive a pension, others were to be
remembered when vacancies occurred elsewhere. Thus
the intimate close world which Milan's son had known
would be blotted out. In its place there was to rise an
abstract picture, the theoretic pattern of an ideal already
worshiped by the nation as its future master.

While all this went on, the reproved Captain of Guards,
Dragutin Dmitriyevitch, appeared at the quarters of the
military commandant to defend an indefensible slip of
tongue. He was faced with a stern indictment for pub-

licly addressing the exalted King of Serbia by the nursery diminutive of Sasha.

Not that this act ordinarily constituted a transgression. Press and populace had for years referred to the heir apparent in just that manner. It was characteristic of Slavic peoples to speak in fond endearing terms of their sovereigns: a queen was a "Good Fairy," an emperor the "Little Father." But such informality could not be sanctioned in Army circles or during ceremonies of an official character. Furthermore, every man in uniform knew this. The highly respectable *Skupchina* had never before witnessed a similarly impertinent breach.

It was to Dragutin's distinct advantage that this venerable body was still in session. All Belgrade, in fact, seemed at the moment to be engaged in making history. The hour of noon had slipped by unnoticed. Was it forgotten, and the Captain's misdemeanor as well?

The tall young man in his shiny regimentals paraded up and down the empty *Slaviya* Square, undecided as to a proper course of action. He had come to be disciplined, yet there appeared to be nobody interested in meting out his punishment. Although his orders did not provide for such a contingency, matters would be worse if he turned about and went home. At length he hit upon a happy thought. Staff headquarters were located in an old part of the city, not far from the river bank. It was only a stone's throw from the *Slaviya* to the lodgings of his friend Mihailo Masin, who dwelt alone along the quay in an ancient Turkish house. Lieutenant Masin was at the moment confined to his rooms, nursing a wrenched hip. The cavalry occasionally went in for that sort of thing; nerve-wracking, yes, and at times attended by deplorable setbacks, but all the same—give him the cavalry. It was the best branch of the service.

Incidentally, Mihailo had not heard about the latest brainstorm of that brotherhood of halfwits, the *Skupchina*. The good patriots were reverting atavistically to an ancestral occupation—barnyard husbandry. Only this time they were going to hatch a king! It was marvelous. Mihailo would be in stitches. Bad for his hip, of course, but so rare a guffaw warranted stitches.

Captain Dmitriyevitch consulted his watch. Five minutes past three, and still only a few orderlies hung about the place. There was no point in waiting further. Perhaps by this time the resourceful Cincar-Marko had picked a foreign princess for the boy King's nuptials and the assembly were in a fog over a name for the next heir.

He made up his mind without further pause. Throwing his blue cape over one shoulder, so that its scarlet lining blazed in the afternoon sun, he veered abruptly and hastened down a narrow street. At its end foamed the turbulent dark waters of the Danube.

CHAPTER III

THE MASIN HOUSE ON THE DANUBE QUAY

LIEUTENANT MIHAILO SVETOZAR MASIN was a gentle nondescript person whom women overlooked and men loved with a shy fraternal insistence. He owned one of the oldest mansions in Belgrade. The massive oriental structure with its intricate latticed windows and balconies had come down to him from his forebears, wealthy wine merchants of the Sava region. It had been built in days when Belgrade was a far outpost of Turkey-in-Europe; a time when the city, dotted with mosques and minarets, beheld on its flat housetops veiled Moslem women lolling dreamily above the masculine bustle of bazaars and thoroughfares below.

When, toward the middle of the nineteenth century, the Mussulman began his retreat into Asia while Christendom supplanted muezzin towers with Byzantine cupolas and Italian campaniles, the dim seraglios of lustful Pashas suffered a similar fate. One by one, they were razed to the ground and replaced by sober post-Renaissance dwellings with a definite leaning toward monogamy.

Rapidly the face of the city had changed. Only the picturesque house of the Masins remained, an obstinate challenge to reform. In part, this was due to the fact that its owners had for generations held their inheritance in almost sacred esteem. But there was also another, more trenchant reason. Most of the remodeling had been done at the government's expense; zealous reconstruction of

35

vast urban portions quickly depleted the municipal coffers and, long before the project was finished, interest in the whole matter had died down. With the Turk at bay, and France and England watching the Dardanelles, the Mohammedan menace gradually vanished. There was no danger of further invasion and consequently no harm in saving a landmark or two of a bygone era.

Ironically this conclusion had been reached by the city elders at a moment when, for the first time in its existence, the Masin house belonged to an owner who wished to be rid of it. The father of the present Lieutenant Mihailo had allowed the family fortune to slip through his fingers. Wine was ever the Masin means of subsistence, but there had been a subtle and progressive shifting from the production of it to its consumption. The last patriarch of the old firm had gleefully drunk himself to death, leaving a harassed widow and two sons whose only asset was a colossal establishment minus the wherewithal for its upkeep. Nor did the sorrowing lady struggle long. Before the older boy had reached maturity they carried her to the cool vault of the Masins where, beside her slumbering and improvident husband, the future held no more pangs.

Mihailo, the heir, had tossed a coin to determine his own and his younger brother's fate. The enormous house no one would buy, so they would have to continue living in it. But the scant wares stored in its deep underground cellars could be turned into gold. Not wealth, by any means, yet money enough to start them both on careers of their own choosing. At first they considered medicine and civil engineering (the fourteen-year-old Voyan wanted to build a bridge). But those were the days of the fourth

Obrenovitch who toyed with regal robes and yearned to clasp the scepter. Young men were exhorted to join the royalist cause and wear its alluring colors. Most of them found shako, rapier and cape exactly what such accouterments were meant to be—irresistible. The Masin boys proved no exception. Voyan, of course, could not actually enlist; but Mihailo rose on the tide of national feeling and soon found himself in company with the country's best blades forming the first regiment of Royal Guards.

He loved the service, and the experiment had cost him nothing. For, in the first glow of benign kingly grace, the newly crowned Milan showered his followers with favors. Equipment, stables, orderlies—all were furnished free. Thus even the dilapidated Masin mansion profited indirectly, for Anton, the trooper assigned to the freshly appointed guardsman, was transformed by the two brothers into a combination valet, matron and housekeeper.

In addition, there was still the money obtained through the sale of the paternal vintages. Since Mihailo's future seemed secure enough, it was decided that Voyan should derive the full benefit from this fund. He would be educated for the diplomatic field. Through Mihailo's position at court the younger brother was eligible for enrollment in the cadet corps, with admission to foreign academies, particularly the fine boys' schools in St. Petersburg. In this manner the impecunious young gentlemen managed to hold up a crumbling palatial home over their carefree heads, by the mere expedient of occupying only two of its innumerable rooms and accepting the gratuitous service of a stoical manservant provided by His Majesty the King.

It was impossible to foresee that Milan I would end his

reign as an exile on Austrian soil. The recent pande-
monium at the palace had come as a shock from which
people were slow to recover. Everyone knew that the
Army had ousted its sovereign, but this did not include
the Royal Guards, the King's own honor troops whose
oath of allegiance was a shade more personal than that of
the rank and file. The very nature of his oath, its solemn
wording, had troubled Lieutenant Masin on the morning
following the King's precipitate departure. He felt himself in a most equivocal position.

Despite a painful concussion he had suffered on the
parade ground only a week ago, Mihailo was able to get
about and could easily have driven to the *Skupchina* for
the mass meeting. But he preferred to stay away. No
matter how unworthy, Milan had been king, and one had
sworn loyalty to him. Let ministers and politicians decide
what was to happen next. He, as an officer, would neither
sully his honor nor perjure his word. Let them elect a
Karageorgevitch; enough propaganda for the Georges
filled the air! It was all right with Lieutenant Masin.
That bloodthirsty Peter, head of the *Cerny* clan, would
be a keen, bold master. Yes, and a ruthless one, which
was always good for a country's foreign policy.

In a way, Mihailo hoped that the Obrenos—blustering
egoists whose deceptive airs of leadership concealed but a
bungling distemper—would ultimately relinquish their
claims, as befitted a dynasty that had failed to prove its
worth. But this ought to happen without the need of
Guardsmen turning upon the monarch whose insignia
they wore. And so he had preferred to stay at home,
nursing his battered hip until the news arrived from the
Skupchina announcing the people's choice. Plenty of time,

then, to assume the obligations imposed by Serbia's new government. A different matter entirely, after Parliament had acted.

How fortunate that Voyan was still too young to take part in all this! Pupils of the cadet academy learned of political changes after their satisfactory completion and not a day earlier. Yes, he would leave Voyan at school and quietly await the outcome of events.

It was Anton, the orderly, who disturbed these reveries.

"Captain Dmitriyevitch to see you, sir."

"Good, show him in." Masin rose carefully from his armchair near the open window. There was a tap on the door and a moment later the dark figure of Dragutin appeared on the threshold.

"Greetings," he addressed the smiling invalid.

"*Zdravo* (welcome)," Masin replied with soft Slovene inflection. "Decent of you to come. I was beginning to wonder if everyone had forgotten me. Well, I suppose it's all over! Where are the others? What made you so late?"

"Thanks, I *will* sit down," mocked Dragutin, taking an unproffered stool.

"Challenge at sunrise tomorrow, for insults on my own premises," laughed Masin as he settled back in his own chair. "Good heavens, man, I'm starved for news—and you stop to notice my bad manners! All right, now tell me——"

"And I'll have a cognac, if you don't mind," Dragutin continued, stretching long legs so that his spurs dug into the thick pile of an Azarbaijan prayer rug. "Incidentally, you'd better take one yourself before I begin my sad tale. And I warn you, it will be a tear-wringer."

Masin's eyebrows rose suspiciously. He reached for the liqueur tray on a near-by tabouret and uncorked the decanter. Dragutin poured. They raised their glasses while, with a quizzical glance at his friend, Mihailo murmured:

"Well, it's the health of *Kralj Petar Karadjordevic,* I take it——"

Dragutin gave a harsh chuckle. "Wrong, old man," he countered; "here's to royal mumps, measles and whooping cough. You are drinking the health of none other than Sasha, our rocking-horse King!"

Lieutenant Masin brought down his glass, staring blankly. "Not really——" he gasped.

"Oh yes." Dragutin wiped his mustache with the back of his hand. "I am not insane and I don't walk in my sleep. You can believe what I tell you. It hasn't been done before, but it's going to be done in Serbia now. We are about to have a nursery king."

"Of course," the other interrupted, facetiously pedantic, "your premise is wrong. One of the Medicis ruled from his cradle, and there's a precedent in Tudor England. Come to think of it, Spain has at this moment a three-year-old Alfonso XIII, born after his father's death. What do you say to that?"

"Not the same thing at all." Dragutin flushed with exasperation. "In each of those cases the power was vested in some surviving member of the dynasty until the majority of the heir in question. But with us the impossible is being attempted. An abandoned boy is to be placed in a sort of laboratory where he will be molded, pulled and twisted by more strange people than will be good for him or anyone else. He is to go through child-

hood and adolescence balancing a crown on his head,
while we—a nation of fighters—bow to a whole damnable puppet show of nurses, governesses, tutors and even
a pious metropolitan or two. Can't you see? Just now,
when we are growing into unity and strength—for the
first time in centuries—now we choose a lad in nursery
bibs to lend us majesty!" He groaned and leaned forward, pressing his face between his hands.

Masin had listened with growing consternation. "Well,
then," he exclaimed, "why don't we learn from Spain?
The widowed María Cristina seems to be doing all right
at Madrid. Why doesn't someone recall our own Queen?"

Dragutin flared up. "Never!"

The other tried to placate. "Children need family ties,"
he said soberly, "I can see it in my brother Voyan. And
that Sasha is not so much younger——"

"He's very backward, due to pampering. They say the
servants still rock him to sleep!"

"Doesn't that prove my point?" Mihailo persisted,
"Hired help won't do. The boy ought to have his
mother."

The visitor's lip curled in ironic amusement. "Right,
old man, but your poultice has already been turned down
by the doctors on the case. You see, I was the first to
suggest it. And where's that going to get me? Probably to jail."

"How so?"

"Something they didn't like about my inflection. As
usual, the *Skupchina* can't stand playing rough. I suppose
I did egg them on, though, about the return of Natalia
Kesko."

"What did they say?"

"Nothing much beyond admitting that poor Natasha
has no sense. Somebody recalled an adage—somebody
always does—about female rulers being worse than none
at all. Unless they're disgustingly clever, that is."

"Rot!"

Dragutin's sardonic expression had not changed. "Besides," he went on, "as Cincar-Marko was kind enough
to remind me, the Queen was exiled by Milan himself and
there's no way to re-instate her after his abdication. The
crown is doubly lost to her."

Masin smiled acridly. "You were always good at
sophistries, Dragutin. As if the dispositions of jobless
kings couldn't be undone by popular wish! For the rest,
I'm afraid it's only too true. Natalia, though harmless, is
a trifle beetle-headed."

"Which makes her," Dragutin added, "in my opinion—
not so harmless."

Masin's manner had mellowed once more. "Maybe so.
But it strikes me that we're needlessly worried about the
child. The whole thing may turn out much better than
we think."

"Sorry I can't share your optimism. Kings are born,
not made."

"I see you know a proverb or two yourself," Masin
teased.

Dragutin frowned. "It may be trite, but it's true."

"Oh, I don't know. Education deserves some credit,
doesn't it?"

"Sure it does, and a great deal too. But real leadership
is a heritage, whereas this sorry Sasha has nothing behind
him but——" He broke off with a gesture of contempt.

Masin looked puzzled. "When we chose his father we were impressed by the man's authoritative air."

"Yes, and found out soon enough that he showed valor only when beating his wife, and majesty only when bullying underlings. Worthless dogs will fool you by their savage bearing, just as horses can show spirit which is followed up by cowardice and treachery, so why not human beings? But there are thoroughbreds among dogs and horses, even as there are thoroughbred leaders among men. Only, you cannot create them by formula."

Masin leaned back in his chair, gazing through the open window at an ever deepening afternoon haze. In the distance, on the Hungarian bank of the Danube, gleamed the lights of Semlin. High above the river rose the symbol of a thousand-year-old kingdom of the Magyars, the Millennium Tower of St. Stephen. Dragutin followed his friend's troubled glance.

"How they'll laugh at us over there," he murmured between tightened jaws, "they've always laughed at us! Little Serbia, playing at kings and soldiers in the shadow of Europe's most ancient crown. How they will patronize us and point across the water to direct our petty destinies. . . . This is our tragedy—that we remain feeble, yet are possessed of such immeasurable faith in our superiority among Balkan peoples!"

They continued to sit, staring dully at the vanishing gold without. The river moaned, and dusk spread slowly over it like a cloak.

CHAPTER IV

PEDAGOGY

THE dining room was large and incredibly high. Sitting alone at the table, the small boy felt swallowed up by all this vastness. He had never before eaten in the official dining hall. When Mama was still with him the two of them had had cozy little suppers in the nursery, while Papa sat at the great board downstairs with a host of loud gentlemen. (Not gentlewomen, since these had gradually disappeared.) At such times it seemed that Papa must have been telling funny stories, for Sasha could hear uproarious laughter above the clatter of his own porridge spoon.

"What is Papa saying?" he used to ask, tortured with curiosity.

But his mother pretended not to hear and urged him to get on with his meal. Of course, that was always the way with grown-ups. One had to make allowances for them. When they didn't know the answer, they simply ignored your question or, worse yet, postponed the whole issue. Like that time, long ago, when Sasha learned the Ten Commandments out of his little catechism. "What is adultery?" he had demanded, for it said, "Thou shalt not——" in front of this formidable word, and Sasha was very much worried lest, unwittingly, he might commit it.

"What is *what,* my lamb?" At moments Mama was very difficult. Thus, when Sasha had repeated his query,

44

she had pulled out her pocket handkerchief and busied herself with it. Then, most casually, she dismissed him with:

"You must ask your father, darling. He knows more about it than I do."

Which had left Sasha exactly nowhere, since he almost never saw his father. In fact, as time went on, that part of his life which had to do with Papa became blurred. Other things too became blurred. Of late Sasha saw no one at all. Even Anya seemed to have disappeared. He was very lonely.

It all had something to do with his being downstairs in the beautiful dining hall that had excited his curiosity as long as he could remember. For some strange reason its heavy doors had opened today, and there—upon the dark oak table—stood his own deep dish and silver drinking cup. In a way, of course, he really sensed the answer. He had grown up. (Growing up must be a lonely business, then.) But it had its compensations, for now he doubtless would eat with men, the boisterous companions who laughed so hard at Papa's jokes. And yet he saw no plates, cutlery or even goblets for anyone besides himself. Quite possibly this was a dream. . . . A very satisfying dream, to be sure, for here he was in the very spot that had long appealed to his imagination. He was thrilled, proud, hopeful—at any moment the most amusing things were bound to happen. His small black eyes shone with an unnatural brightness while his nerves tingled in suspense.

But nothing happened. Nothing, that is, beyond the opening of a narrow service door through which came a footman bearing a tray. Above the tray hovered a familiar aroma of cinnamon and clove. And now the spell was broken.

Sasha knew exactly what this meant. He was to go on eating his usual portion of rice, cooked with milk and topped by a mound of apple sauce, and the most elegant setting would not save him from being chided for harmless dalliance over unexciting food. To think of outgrowing one's nursery for this!

He felt restless. He wanted suddenly to escape from the rigid armchair that seemed to close about him, hiding everyone from sight. He wanted to find Anya. Perhaps Anya was sick with the toothache and Doctor Dokich had locked her up in her room. He must go and see.

Folding his napkin, he slipped from the chair and ran across the room. He was about to open the carved double doors leading into a series of antechambers when the sound of muffled voices reached him.

"Anya?" he said faintly. The syllables were drowned in all that space.

But now the doors were thrown wide and Sasha caught a rasping whisper. "Please follow me. You know your instructions, gentlemen!" With this a group of strangers appeared, as if from nowhere, in the arched doorway. The boy regarded them in amazement and delight. One of the strangers wore a bright uniform, the next a black sack with a long row of buttons down the front, and still another was dressed in a plain garment unlike anything Sasha had ever seen—just gray, sort of.

Fascinated, the child stood motionless. Then it was going to be a nice dream after all! Here were all those gentlemen. In a few minutes they would surely bellow with laughter. And Papa, too, was probably behind them.

Sasha stretched himself to take a good look. But the man in the *soutane* placed a lean hand on his shoulder.

"Alexander," he said in the dry rasping voice of a moment ago, "that is unbecoming. You must remain seated at table."

What was this? Sasha felt immensely disappointed. But the man in black had not yet finished.

"I am Father Milutin," he pronounced slowly and with unction, "please remember."

Sasha understood. His mother had been very fond of gentlemen with tight round neckbands, whom one addressed as "Father." They commanded respect because they had special dealings with God.

"You are Father Milutin," the boy repeated quickly, for he wanted no trouble with this thin black man. And then, as if to forestall unseen dangers, he hurried back to the table. He looked up with an ingratiating smile. "I never eat my dinner very fast," he said, "but I eat it."

The grim man (he was, in truth, needlessly grim) did not return the smile. Instead, he bowed with great solemnity and signaled his companions. The figure in uniform stepped forward. Milutin introduced.

"This is Master-of-Cadets, Colonel Gorlice, from whom you will learn the soldier's trade."

Much clicking of heels and the rattle of a giant saber accompanied this presentation. Sasha beamed. Oh, he knew! He was a big chap now. And soon, no doubt, they would bring him a uniform. If only his mother and father were here to tell him how soon. Perhaps he might even have a uniform tomorrow! Perhaps this was his birthday? Sasha loved birthdays.

He wanted to shake hands with the festooned Colonel

when Father Milutin beckoned again. This time the little man in gray came to the table. He nodded continually, as if his head had come loose, and an eager smile was spread across his features.

"Seminar Instructor Abramovitch, who is versed in sciences, numbers, reading and writing."

The child peered into the birdlike face of the schoolmaster and sensed its kindliness. Bonds of sympathy spun lightly in the air. Sasha reached for the nondescript gray sleeve.

"You can come with me," he said, "I was going to look for Anya."

Father Milutin thwarted this intention.

"Nonsense," he was snorting through lips that scarcely parted, "the—er—woman called Anya is gone. Surely there is no further need for a nursemaid, is there, gentlemen?" The last remark was directed to the room at large.

Sasha paled. Like his mother he was tender-hearted and easily moved to tears. Like his father he was subject to impetuous changes and quickly frightened. What did all this mean? Where was Anya? Everything seemed to be dropping out of his world at once; even Nushka hadn't looked the same when he caught sight of her in the corridor a short while ago. Was it because she too would disappear? Panic seized him. Suddenly great salty tears streamed down his round cheeks.

"Anya!" he wailed.

The mild little schoolmaster fell to his knees and patted the grief-stricken head.

"There, my lad," he whispered, "Anya has just gone on a holiday. She may be back in no time at all——"

An icy voice interrupted him.

"Abramovitch, I am the boy's governor. It is your business, as his tutor, to concern yourself with texts and copy books. Exclusively, Abramovitch!"

The schoolmaster reddened. "Yes, Your Reverence," he stammered, "texts and copy books—exclusively." He retired behind the broad shadow of his military colleague, while Milutin took Sasha by the hand.

"And now," the disciplinarian's tone had softened unexpectedly, "we shall go to meet the Countess Eudoxia and Mademoiselle Vera." Sobbing helplessly, the boy allowed himself to be dragged away.

They walked some distance down the large vestibule and entered what was known as the Crystal Salon. This was a circular reception room hung with huge chandeliers from which, on gala occasions, a deluge of candlelight flooded the mirrored walls. Here, not so many years ago, King Milan and Queen Natalia had held their first official court. Here, after his baptism in the old cathedral, Sasha himself—asleep on a satin pillow—had been acclaimed as Serbia's heir apparent.

Milutin opened lacquered doors and coughed discreetly. There was a treble of women's voices within, drowned by the boy's sobs.

"There's not a thing to cry about," came a final stern admonition from the frocked governor. Sasha, aware that everyone including the gentle Abramovitch had been left behind, choked back his tears. Together they entered.

Two women rose from a plush divan and ran forward to meet them. The elder, a brisk middle-aged lady with reddish hair and ample bosom, exclaimed in voluble crescendoes: "You have kept us in suspense, Prota Yacov

Milutin! But there you bring him at last, the little duckling, the precious *pitushok* (chick)—what a dear boy! So serious, though. How can he be so serious with that jolly dimple in his chin?"

Sasha felt repelled and sickened as she stooped down to place her heavily jeweled hands around his solid waist. "I am Eudoxia," she cooed, while a strong wave of perfume surged upward from the fullness of her décolletage, "Eudoxia from Russia. And you, my child, must call me Auntie."

"In the interest of etiquette, Countess," mumbled Milutin, bending forward as if to absorb the exotic fumes more deeply, "I have already arranged for the proper manner of address." His exquisite politeness left no doubt that "Auntie" would be out of the question. The lady accepted his correction with grace.

"Forgive my impulsiveness," she breathed, "we know the Regents have decreed that your judgment is to prevail in all things."

She regained her feet and henceforth seemed to hang on the cleric's every gesture. Milutin smiled almost imperceptibly so that Sasha could see crow's feet forming across his temples where the hair showed a tinge of silver. It was the first time he had seen this man smile; he found the experience not without a certain grisly enchantment. For, when that gaunt face showed even so feeble a trace of emotion, the nostrils quivered visibly. Sasha observed this phenomenon with interest and, forgetting his grief, stood lost in awe.

At this point the second lady came forward. Much younger than her companion, she had a lemon-colored complexion, and faded blonde hair which she wore in an

enormous pompadour on top of her head. Her manner
was nervous. She fluttered, waving her fingers in futile
spirals and lowering her lids (she could do this with
either eye) in an unaccountable wink. These movements
seemed to be spontaneous and quite unintentional, for they
did not coincide with an otherwise formal demeanor.

"Here," introduced Father Milutin, "is Mademoiselle
Vera Pellingre who speaks French and English. As for
Countess Eudoxia, she will supplement my religious instruction and watch your deportment." He glared solemnly like old Doctor Dokich who took care of Sasha's
bad teeth.

The boy listened, bewildered. Like all royal children
he was accustomed to being addressed by adults in stilted
adult fashion, without paying particular attention to it.
But this was different. The full import of "governor,"
"French," "deportment" struck him at last. All these
strange people whom he had just met would henceforth
be around him, and those he had once known—Papa,
Mama, Anya, perhaps even Nushka—were in some incomprehensible manner gone forever.

There sprang up somewhere inside him a dreadful all-
engulfing ache but he did not know what to do about it.
It was just there, tearing through his stomach so that for
an instant he felt nauseated. What would they do if he
became ill—right here on the elegant parquetry? Oh,
they didn't know how he needed Anya! They didn't
know a thing about his bedtime confidences, his games
in the bathtub, his eggyolk-and-sugar reward for taking
afternoon naps. Why, for two days now he had pretended to sleep, despite his preoccupations, but the afternoon wore on and no one thought of Sasha's favorite

tidbit. Most appalling of all, they didn't know about his fears at night. These puzzling men and women who seemed all to have combined against him—they didn't know that he must have a strip of light under his mother's door, and Anya keeping watch far down the hall. They didn't know that after dark, in his own bed, he suffered the primitive agony of elemental creatures—a blind, deep-rooted dread of something that might be death.

Once more the monotone of Milutin's voice filled the chill room. "I anticipate no difficulties," he was saying. "Children taken in hand at an early age can be shaped according to noble patterns. It is my purpose and your duty, ladies, to further the development of our charge. Ours is a great responsibility toward Serbia. I need your unconditional co-operation in this task."

He was obviously satisfied for, as his narrow eyes rested upon the two women, a benign smile spread again over his face. Mademoiselle Vera, considerably affected, changed from yellow to a faintly purplish hue. Her clammy fingers clasped Sasha's fat warm palm, holding it in an ecstatic clutch. But Countess Eudoxia continued totally unconscious of the boy. Her gaze was fixed with bovine concentration upon the countenance of Milutin, whose nostrils, Sasha noticed, had again set up a vibration.

"Pray rest assured," the Russian murmured in her dulcet tones, "there shall be obedience to your slightest wish."

With a flourish she drew forth from the corsage of her dress a lace-bordered kerchief and gently dabbed her eyes. The fragment of cloth exuded new and more vigorous gusts of that intense smell which enveloped its owner.

Sasha became interested.   Subtly at first, and then with
rapidly diminishing restraint, his attitude toward this
extraordinary creature changed.   Revulsion gave way to
curiosity.   He suspected that in the picturesque composi-
tion of the Countess Eudoxia there was much to explore.
He did not know that her gaudy tastes and simpering
mannerisms passed for that spurious conceit called glamour.   He had a small boy's very neutral reaction toward
glamour.   But he more than vaguely sensed a difference
between the full-blown Countess and the vestal person
of Mademoiselle Vera.

"Perhaps," he speculated, sniffing the scented air, "perhaps *she* will come to visit in the nursery.   If so, I must
think how I can make her stay."   Only recently he had
taken two alarm clocks apart to see what made them tick,
besides opening up Toyo—his Japanese doll—to investigate its interior.   Toyo, it developed, had been stuffed
with newspaper.   You never could tell.   The Russian's
dress rustled even more crisply than the puppet's kimono.

But now he grew aware of something damp and sticky.
It was the hand of Mademoiselle Vera, still wrapped
around his own.   It felt like a frog out of the pond in the
park.   He shivered, but was afraid to withdraw from the
contact.   Biting his lips, he forced himself to endure it
until, presently, Father Milutin led him from the room.

"Next we go to chapel," said the priest, brushing a
particle of dust from the cuff of his cassock.   He must be
very tidy, Sasha reflected.

The voice went on.   "I shall rehearse the prayers with
which we are going to begin each day.   At night, Countess
Eudoxia will hear the evening recitation and report to
me later.   You must pay close attention."

Almost immediately Sasha felt happier. Then she would come! She would watch him speak his verse before the holy ikons at the head of his bed—the ikon of Our Lady of Vladimir and the sad Byzantine Christ—in their twin silver frames. And like Anya, she would doubtless check up on his poor memory, since God, although He looked at Sasha's heart, apparently did not enjoy a bungled psalm.

The perfumed Countess would discover numerous inconsistencies in Sasha's very personal conversations with God. But he hoped she would be charitable and tolerant like Anya. And he wished, oh, so earnestly, that he might again find someone—someone who would stay close by, and who would be fond of him.

CHAPTER V

Anya Goes Home

THE old woman chose to travel over land by stage. It was thus that, more than forty years ago, she had first left her village home of Provo and moved to the city. She saw no reason why today—after a life of service which had culminated, and found an ignominious end, within the gates of a regal palace—she should return to her native heath amid the clamor of a newfangled railroad or the even more pretentious hubbub of a river steamboat.

In all these years most of her kinsfolk had moved on to eternity. Did any of them survive to welcome her? For the moment she could not remember. It didn't matter how she came or where she went. It mattered only that she must leave Belgrade with her little bag of shiny dinars, her "pension." Pay-off, she called it! Bribery, to keep her away from the apple of her eye, the boy over whose life she, Anya, had watched from the first minute of his difficult birth. She had done the same for his father. (These large-boned Obrenos all but killed their mothers for giving them life!) And now that her usefulness was thought to be over—as if, just because he was king, her little Sashino could do without a nursemaid—they packed her off with orders to mind her memories and hold her tongue.

As if she cared to talk of such distress as had befallen her! As if the simple folk in the back hills whither she was now returning would remember, or indeed, lend credence to the things that she might tell. . . .

Huddled into a corner of the rumbling coach, she peered through the grime that caked the window nearest her. The paved streets of the capital lay far behind, but still the road was alive with marching soldiers, prancing horsemen and the clatter of moving artillery. Oh, she knew what that meant. Whenever important political measures were afoot, it was deemed prudent to distract the military. Especially the temperamental Officers' Corps. Those fellows were apt to get out of hand unless engaged in the more strenuous exercises of their trade.

Shortly before adjourning, the *Skupchina* had ordered army maneuvers to be held in the valley of the Sava River. The center of operations, Anya had heard, would be the little town of Obrenovatz. She did not enjoy passing through this spot, for it held painful memories. Here, during girlhood, her path had first crossed that of a future dynasty, when her father brought the young Anya to work in the rich house of the Obrenos. From here her entire life took its form, since she had never wished to do service for any other family.

Even now she could discern, through clouds of dust, a crumbling turret etched against the horizon. Soon there would be a turn in the road disclosing the fertile banks of the Sava, the lovely Danube tributary which at Belgrade joins its mother stream. And down near the water's edge there stood—Anya remembered—the busy mill of her godchild Mara, who had married that good-for-nothing Lunyevica rake, a harlequin if ever there was one.

The old woman stirred in the creaking seat. This

recollection of some one who belonged to her, the vision of some haven where for an hour she might find shelter and a chance to assemble her thoughts, seemed like a godsend. She had made no plans for the short span of life left her. It was high time to come to a decision. What if she were to call on Mara?

Of course, the whole idea might prove preposterous. So many years had passed. For all she knew, the mill belonged to strangers and Mara was dead. Such a pretty wench, too. It was a shame. But on the other hand, there were the children. Three or four, Anya recalled, had been mentioned in some letters. Still, the last time Mara had written must be more than a decade ago. Much could happen in that time!

The old woman was too busy with her thoughts to notice that the carriage had slowed down for the gates of Obrenovatz. In another second the horses had come to a halt. Doors were opened and amid a confusion of bundles several peasants piled in. Their shouts and vehement oaths roused Anya from her melancholy reveries. She looked about her in dismay and realized for the first time that she had forgotten the boisterous ways of country folk. She had been servant to royalty, albeit such ill-bred royalty as poor foolish Milan, and she had acquired the airs of a noble house. Although the King, her master, had picked his teeth and spat on his wife's carpet, he did these execrable things in the grand manner. That was it: Anya had become used to the grand manner.

She withdrew from the aggressive newcomers and smoothed her crumpled shawl. One of the men pushed her satchel with his boot and bellowed cheerily:

"Well, Little Mother, and where might you be going? On a lopsided honeymoon?"

Anya's sharp nose grew a trifle sharper. Little Mother, indeed, and from such a lout as this! Instantly her mind was made up. She would go on to Provo, that was certain.

"I've reached my destination," she snapped and, picking up her effects, rose from her seat.

The other passengers gaped blankly and then fell to jostling her through the open door. With haste she scrambled from the carriage. It was not a moment too soon, for the horses had been watered and she could hear the driver's horn. Only a split second and she might have been compelled to share the coach for hours with the ruffians she had just escaped.

And now there she stood on the sidewalk, shaking her wraps. A few casual passers-by regarded her curiously. She did not mind this, for she knew that her appearance must betoken the great city. A lone cabman hailed her with elaborate courtesy, inquiring about her destination. This brought her back to reality. Whatever else she intended to do, it was impossible to remain here in the town square of Obrenovatz without plans for the night. She must hurry to the end of this street where the open road could still be seen, branching off to the left. From there it would be a short walk toward the river where, she trusted, a kind fate awaited her. For down behind the mill lived, if the heavens so willed it, her godchild Mara. Resolutely the old woman picked up her bags and set out for the wide country.

It was mid-afternoon when she arrived on the bank of the stream and skirted the mill's big waterwheel. A dog ɔarked through some fence boards behind which could be seen a tall swarthy boy weeding a vegetable patch. From the solid peasant house near by issued a clear voice:

"Nikodem, there's someone at the gate. See who it is."

The boy in the garden looked up but he seemed loath to bestir himself. Through the open doorway of the house, meanwhile, emerged a bronze-skinned woman of perhaps forty-five with an infant at her breast. The saints be praised, this was Mara—Mara with another baby in her arms! It was too much for the old nurse. Tears rolled down her parchment cheeks as she ran trembling up the path.

"Mara, my godchild, don't you remember me?"

The other's eyes grew fixed, then there came into them a quick sign of recognition.

"Mother Anya!"

Loudly the two women wept while the babe and the lanky youth who ambled lazily across the courtyard stared in wonderment.

"Call your brother and sisters, Nikodem," Mara ordered her son between happy sobs, "tell them to come at once. Our kinswoman is here, Godmother Anya, who has lived at the *Konak* and is an honored lady."

At this the old nurse blushed with modesty and her weeping gained fresh impetus. So joyous were her sniffles and gulps that the starched white *hauba* (bonnet) on her head threatened to dislodge itself. As it was, the fine batiste crown remained tilted at a most precarious angle. But Mara's son had not stirred in his tracks.

"Go, then, Nikodem," his mother urged him a second time, "don't stand there like a stricken calf." And to

Anya she said: "Let us sit in the best room; you must be very tired."

They went indoors, with Nikodem at their heels. He was determined not to miss anything.

Once inside, Mara again caught sight of him. "Niko, what did I ask——" she began, but he interrupted her.

"Mother, you know how crazy the girls are—especially Draga—with all those soldiers in town. They got Paul to take them to the review today and there's no chance of your seeing any of them before dawn." There was a note of resentment in Nikodem's voice. Paul obviously ranked as his sisters' favorite.

The old woman's ears were sharp. Nikodem, Paul— gentlemen's names. And Draga! Yes, the Lunyevicas showed class. Even if their father never did amount to much, their grandfather owned the best pastures in the Choumadia district. She turned to Mara, noting the dignity of her well-embroidered regional dress.

"As yet you have not mentioned your husband, Panta Andreas. Where is he?"

There was a pause before the younger woman answered. "Oh," she said lightly, "he's gone to America."

"America!" Anya felt the ground giving way under her feet. A land of red-skinned savages who carried hatchets and scalped one another alive—to think that a fellow countryman, and one who was her kin, should meet with such a fate. "Did he *have* to go to America?" she asked faintly. For quite possibly Panta Andreas had committed some folly which obliged him to flee. But Mara laughed loudly.

"No, no," she protested, "there was no way of stopping him. Someone said it was the land of opportunity, so he decided that was where he belonged. There never were any opportunities here. That is, none he would bother about."

Anya nodded angrily. "Well, and did he leave you anything besides"—she pointed to the baby in Mara's arms—"another head to care for?"

The other rallied to her worthless husband's defense. "Oh yes, I have this property and the income from the mill. I don't complain."

The old nurse snorted. That was the trouble with Serbian women, from Queen Natalia down to this forsaken mother with her brood of five. They would tolerate no contumely against their menfolk.

Wistfully, Mara went on. "Andreas—he was always a good mate, kind and very tender. My only worry is——"

Anya's eyes narrowed triumphantly. "Ah—then you do have a worry?"

The other's face grew somber. "It's nothing," she murmured as if to herself, "that is, nothing so bad as trouble. Only, the children, they all take after him. They're not like me, soft, easy to manage. They're hard. You can't reason with them."

Anya stroked the baby's mop of black hair, while the mother continued her soliloquy.

"Look at these two here. Nikodem is always *The Turk* among his playfellows. And even Voika, scarcely a year old, glares at me like a gypsy. They're wild children, heedless, irresponsible—I tremble for their future."

The youth standing on the doorstep flashed white teeth and laughed. "You never know, Mother," he taunted; "if this is Aunt Anya you've told us so much about, it just proves what funny things do happen. *She's* been under a king's roof, hasn't she?"

The old nurse did not dislike the reference to her former haunts, although it pained her to admit that this part of her life was done. "True, my boy," she sighed, "but that's over now. The *Konak* has closed upon King Milan's household, of which I was an insignificant member. Anya is without home and without purpose."

"You have my home," said Mara simply, "and who knows but what your sad example will teach these fledglings to seek humbler goals. Especially do I need help with Draga. She has her father's hunger for adventure. No menial tasks for that young lady! I have to whip her so she'll make her bed."

"It's not the kind she wants to lie in," mocked Nikodem, stretching himself impudently.

His mother looked up in anger. "Brazen rascal," she cried, "off to town with you, to get those children."

He checked her fury with a kiss and finished chaffing: "Sabine will love that! She's already an old maid. As for Paul, Aunt Anya, he is practically my twin. So you see, I am going to fetch the 'children.' . . ."

"He needs the seat of his pants thrashed," groaned Mara in desperation. "Only seventeen and thinks he knows it all. Wants to be Shah of Persia or Grand Mogul if nothing better turns up. And that chit, Draga, is even worse. Together, I tell you, they turn this place into bedlam every day."

Anya was fast forgetting her sorrows while hearing of her godchild's complicated life.

"Are the boys occupied?" she asked soberly.

"They didn't do so well in school, and neither would

learn a trade, so I'm letting them apprentice in the mill. It keeps them busy and out of mischief, but of course there's no future in that, since the fad for modern inventions has hurt our old-fashioned methods. Grain is taken to the city nowadays to be milled in large quantities by machines said to be a thousand times faster than our wheel, although I've yet to see flour that is any finer and fluffier than that which my boys turn out."

"Then they do take pride in their heritage?"

Mara shook her head sadly. "As long as the mood lasts, which is never very long with a Lunyevica. My constant terror is that their father's venture across the seas will lure them. Nikodem would love nothing better right now than to tie up his belongings in a length of calico and trundle off to America by steerage."

"And Sabine, what about her?"

"Oh, Sabine—she has oil for her lamp, as the saying goes, but no bridegroom in sight. I'm afraid she is not very pretty, my Sabine. Of late, her fancy has turned to religion. Though, mind you, she is as foolish about a handsome hussar's uniform as any minx. Still, I shall be relieved if she decides ultimately to take the veil."

Anya approved. "There is a nunnery this side of Bilna."

"The Ursulines. But"—Mara's tone was apologetic—"they are sisters of the poor and go barefoot. Sabine couldn't——"

"Of course not," said the old nurse with conviction.

"Now, about Draga—well"—a little archness crept into the maternal voice—"there's cleverness in that girl. She's still in hair ribbons but already I am being asked what dowry I've in mind to give her! If one of them does, it's

Draga who will make her way—if I can lock her up, that
is, before she loses it."

The gray head nodded sagely. *"Devishtvo* (virginity)
gone, you can throw out the wench."

"Yes," Mara mused, "I must bolt the door."

They chatted on, confiding, counseling, conjuring up
the unborn future and a past long dead. The room darkened slowly as evening crept through the windows. But
when Mara put down her sleeping youngest and fetched a
burning lamp, Anya, the nursemaid, knew that her wan-
derings were over. She had come home.

CHAPTER VI

VILLAGE BRAWL

THE military band which had assembled in the kiosk on the principal square was playing. A multitude of listeners poured down from the hills beyond the town where lights glowed like pale jewels on the throat of night. In the distance rose the deserted ruins of an ancient manor. From its ramparts the river below could be seen for miles, but no one ever went there to enjoy the view. Obrenovatz, the stronghold once forsaken for royal Belgrade, offered now no shelter to its brood. King Milan, driven from his country, dwelt shabbily in foreign rooming houses while his erstwhile wife sought consolation in that paradise of royal exiles, France.

The town itself, however, was not concerned with this. It had enough to do getting the womenfolk home after the big show—for, as usual, when even the smallest brigade was quartered in Obrenovatz, giddy skirts turned out in flocks while local Romeos suffered pangs of impotent jealousy. Almost invariably events of this sort led to stark domestic tragedies, fisticuffs in the more frequented wine shops and, oddly enough, a growing number of enlistments on the part of enterprising citizens. If uniforms proved so dazzling that they turned the fatuous head of every female, whether weaned or wizened, it was about time for the rural lads to enter into competition. Annually, autumn maneuvers brought first discontent, then inspiration, to peasant males who watched

their sisters, sweethearts, wives, sighing at the mere
glimpse of a rakish *kalpak* or a bright dragoon *levitka.*

Today had been no exception. Streets were thronged
with damsels of every age and description. Many had
come from far away, wearing the garb of their particular
district. Southern women appeared in richly ornamented
tunics topped by extraordinary metal discs which dangled
over their stomachs. These cumbersome "pinafores" had
a grim history: in years gone by the barbarous Bashi-
bazouks, while seizing Serbia for the Sultan, had supple-
mented their deadly work on the battle-fields by rounding
up pregnant Slav mothers and kicking them in the abdomen to cause miscarriage. Each child thus lost diminished
Serbia's strength. In self-defense, therefore, peasant
women of Macedon and the Voyvodina had devised an
armored plate to wear suspended from their waist.
Through passing generations this safeguard became asso-
ciated with the particular style of the region, so that, long
after the Moslem had vanished, the trinket (later much
reduced in size) was regarded as a dress trimming.

In point of fact, other portions of the Balkan peninsula furnished contradictory legends on the same subject.
There wandered about the square of Obrenovatz buxom
maids in Croatian garb, which consisted of voluminous
and billowing skirts supported by incalculable layers of
starched linen underneath. And, as though this were not
enough, many had tied around their middle a properly
stuffed pillow, the more to distort their shapes. Legend
reported that the ancestors of these sturdy beauties had
likewise suffered under the Ottoman scourge in rather a
different way. Periodically the Sultan's harem needed

replenishing. Accordingly, from far and wide, girls and young women of conquered races were carried to the slave markets of the Orient. Only expectant mothers were spared. As a result, the territories in question suddenly abounded in grotesquely inflated females, each of whom was loath to be the Sultan's bride. Again the historic motive had been obliterated, but the symbol survived. The little cushion, decked with ribbons and fancy stitching, was deemed a very convenient place to rest one's hands. Thus everyone, in the end, appeared satisfied—even the Turk, into whose boots every conceivable atrocity had been shoved for so protracted a spell that no one knew, and scarcely anyone cared, how much was truth and how much fiction. The Mussulman had long become Europe's favorite alibi. If crops failed or rain was slow in coming, people said: "The Turk did it. He destroyed our forests to trade lumber in Egypt!" It was extremely simple. Everything that happened could be blamed on the Turk. Even the discovery of America.

In the riot of color which, then, owed so much to the invader, Obrenovatz made merry. Frolicking through the crowds, with a mischievous glance here and a wanton outcry there, was Mara Lunyevica's youngest, the unbridled Draga. She had broken away from her brother and sister during the band concert and now roved idly among the throngs. This surging of humanity intoxicated her, the alert fifteen-year-old. With the strange precocity of adolescence she longed to attract attention. Her overtures were directed largely toward virile men whom she strove to entice with a pretense at knowledge she did not possess. Made conscious of womanhood by the rapid budding of her figure, she, who had been a torpid urchin, now tingled in every fiber. Though lazy as a child, today she loved to wander tirelessly in conspicuous places.

The eyes of men, puzzled, amused, followed the conscious swaying of her small hips, the quiver of her ripening bosom. There was neither good nor evil in her—only the stirring of blind forces awakened by a new scent. The country child's early familiarity with physiological facts precluded timidity in matters of sex and hastened the need to complete a creative cycle. The pulse of nature throbbed particularly strong in Draga. Outwardly demure, almost shy, she perverted demureness and decorum to romantic ends. Yet when openly accused by her less daring sister who, at twenty-three, was fast wilting into frustrated spinsterhood, the half-knowing girl denied all flirtatious intent.

As she elbowed her way through the mob her delicate head with its tight black curls seemed to vanish and reappear everywhere at once. The ringlets which she tossed coquettishly were the product of nightly winding around bits of tissue paper—a painful and tedious process made endurable only by its jaunty daytime results. During the late part of the nineteenth century the fashion for shorn "Roman" coiffures had taken the Western world by storm. There were few young ladies of Draga's age (in the cities, at any rate) who had the fortitude to boast heavy braids when everyone they knew wore provocative "Emperor Titus" curls.

Naturally there were always people who disapproved and wondered what the next generation was coming to. Stuffily they lamented the ravishment of that feminine fetish, "woman's crowning glory." Sabine allied herself with these and steadfastly clung to her stringy brown strands. Daily she brushed the limp growth, rubbing her scalp with butter and coaxing salves. Two or three times a year—no oftener, since this was very bad—she washed it with soap, water and orris root. But even such ministrations did not provide the anxious maiden with a husband. The village swains had a way of looking right past Sabine's angular figure and her lubricated tresses, toward the comely Draga whose pert nose, flashing eyes and frivolous antics totally eclipsed her sister's plain and reactionary person. This much the sensitive and feline Draga knew: that it was infinitely better to be a pace ahead of fashion than the merest fraction of a step behind. Also, she was well aware that city grooming combined with native costume made a piquant picture. And so, in defiance of maternal criticism, she would have her ringlets despite the discomfort entailed by their manufacture. Regardless of anyone or anything, she would always reach out for that which loomed within her grasp, no matter what the price might be. For she was Draga Lunyevica, and there could be only one of her. There was no drop of happiness which she intended to forego.

It was late when Nikodem reached the festive square. He had seen his younger sister darting past a group of tambours whose drum-sticks whipped the flounce of her swirling petticoat as she danced. Twice he had called her name but apparently she did not hear him. Anyway, he knew she was not ready to go home, and nothing short of violence could induce her to change her mind. Their poor mother had best get used to this. During army maneuvers, the harvest feast or the great processions just before Lent, Mara could never count her vagrant offspring until she saw them. For they had mind for neither food nor sleep.

After some aimless meandering Nikodem had also discovered Sabine, sitting modestly on a bench while near by, joshing a bevy of fat peasant wenches, stood Paul, his cheeks aglow from repeated sampling of cheap wines. On recognizing Nikodem, Paul waved uncertainly with an empty goat skin from which still dripped the cloudy dregs of its odorous content.

The brothers differed a great deal in temperament. Paul, by far the better looking, knew how to win his mother, sisters and the fair sex in general by little gallantries which Nikodem scorned. But both boys were in complete accord on the subject of drink. They liked a jug of the grape whenever and wherever proffered. Since the wine of the Sava region was not heady, the Lunyevicas were guilty of only mild excess when falling under its spell. At best, the sweet juices led to a brief exhilaration of the spirit, which, more often than not, ended in a good-natured brawl with youths of equally sparing dissipation.

It could not, therefore, have been alcohol that brought about the evening's scrimmage in which both soldiers and townspeople were suddenly involved. Quite unaccountably, an enormous rumpus set up in the vicinity of the kiosk. Whether it had been provoked by some female's flirtatious abandon, or the foolhardy advances of a uniformed dandy, could not be determined once the fight started. Before any motive became known, yokels and swordsmen were at one another's throats in a fierce mad scuffle. It was something the sons of Obrenovatz could not afford to miss—this chance to pull the brass buttons of the Army. Nor were the troopers slow to bash in a

couple of rustic skulls. From the start, Nikodem and Paul
had joined the fray; there was strength in their sinews
and an accumulation of rancor in their chests. The turmoil, which very nearly razed the band pavilion, was
reaching impressive proportions when the worst happened—the commandant arrived.

There had been too much noise for the trot of approaching cavalry to be heard. But now, out of a dark
side street, a mounted detachment charged against the
crowd. Foremost among them towered the well-known
director of maneuvers, Captain Dragutin Dmitriyevitch,
followed closely by his aide, Lieutenant Mihailo Masin.
While the latter restrained his horse to avoid injuring
trapped bystanders, Dragutin plunged relentlessly ahead,
cursing soundly and brandishing the gleaming steel of his
sword. The thunder of his voice shook the air, falling
like a weight upon the tense climax of the combat. Silence
followed, while the stunned contestants paused, reeling in
a fog. No one understood the secret, yet all reacted mechanically to the dominating force of this man's presence.
He was an officer, Dragutin, in the fullest sense of the
word. He embodied authority and he knew it.

"Every man to the barracks at once!" he bellowed.
"I'll tend to those responsible for this in the morning. I'll burn the hide off everyone, as long as it's a
beating you're asking for!"

Sheepishly, spectators and active participants began to
disperse. Some ambled along, rubbing bruises caused by
charging horsemen, while others took sorrowful stock of
abrasions suffered in battle. Gingerly, the band made its
way through this confusion, casting glances of devout
gratitude in the direction of Dragutin, who had arrived

just in time. For the drummer and the trombone player found themselves in a dire predicament. Both had dived into the former's instrument where, for lack of ozone, they were threatened with extinction.

As the place gradually cleared there remained in its center, perched safely on a balustrade of the kiosk, the figure of a panting radiant girl. Short black ringlets hung damply about the triumphant face of Draga Lunyevica. She had been the cause of it all, and she was very proud.

She smiled, with a hint of challenge in her bold eyes, at the menacing Dmitriyevitch. His masterful demeanor thrilled her. His martial elegance held her spellbound. Here was a man of rank, of importance, whose fury had been aroused by a disturbance which she—Draga—provoked. Willfully, too. For she had known full well that, while clinging to the arm of an attentive dragoon, it was unsafe to ogle some peasant suitor whose responsive signals were certain to be intercepted. Yet that was precisely what she had done—ogled. And with what spectacular results! Yes, Draga Lunyevica was proud. She swung seductively from the stone railing and smiled at the commanding captain. Dmitriyevitch caught the hidden sparkle in her gaze. Instantly appraising the situation, he raised his roaring voice:

"You there—it's chits of your sort who are always at the bottom of a row! Silly brats who should be sent to bed without supper——"

He followed up the stinging words by roughly pushing his mount against the balustrade, forcing Draga down. Hurriedly the girl skipped to the ground. She was mute with rage and surprise. Her cheeks crimsoned under this intolerable insult, for nothing could have been more wounding than a reference to her immaturity. She who had begun to consider herself a creature of fatal allure, and had at that very moment hoped to test her power against the first man who really stirred her, was being driven off like a street urchin by the brutal advance of his horse. Even as she picked up her skirts to run, hate and humiliation stormed within her. She knew she was cutting a ridiculous figure, not at all like the siren she fancied herself to be. The indignity of it would eat out her heart. She would be laughed at by all who had witnessed the scene, though fortunately the square did look almost empty.

She sped along. And now angry tears blinded her eyes so that she stumbled against a large clanking mass that obstructed her path. Something sharp dug into her shoulder and she gave a little cry of pain.

"Look out," said a kindly masculine voice, "not so fast, child, not so fast!" Spurs jingled. A hand reached down from somewhere to pat her head.

At this she could contain herself no longer but burst into desperate sobs. The friendly voice drew nearer. It was sympathetic, even though one could detect in it a faint undertone of amusement.

"Why such a rush? There's no one chasing you."

"Oh yes, *he* did!" She turned furiously, only to discover that her pursuer had remained far behind. Completely unmindful of her, Dragutin was rounding up lingering stragglers and heading them toward the barracks.

"See? I told you." The stranger who was so eager to comfort had a kind face topped by a fringe of sandy hair.

Draga took no further stock of him.   She asked with a shrug:

"Who is that one?"

"The Captain?"

"Of course!" She stamped her little foot. "What is his name?"

The man laughed. "Dragutin Dmitriyevitch! . . . But he is a soldier, every inch of him, that's why he seems a bit rough. Not for a *ta mlada* (small lady) to play with."

Draga resented this banter and turned away. The man looked about with uncertainty, as if searching for someone.

"Are you alone? Have you no one to take you home? It's much too late for those nice red cheeks to be on parade."

The girl's tears had subsided. True, she did not think much of this odd person who persisted in treating her like an infant, but he had—after all—noticed her cheeks. It was just what she needed. Only an ounce of encouragement; give her that and she would know how to gain ground.

"I came with my brother and sister," she said demurely, "but we were separated in the crush."

To her supreme satisfaction he dismounted. There was a click of heels. "Then, perhaps, I may have the honor?" Throwing the reins over one arm, he bowed and introduced himself. "Lieutenant of the Guards, Mihailo Masin. Where can I escort you?"

She caught her breath. A Lieutenant of the Guards, indeed! Well, what if that other one had snubbed her—here was balm for her wound. A cavalier had turned up to offer his arm. She took it eagerly, smiling up into his eyes, when an ungracious fate intervened once more. From the far end of the square three figures stalked toward her, waving frantic arms and shouting:

"Draga, Draga! Wait until Mother hears of this— it's a whipping you'll get, that's certain."

Despair overshadowed her young face. "There they come for me," she moaned, "and they've spoiled everything. But I don't get whipped," she added stubbornly, for she felt that he might laugh at her; "if I did, I'd run away."

The officer suppressed a chuckle. "I should do exactly the same. Only don't run straight into more trouble, the way you did tonight."

She was very serious. "I'd go to Belgrade," she told him.

His voice was still friendly, amused. "Fine," he agreed, "look me up when you get there. I've a lonely house on the Danube, and you might like it——"

With this he turned and leaped into the saddle. Touching his cap, he was off just as the distracted Sabine arrived, leading her less hurried brothers. The departing officer had not failed to make an impression; Sabine's face was white and pinched with envy. Her long fingers dug into Draga's shoulders as she shook the girl.

"Always starting something," she screamed venomously, "everybody knows you stirred up the fight. The whole town will be gossiping about us by morning!"

Draga sniffed. Her impudence was very cutting to the embittered sister. "Don't worry, Sabine—no one will mention you."

The others had meanwhile approached. With the astuteness of a kitten, Draga slipped her hand into that of the mellow Paul. Meekness, she knew, would soothe even Nikodem.

"If we hadn't got here in the nick of time," Sabine upbraided them all, "she would have made off with that vagabond!"

"He is a Lieutenant of the Guards," Draga murmured coyly, "and I can't help it if he shows me attention, can I?"

Nikodem, recalling the visit of Anya and the impatience with which they would be awaited at the mill, pushed resolutely toward home. "Sabine is right," he snorted, "the whole place will be talking for weeks. Mother won't like it a bit."

They moved on, Draga trailing quietly behind. Her eyes were fixed on far horizons. Over toward the east, where the starry heavens shone brightest, lay the royal town of Belgrade. The city of two rivers, the city of dreams!

"I don't care what people say," she whispered to herself, "just so they don't ever ignore me altogether."

Paul walked limply at her side, drowsy with sleep. Paul never scolded. He liked her. She squeezed his arm and exulted in her power over him. She was very grateful to Paul. He made her forget, for a moment, the unforgettable insult of Dragutin. He made her think of the sandy-haired lieutenant. What was his name? Mihailo—yes, Mihailo Masin. She must hold on to those whom she could conquer. The Pauls, the Masins, even the Nikodems—she must use them to win out in life against the Dragutins! She must, and she would.

The young Draga had become a woman.

CHAPTER VII

More Pedagogy

THE Council of Regents had reason to be satisfied. Six weeks had elapsed since the Serbian throne was vouchsafed to the child Alexander, and not a sign of unrest threatened the land. In thus retaining without murmur the heir of an unworthy king, the nation had given proof of the most scrupulous fair play. To allow the dynasty another chance was liberalism of a high order.

True, there had been the usual hotheads who were constitutionally incapable of accepting any *status quo* with grace. But fortunately these conscientious objectors were army men who could be safely ordered to the provinces. Here they could release the evil vapors of emotion without doing any particular harm. The civilian population, especially that of rural sections, gave Belgrade no cause for worry. The average Serb was far too busy with his own affairs to bother about politics. He asked for one thing only, *pravica* (justice), so that he might till his fields or ply a trade and attain economic independence— the goal of modest burghers everywhere. To the Slav peasant it was a matter of supreme indifference whether taxes were levied for the upkeep of kings, popes or sultans; it was the size of the tithe, not the identity of its collector, that occasioned many a pang.

Next to social justice the nation hungered for peace. After centuries of military conscription by foreign masters Serbia wanted a respite from war. Yet peace in the

Balkans was a dream almost too fanciful to cherish. It seemed unattainable under the blustering tactless Milan whose misrule brought frequent reproofs from his neighbors. Perhaps because of this the vision of an unformed child upon the throne held a peculiar and naïve promise, for was it not written that to the innocent belonged the kingdom of heaven? The boy Alexander would become the Prince of Peace!

To a large extent even the soldiery shared this view. Reports at headquarters indicated that the annual army maneuvers had served their purpose in diverting a possible uprising. Campfires on the Sava banks brought a zestful and most welcome change from city restraints. Germs of insubordination, bred under close discipline, were easily scattered to the winds in sham skirmishes on bucolic drill grounds. Here the more aggressive warrior had his say and felt better for it. As a result, the troops were gradually returning to their regular posts; two of the most spirited regiments, the Royal Dragoons and the Cavalry Guards, had been among the first that were recalled. They occupied their usual quarters near the *Konak,* without any further note of discard. Even Captain Dragutin Dmitriyevitch, a fellow with radical ideas who bore watching, conducted himself creditably and bridled his caustic tongue.

At the palace the new program was in full swing. A capable monitor, Father Milutin, had put his talent, his ingenuity, indeed his very soul, into the task of kingmaking. Under his expert tutelage the royal boy, free from family ties and tribal inhibition, was to be shaped into the ideal of objective education. In this Alexander the world must behold the man of the future who, deprived of parental dominance and reared by the State, would be fitted into public office like a peg into its hole.

Each morning, according to schedule, heavy footsteps resounded on the wide central staircase. Puffing audibly, Colonel Gorlice always paused on the landing to compose his pompous and asthmatic self before entering the school-room on the second floor. It was ten o'clock and Sasha's French lesson had terminated. Mademoiselle Vera's voice could be heard through closed doors:

"*Alors, Altesse, vous avez bien entendu? A demain, Altesse.*"

And, after awkward silences, the slow guttural reply: "*Parfaitement, oui.*"

Colonel Gorlice knocked once and was instantly admitted. Mademoiselle Vera was fanatically prompt and prided herself on the fact that she had never in her life kept anyone waiting. At the same time she had not permitted herself to find out whether, failing this virtue on her part, anyone would ever wait for her. Gorlice's peremptory morning knocks led to the uneasy assumption that the cadet master tolerated no delay. There were days when the governess scarcely found time to flutter across the room before the knob was sharply turned and the officer's basso rolled forth:

"Attention! It is the riding hour."

Invariably Sasha paled. Much as the prospect of becoming a soldier attracted him, he did not relish saddle drill. To begin with, although sturdier than most children of his age, he was somewhat short-limbed. The best pony available in the royal stables happened to be wide of rump, stretching the boy's legs unmercifully so that he had practically no hold whatever. Besides this, Sasha was timid by nature and had an instinctive dread of horses. It was a trait which the riding master had soon recognized and hence strove with unrelenting firmness to overcome. His efforts met with lamentably small success.

Quivering, the boy saluted and bade a halting French farewell to Mademoiselle Vera before preceding Gorlice from the room. In a few minutes they had reached the outer courtyard below. At least this was summer, and that icy wind blowing down from the Hungarian flatlands would not bite Sasha's cheeks. At least the pony would soon get hot and slacken its pace, regardless of the drill master's orders. The boy reflected on the inevitable compensations in human experience; if a thing was bad, it could apparently always be worse.

Resigned, he allowed a footman to help him onto the oversized Shetland. Yes, there was the pain in his groin. He would have to sit still for a moment and get used to it. The feeling passed and Sasha reached for the double reins, holding them in prescribed fashion: a strap of bridle and one of simple rein between the three outer fingers of each hand. This, he had memorized, allowed a good thumb-lock over his closed fists and was necessary for fast riding. Later he would learn to hold all four straps between the proper fingers of his left hand and a drawn saber in his right. He shuddered at the thought of what might follow after that, for he had already seen great hurdles bordering the parade ground where men leaped through the air in the best manner of the Spanish Riding School at Vienna or the newly planned Tor di Quinto Academy of Rome. Sasha hoped that long before such a contingency the galvanic cadet master would be wheeled about in a chair like old Crakow, the stable hand, who years ago had been thrown by a filly and broken his spine. For the present, however, Gorlice's health remained painfully robust and there was nothing for Sasha to do except obey his teacher's exacting demands.

A particular difficulty needed to be overcome. Terrified lest he fall from his mount, the child had from the beginning thrust both feet through the stirrups and caught himself firmly with the heels of his boots. But this was wrong. Colonel Gorlice tore his hair, he swore, he fumed. A gentleman placed only the ball of his foot in the stirrup, depended solely on the grip of his thighs for safety.

"It is gross, ignorant, vulgar, plebeian—to use the heels!"

Well, if it was all that, Sasha mustn't do it. He suffered. For the fine points of equestrian virtuosity were precarious. He fell innumerable times and believed himself badly injured, but since the pony was not high these tumblings were regarded as inconsequential. At length the ordeal was over and a happy interval beckoned. He would return to the palace where Nushka, who miraculously still remained out of a fast-fading past, waited for him with his toddy on a silver tray. After gulping this delicious drink he would have a steaming bath.

There had been some discussion about a royal bather who, Father Milutin decided, should henceforth be of male sex. But the Swedish masseur, engaged for this purpose after a most discriminating search, would not arrive before the first week in August. It was this circumstance which explained the presence of Nushka, who, for the time being, must continue to perform her accustomed duty.

Sasha enjoyed his bath far more than the riding lesson. Strangely, although his forebears were hardy mountaineers, he disliked the outdoors. He loved shelter, coziness, the intimacy of things he could touch. For he had inherited from his mother—who, after the manner of well-bred ladies, had spent two-thirds of her existence doing useless fancywork—a pronounced myopia. Although no one (least of all the child himself) knew it, Sasha found woodlands, gardens, parade grounds or streets an unmitigated bore, for the simple reason that there was so little in all this which he could really see. Indoors, where all experience lay close at hand, the infirmity remained unnoticed. While other short-sighted children gave themselves away at school, by their inability to see a far-removed blackboard or map, the privately tutored boy kept his secret. He would keep it perhaps for years, until the most casual chance brought out his handicap. It was Nature's most subtle joke, to work thus erratically under isolation.

Even with kind Nushka waiting for him on the second-floor landing Sasha found it a severe task, after two hours in the saddle, to make the steep climb. Sometimes, when no one below was looking, the girl came half-way down to meet him. She would help him the rest of the way, clasping him with her strong bare arms. He leaned against her then, happy beyond words. Vaguely he thought of his mother and Anya, but there was no longer the vivid reality to these mental pictures which, a long time back, had troubled him so much. Nushka now had taken Anya's place and as for his mother, the elegance and lingering softness of Queen Natalia had slowly become fused into the figure of the Countess Eudoxia. Only there was that difference—a disturbing sort of excitement which, with his dear mother, Sasha had never felt.

Weird, that intangible something, of which the boy himself was hardly conscious. Yet daily, during the hour of his bath, he experienced it. As he sat in his tub playing with water toys while Nushka gently rubbed his body he could hear the Countess Eudoxia moving about in an adjoining chamber. She would be supervising the preparations for their luncheon, he knew, for the bath was always followed by this repast in the company of the two governesses. At the sound of the Russian's voice Sasha's heart skipped a few beats. He visualized with terror how at any moment the bathroom door might open and the perfumed lady . . . Of course, this never happened. Nushka seldom forgot to lock the door, though when she did forget he noticed and reminded her of it.

At times Mademoiselle Vera's voice also could be heard, but this never bothered him. Any more than it disturbed him to gaze curiously down the loose neckline of Nushka's dress as she stooped over to scrub his toes, the while he calmly explored the brown shadows of her skin. For Nushka, the Frenchwoman, Gorlice, Father Milutin, not to mention the teacher, Abramovitch, were all alike in that they were unlike the Countess. They were, well, just people like Sasha and everybody else. They didn't sound, smell or look mysterious. They couldn't, even in anger, make him feel confused as he did when Countess Eudoxia moved about outside his bathroom door. In this she differed even from his mother, and Sasha had thought his mother the most beauteous creature of his phantom dream world.

His somewhat erotic emotions vanished during luncheon. Exercise, sunshine and the subsequent bath had given him a strong appetite, and at sight of his food he forgot the alluring lady altogether. Unlike his earlier habit, he now ate fast and with concentration until reproved by the mincingly fastidious Mademoiselle Vera. After the repast he was overcome by sheer exhaustion. Nushka came in at once and led the child to a near-by divan where he dropped into deep slumber. The others tiptoed from the room.

Over-fed and over-stimulated, the little majesty slept. Behind Venetian blinds in an adjoining salon the Countess Eudoxia planned his royal afternoon. She chatted softly with her spiritual counselor, Father Milutin.

CHAPTER VIII

Sasha Learns to See

IT WAS the schoolmaster, Abramovitch, who in the end most deeply affected Sasha's development. The small gray man who arrived each day, after breakfast was over, to review the child's grammar and numbers (before Mademoiselle Vera put in a very Gallic appearance) was possessed of rare intuition. In the first place, he had a natural affection for the young. Teaching was his vocation. He loved it. Knowing well how few men were permitted to follow a career of their own choosing, he felt himself to be most fortunate. Again and again this realization filled him with an inner glow of tranquil satisfaction. As a consequence, he was an excellent pedagogue—a peaceful, sympathetic soul in whose very presence the awakening mind of childhood found thriving strength. Whether he dealt in conjugations or a complex algebraic formula, he had a way of breathing life into these things. Teacher Abramovitch refreshed stale platitudes and axioms with the dew of his imagination. And he had often been rewarded by the sudden bursting into bloom of just this quality in his small listeners.

But with Sasha things were different. Sasha did not learn well. From the beginning, Master Abramovitch had felt attracted to the round-faced boy whose loneliness touched him so profoundly. He had liked the child's unaffected manner, his trusting simplicity. There must be a good brain at work under those black unruly locks,

85

for the boy's instinctive logic seemed at times uncanny, and his grasp of the spoken word ranked far above the average. With what passionate rapture, for instance, did Sasha listen to the ancient saga of the Serbs. He would sit entranced while Abramovitch recited the ballads of Tsar Lazar, Milosh Obilitch, the wicked Sultan, or Vuk Branko whose bravery in battle made a legend. Then there was the famous Kralyevitch Matías living, like Barbarossa, in a cave under the earth and watching his white beard entwine itself about a marble table until the time when he would return to bless his people. It was with especial eloquence that Abramovitch next dwelt on the heroic Slav mother who had lost a husband and nine sons on the tragic plain of Kossovo, yet wept only because she had not more to give.

"I don't believe that," said Sasha quietly.

"But she is the symbol of our Serbia," insisted the disconcerted teacher.

Sasha remained firm. "She cried because she saw them killing all those children, and their father too!" To him the sons of the Slav mother were defenseless boys, not unlike himself. He knew very well that Mama, even as dimly as he nowadays remembered her, would not have wanted another Sasha to be disemboweled (the Turks did that) after her only Sasha had already been disemboweled. No indeed.

Following this embarrassing clash of opinions, Abramovitch had deleted the offensive folk tale. In his heart he knew that if a child rejected it, it most certainly could not be true. Instead, he retold the tender story of the lovely maiden of Kossovo who, like a Valkyrie, shielded the brave troops of the Tsar. She was of course a *vilya*, this maiden, and did not exist in the flesh. For the hills and valleys of Serbia were full of fair wood nymphs and benevolent sprites who, if people were kind and deserving, brought untold blessings in their train. Sasha firmly believed in *vilyé;* he had several favorites hovering about the *Konak* gardens. He would conjure them up to his window at night, so that they might ward off evil dreams. In short, the maid of Kossovo suited him perfectly; he knew all about her.

No, as regarded Sasha's grasp of his country's remarkable history, Abramovitch could not complain. It was in other, rather more essential fields, that the boy showed alarming weakness. After months of steady effort Sasha's reading continued faulty, his script illegible even to himself. Although he recited mathematical tables with relative accuracy he was utterly unable to solve written problems. While copying his teacher's corrections the boy still made mistakes which left Abramovitch in a quandary. What, then, was wrong? Never before had the patient pedagogue known his methods to be so fruitless

Not until now were the child's powers of vision questioned. Abramovitch himself undertook the first practical tests. Sasha's eyes behaved abnormally at close and far range; he was on the threshold of adolescence without having ever beheld the world about him as others saw it. He needed glasses and needed them badly. When he got them they became a permanent fixture.

The boy's reaction to this innovation was astounding. For days he could not be held in check and it seemed that he had time neither to eat nor drink. He flatly refused to lie down for his usual nap; he would not sit still for a moment. Too much newness had suddenly rushed down

upon him. He must discover all that he had missed!
Outdoors there were big trees shaking a myriad tiny
leaves where before he had seen only a blotch of green.
From his balcony at night the heavens looked like a mass
of glittering points where until now he had never noticed
more than a faint gleam piercing the darkness. Such darkness of dull black as he had known! No wonder he was
afraid of the night and her veil of shadows. . . .

Within the palace many more surprises awaited him.
There was the Crystal Salon. Here, on rare occasions,
the boy made polite answers to a group of solemn gentlemen who, he was told, safeguarded his future. But now
this cold white space, which had seemed to him like the
Ice Queen's hall in the fairy tale, was transformed into a
gigantic jewel box encrusted with ornament and set off
by a thousand facets. Staring through his thick-lensed
spectacles Sasha counted the bits of crystal in the scintil-
lating chandeliers. He also scrutinized each delicate line
etched upon Mademoiselle Vera's anæmic face, and his
fascinated gaze lingered upon queer discolorations in the
copper tresses of the Countess Eudoxia until that lady
made silent vows to employ greater skill in her use of the
dye pot.

Having awakened to this new reality the child's temperament suffered a sharp change. Always of an intensely curious disposition, his hunger for concrete
information now exceeded all bounds. Not that his interest in lessons grew. Their daily recurrence long ago had
palled. Governor and tutors alike had drummed their
knowledge into him with such unfaltering constancy that
his tympanum throbbed at times with their incessant

drone. He had come to regard bookish learning with a hearty distaste.

But Sasha's attention was directed elsewhere. In a muddled way he knew that important circumstances were attached to his birth. Yet the real significance of his position had so far escaped him. Nor was this in any way unusual. England's Queen Victoria is said to have reached her eleventh birthday before discovering that she was heiress to a crown.

In Sasha's case a trifling incident had aroused the first suspicions. Nushka, the last link with a past that now was gone forever, had finally been sent from the palace. In her place functioned the Swedish successor from whose lips Sasha's ears had caught a strange remark. The bather and gymnast, henceforth in charge of Serbia's royal child, had nervously inquired if His Majesty used a bath shirt. Sasha had never heard of a bath shirt and he had never been addressed as "His Majesty" before.

Father Milutin, hearing of the incident, took the manservant aside for consultation. Bath shirts, then in use among prudish gentlefolk who employed attendants for their cleansings, were approved by the ascetic governor, but further reference to Sasha's kingship was barred. The time for such a revelation had, in Milutin's opinion, not arrived. But its postponement was no longer possible, now that the *lapsus linguæ* had occurred. For the novelty of wearing a soaked garment under the clumsy folds of which only the most inadequate ablutions could take place, eventually wore off. But the mystery of the bather's first address remained.

His Majesty! He, Sasha, had been called by a name

which belonged to—everybody knew that—emperors and kings. Of course, it was quite possible that the servant had been jesting, like Anya when she spoke of her princelet, her lambkin or her cub. Sasha himself used these pet designations; his loveliest *vilya* was a princess.

But what if this thing were true? What if he grew up some day to be an emperor? Maybe that was what his father had been. The gentlemen who came to the Crystal Salon always spoke in whispers about his father. And how their faces changed when they talked among themselves! In fact, faces took on the most amazing expressions, now that Sasha could see. People who weren't servants at all, tall soldiers and elegant ladies, lowered their eyes like servants when the boy happened to meet them in the palace. Foreigners came at times to visit Mademoiselle Vera or the Countess Eudoxia and Sasha observed that in crossing his path they were overcome by the same subdued gravity.

His faulty reading having rapidly improved, he noticed other things: inscriptions under family portraits, book plates, letter heads. There were small coronets embossed on all these things, but of course he did not know that other people had no coronets. Such symbols were not nearly as attractive, and to him far less important, than the elaborate polychromes which embellished his collection of cigar boxes and bands.

From still another source he gleaned more substance for speculation. Occasional newspapers carried photographs on which he recognized himself riding Krasny, the Caucasian thoroughbred (he had graduated from Shetland ponies). The captions read, somewhat cryptically, "Alexander in the *Konak* Gardens" or "Our

Sasha at Play." Our Sasha! Whose Sasha? What did it mean?

He asked Abramovitch point-blank. "Who am I? If you know who I am please tell me."

The little gray man turned, if possible, a shade paler. "Why," he groped for words, "you are Alexander Obrenovitch who will some day——"

The boy's eyes were pinned to his teacher's lips. But now the timid pedagogue grew evasive.

"—who will some day do great things for Serbia," he finished carefully.

"Like Colonel Gorlice," asked Sasha perplexed, "do I have to train soldiers and show them how to ride?"

The teacher sidestepped hurriedly. "Better than that," he said, "but you must ask Father Milutin. He knows everything. Abramovitch knows only books and figures."

The boy felt disheartened. The prospect of going to Father Milutin for enlightenment was depressing. The stern governor whose religious precepts Sasha obeyed conscientiously, even to the point of wearing the obnoxious bath shirt, did not inspire confidences. But in the end it was the only thing to do.

Sunday afternoon. Mademoiselle and the Countess had retired to their own quarters for a period of privacy and rest. Sasha wandered through long corridors toward the wing occupied by Father Milutin. With beating heart he approached the governor's room and knocked on the door. A rustling movement followed within but no answer. Bewildered, he put his hand on the knob and called out softly:

"Father Milutin—it's Sasha—please, I've come to see you."

There was a pause before the door opened. Rigid and gaunt, the governor stood in its frame. "What do you want? This is no time, Highness, to meander about the halls."

"Highness," Sasha reflected. Quite recently they were beginning to call him that. It had something to do with, perhaps even led up to, all this mystery. "Please," he asked, "may I come in and talk to you?"

Father Milutin jerked the door another inch and indicated a chair. Sasha sat down on the edge of it. He drew a short breath. The air in the room was strange, not unpleasantly soothing, and somehow almost palpable. Sasha relaxed. The interview would be easier than he had anticipated.

Milutin stood silently. He had not moved from his place near the door. He was waiting. Suddenly the child blurted out:

"You can tell me, Father, so I've come to ask you. Who am I? Where do I belong?" Through shining spectacles his small black eyes met those of Milutin. The priest stared stonily ahead but said nothing.

"Why do you call me Highness?" the boy asked again. "It means something. I want to know what it means."

Milutin's fists locked until the knuckles showed white. "I expected this to happen," he said slowly, "although not quite so soon. But I determined to answer when the time came."

Flushed and breathless the boy jumped to his feet. Milutin stiffened into a granite-like statue as he uttered the next words:

"By the grace of God, you are the *Kralj!* You inherited the throne of Serbia at a tender age. . . ."

Sasha sat down again. So that was it! In a way, he didn't really feel surprised. For a long time he had clothed himself in imaginary greatness, wondering only whether he had been kidnapped by the wicked Turks and brought here from some distant land, or whether—and this he far preferred—he might be descended from one of those heroic figures in the Slavic *pyesmé,* the song-poems recited by the faithful Abramovitch. To be the heir of kings, or better still, of glorious Emperor Dushan (there was a difference between being imperial and merely royal) had been an issue often debated in his dreams.

The question troubled him. Again he turned to the man in the cassock who seemed to have authority over everything.

"But my mother and father—tell me about them! Where are they? Doesn't this house belong to them?"

Milutin shook his head. At last he answered, ambiguously. "They came before you, and their day is done."

This was no help at all. A wave of childish impatience swept over Sasha. "But if I am King," he persisted, "nobody can tell me what to do, can they?"

The governor's eyes narrowed. "Since you are not of age and as yet only an uncrowned Highness, I am responsible for your actions until your eighteenth year. Do not forget that for the present you are King in theory only."

The boy's brain reeled in confusion. What sense did all this make? One moment he was a sovereign with a throne, and in the next he must behave like a school-boy.

"When I am eighteen I can see my mother?" he asked

half-heartedly. He was not nearly so happy as a minute ago.

"Perhaps," Milutin said, "though I advise strongly against it. A step of this sort is easily misconstrued, it will be best to go on—er—as before. Was that all you wished to know?"

The boy nodded and rose with the uncertain movements of a somnambulist. A moment later he stood alone in the hall, the door closing softly behind him. He pressed a cold hand against his throat. What had Milutin said? Eighteen. When Sasha was eighteen he would come of age. He would be a real king—a king whom even Milutin could not defy! The thought of his mother returned to him again. Ah, yes—he would visit her! He must find out now where she lived and plan everything beforehand, even though years would drag by with intolerable slowness until he finally reached her. But Sasha's mind was made up. To go to his mother would be his first act of kingship.

Stirred by these emotions he now remembered something else. It had to do with that baffling—yet somehow familiar—atmosphere of Father Milutin's room. There had been a quality in the air, a scent, an overpowering sweetness. . . . That was it! The perfume of the Countess Eudoxia.

How odd. Where did Milutin get it? And why had no one opened the door when Sasha first knocked? Milutin had been in the room all the time, yet he delayed in opening the door. And the Countess, did she give away her perfume? This thought somehow rankled so that he felt a twinge of jealousy. Oh, there were many things he must find out. Could it be——? Did that rus-

tling sound behind Milutin's door, and the long pause
before it opened, argue that the sanctimonious governor
was not alone? Was the red-haired Countess——?

The boy's imagination was feverishly at work. As in
the Roman Church, Greek Catholic laymen knew the
Scriptures only through interpretation from the pulpit,
but Sasha now recalled Biblical passages scanned furtively
while Father Milutin was absent from the oratory. He
also remembered having pored, one recent afternoon, over
a book of African travels which he had discovered on a
dusty shelf in the palace library. Mademoiselle Vera
had found him crouching in a stuffy corner behind the
terrestrial globe. She had fairly screamed with shock.
Like a hawk she had pounced upon the "unseemly"
volume, snatching it from his hands. He never caught
sight of it again. But he reconstructed what he wished
from memory. There had been pictures, in the book,
of brown naked women who reminded him of Nushka—
Nushka who had been so careless of her dress while bathing him. Yes, he remembered. There was a look of
sudden age upon his face, as he crept stealthily back to
his own room.

CHAPTER IX

ADOLESCENCE

As IF by the swift strokes of an artist's brush Sasha's world began to gain perspective. The boy grew daily more conscious of his own unique position and began in a childish way to speculate upon its possibilities. Gradually he realized, and was somewhat taken aback by the discovery, that all the anxious disciplinarians who at present controlled him were in reality his subordinates. The day was approaching when they would bow their heads before him, obeying his commands, where now he must bend to their bidding. A strange thought and a slightly terrifying one.

From the balcony of his bedroom the puzzled boy looked out upon the paved *Teraziye* which formed an impressive approach to the *Konak* gardens. So he was foreordained to be King of Serbia! But this, the wide space out there and the long strip beyond called Milosh Street, was all this Serbia? And did it belong to him as his bed belonged to him, and his air pistol, and his dog-eared *Robinson Crusoe?* If so, what was he supposed to do with it? Why wasn't he out there now—in his Serbia—right this minute, talking to those amazing children who collected daily at the park gates and watched the sentry change! Who were they? And did they know that he, Sasha, was the King? Well, if he was the King, why were there so many things he didn't know and couldn't do? Contriving to get those children in here, for instance, and telling them about himself. Or finding his mother. Oh, he remembered his mother with particular ardor, especially since lately there burned in his breast this fierce resentment against the Countess Eudoxia.

He smelled again the perfume in Milutin's room. It was wrong for his governor and the Countess——

Sasha realized abruptly how long he had hated Milutin. Ever since those twilight hours on the garden terrace when, years ago, Countess Eudoxia read Russian fables to him and Milutin joined them. ("Happened along" *he* put it, but Sasha knew better.) Of course, that disrupted the happy idyl. Invariably the boy would be sent on stupid walks among the flower beds below, a form of exercise he heartily detested, for it entailed the cheerless company of Mademoiselle Vera. True, on such occasions the Countess kissed him on both cheeks and promised a nice surprise at supper time, but generally the surprise turned out to be that Milutin's presence dispelled Eudoxia's urge to keep a pledge of any kind.

Well, at least he had overheard their frequent whisperings about his mother. This he had ferreted out: that she lived alone in France, the place where Mademoiselle Pellingre came from. And now he swore to himself that nothing should stop him. He would go and find her. He would bring his mother back to the *Konak*, to stay with him forever. And she would use a perfume many times sweeter than that of the faithless Countess! She would love him, too, as he wanted to be loved. She would live only for Sasha.

Little did the lonely boy suspect that twice within the past few years Natalia Kesko had made clandestine visits to Serbia. On both occasions she had reached Belgrade,

determined to assert her rights as former queen. With
equal pertinacity, though less tact, the Council of Regents
had in turn informed her that—as a private citizen—she
would not be permitted to reside at the palace. Whereupon, in a paroxysm of tears and bitter remonstrations,
the fretful lady departed. She had lacked the humble
abasement necessary for a reunion with her son.

In like manner King Milan several times returned to
his former capital, availing himself of the privileges
granted in the divorce. By these provisions an annual
visit between the royal child and his estranged parents
might take place in an audience chamber of the *Konak*.
In awe and trepidation Sasha heard the reports of his
father's arrival. Consumed with a wild curiosity he
waited each time for the long-expected visit. But Milan
was unavoidably detained. On his way to the palace the
incorrigible philanderer was wont to pass the house of a
former mistress, Artemisia, wife of the ex-King's private
secretary. The time allotted for Milan's sojourn in Belgrade being brief and strictly defined, it was impossible
to take cognizance of Sasha's development on the one
hand, and the imminent decline in Madame Artemisia's
charms on the other. A choice between these two being
imperative, the kingly rogue obeyed a greedy impulse. In
years to come there still would be young Sasha, but with
Artemisia autumn had begun. . . .

Hurt by repeated disappointment, the child grew moody
and silent. His days and nights were filled with brooding.
He was beset by the morbid impulses of adolescence and
became increasingly difficult to handle. For the first time
in his life there now sprang up within him all the self-
willed obstinacy of his breed. In an effort to test his

authority he began to torment footmen and other palace servants, shouting at them or giving absurd commands. During school hours he dismayed Mademoiselle Vera and the harmless Abramovitch by refusing point-blank to answer their questions.

His fourteenth birthday was observed with a boat excursion to the river town of Shabatz. Somewhere along the way the boy observed, with cold and sullen eyes, that a cheering multitude thronged the Sava banks. He turned to Minister Chedo Mijatovitch.

"Why do they make all that noise?"

"It must be," the Minister replied, "because they love you."

Sasha's face darkened.

"I don't believe it," he said petulantly. "If they love me, let them prove it. Let them throw their hats into the water."

There was an embarrassed interval. Seeing his entourage at a loss for an answer, the boy suddenly turned shoreward and raised his voice:

"Mijatovitch says you love me! If it's true, throw your hats into the water!"

At this the cheers were doubled. Jubilant over the fact that their little sovereign took notice and asked for so paltry a sign, the good people of Shabatz bared their heads and parted with their Sunday raiment. In less than a minute the river was gaily dotted with a flock of kerchiefs, caps, bonnets, spreading like a sea of mushrooms in the sun. On deck, standing apart from his companions, the boy looked on, baffled, gratified.

The memory of it never left him. So! At the merest utterance of a whim, grown men and women were willing,

nay eager, to obey. Then he must test his power again,
just to make sure. He must see if it worked twice.

On the parade grounds during drill exercise, shortly
after the river journey, Sasha suddenly cried out:

"Battalion, salute!"

To his delight every soldier present, including Colonel
Gorlice himself, stood rigidly at attention. At sight of
these giants falling into line like row upon row of toy
marionettes, the lad's eyes glowed behind their concave
lenses and he burst into a proud laugh. The son of Milan
had come into his own. For it was plain to see, his would
be the heritage of the Obrenovitch, the heavy temper of
their truculent clan.

From the parade grounds that day a tall figure on horseback departed with angry clanking of spurs. Along
the path to the barracks another rode slowly, peacefully,
as if lost in leisure daydreams. Without looking to right
or left, the first man stormed past and nearly collided
with an unobliging lamp post.

"You might watch where you're going," Lieutenant
Masin called after him good-naturedly and, having done
so, fell back into his reverie. The other turned furiously
about. His summer-bronzed features were flushed, and
through tight lips he emitted a salubrious oath which
caused Masin to stare up into his face.

"Well, of all people—Dragutin! *Zdravo,* old man!"

"Oh, it's you——" Dmitriyevitch grumbled inaudible
apologies.

"Yes," Masin agreed genially, "and, I believe, you!"

Black eyebrows frowned. Their owner growled omi-
nously.

"If I could help it, it wouldn't be. Not in Serbia at

this moment, anyway, forced to witness the comedy that is about to begin. We, who should be leading a Balkan federation, spend our time clowning in full regalia for the amusement of a puppet-show court."

"My dear fellow," Masin interposed, "you do work up a lather over trifles. Just because we had to salute at the boy's command——"

"You mean His Majesty," sneered Dragutin.

"Very well. It's true, isn't it? You saw even Gorlice presenting arms. We all know that the Regency has only a few more years to go. As for a court—when there is no one but the child—I don't get your drift."

Dmitriyevitch glared impatiently. "I suppose you didn't see the *Konak* windows plastered with leering mugs of lackeys, footmen, serving wenches and that fakir Milutin. They make up the distinguished court I had in mind. It's for their elation that we prance about like the chorus in a provincial theater."

Masin laughed. "At that, you're a very effective *basso profundo*," he said. The remark went unnoticed.

"Judging from advance symptoms," Dragutin continued, "young Cæsar is beginning to feel his oats. Looks as if there'd be lively times ahead."

"Which isn't going to worry me a lot," Masin announced with apparent indifference.

The two men had resumed a light trot toward the barracks. Dragutin now gave his companion a sidelong glance. In a frozen voice he retorted:

"That's no news. We've all known for some time that you're not interested in the things that matter to your comrades. You don't care a rap for the dignity of the Army."

Masin's eyes widened. "What on earth do you mean?" he bristled.

"Nothing much. You've stayed away from the Casino for months, when in former years you practically owned a bunk there. You can't blame people for noticing the difference."

"I've been busy."

"Oh, yes. No doubt about it. That's exactly what everyone is saying; you're busy—elsewhere."

Mihailo bridled in defense. "You don't understand, Dragutin. Damn it, I've had Voyan's future on my mind. The boy finished school in St. Petersburg this spring and we had to find a place for him. You realize how responsible I am for my brother's career——"

Dragutin interrupted him. "It isn't Voyan," he said coolly, "it's that other business. They tell me you are contemplating wedlock with a lady of—well—very obscure antecedents. Or so your reluctance to confide in anyone has led people to believe."

The color had faded from Lieutenant Masin's face. "I think, Dragutin," he countered slowly, his lips set in a white line, "that you have said quite enough. My private life happens to be strictly my own affair."

"Then it is true," the other flashed.

"What?"

"That you're in love like a silly schoolboy."

"Right." A faraway look came into Masin's pale eyes. "Like a stupid, sentimental schoolboy. Love rather shunned me when I was younger; today I welcome it with all my heart. Do you mind?"

"At least you explain your present tastes. I hear that the lady of your choice is only half your age. That on top of the discrepancy in your respective stations——"

Masin cut in sharply. "The small discrepancy, my friend, has been taken care of. The lady in question already bears my name."

Dmitriyevitch was petrified. "Ah!" he gasped. "Then you pattern your life without regard for the canons of our class, you, a Guardsman——"

"Perhaps. At any rate, Draga Lunyevica and I were married more than a month ago."

With ironic emphasis the other repeated the name. "Draga—*The Dear One*—in the dialect of Rudnecker mountain folk!"

"Yes," Masin nodded exictedly, "lovely, isn't it?"

"The Lunyevica part reeks a bit of the soil."

Masin shrugged his shoulders. "Too bad about that. It happens that our national existence is bound up with the soil. Serbia was always a country of swineherds."

"Oh, come now, we've developed a few new trades."

"Not enough to make much difference. We still recognize no nobility and consider titles illegal unless foreigners use them. Even our dynasty lacks royal blood. Do you suppose our Sasha shows the necessary quarterings in his escutcheon to win himself a Romanov or Hapsburg bride?"

"Your democratic views are refreshing, especially since there was a *Knese* (lord) among your ancestors. I should think this fact would prove an asset to Voyan, now that you are grooming him for the diplomatic service."

"Voyan doesn't need to play with extinct honors."

"No one would criticize him if he did. We should deem it rare judgment on his part if he were to revive a patent conferred by Tsar Dushan."

"Let me catch him at it——"

"On the other hand, you're the one who offends the social credo by choosing a rustic mate. I trust you're prepared to face the consequences."

"Don't worry. My wife is unaccustomed to city life and sets no store by pomp or circumstance. We shan't cause you the faintest embarrassment."

Dmitriyevitch felt plainly the gap that widened between him and his life-long friend. He wanted to dismiss caste prejudice and clasp Masin's hand, wishing him happiness. But he mocked instead:

"Although she's not from Belgrade, I assume your bride to be at least of Serbian birth?"

Masin caught the implication. "Neither Moslem nor Jewess," he replied calmly, "but as good a Slav as you. In fact, I might as well admit that it was you who brought us together."

The other stared aghast. He opened his mouth in protest but could think of nothing adequate to say.

Masin laughed aloud.

"You don't remember," he explained, "since you could scarcely have known it at the time."

"I'll report you for slander," Dragutin snorted. "No man will ever blame me for his own tangle of domestic apron strings."

"What, a woman-hater?"

"Yes, and a confirmed one."

"Understand, I don't claim that you introduced me to my wife. Only, some years back, you happened to break up a brawl in the public square of Obrenovatz."

"Go on. Sounds very promising——"

"In that fracas an innocent girl was nearly crushed

under your brute of a stallion. I tried to extricate her from her plight, that's all."

"You don't mean the vixen who caused that rumpus and then sat back to enjoy it like a pantomime staged for her own pleasure!"

"Oh, no," Masin protested guilelessly, "my Draga would never do that."

"Perish the thought. Well, tell me the rest. As I remember we left within a fortnight; how and when did you two reach an understanding?"

"We didn't. I just told her that if she ever visited Belgrade and I could be of service she must call on me."

Dmitriyevitch nodded with bland comprehension. "Which she promptly did?"

"Not soon enough," murmured Masin, wearing a pensive look, "it was not until recently that I saw her again. She ran away from home where they didn't appreciate her."

"Seeking her fortune in the city, is that it?"

Mihailo was swept on by the waves of his devotion. "Dragutin," he declared with bathos, "you don't understand. You know nothing of Draga's beauty, her trusting nature, her helplessness!"

"Hm——" commented the other without regret.

"It was I, of course, who fell in love with her," Masin rambled on with superfluous candor. "All she wanted in Belgrade, poor darling, was work."

Dmitriyevitch could find no hold for the hooks of his cynicism. Also his own emotions betrayed him, for he was unable to discount the very real fondness that linked him to Mihailo. He decided to give up the struggle and to retreat as gracefully as possible from his earlier carping standpoint. After all, since Mihailo had got himself into this mess one must make the best of it.

"Well, you crazy buzzard," he grumbled, a shade of brusque tenderness creeping into his tone, "I guess you've cooked your dish and now you'll eat it. Here's luck." He held out his hand. Masin took it.

"Thanks!"

"By the way, how did Voyan take the news?"

Masin paused uneasily. "He doesn't know yet. You see, he was in Montenegro at the time, winning his spurs with the Foreign Office. But I've given Voyan the best years of my life, so he's bound to approve. Wait till he sees Draga! Those two youngsters will be mad about each other."

Dmitriyevitch whistled through his teeth. "No doubt they will," he said.

Aware of the near-by stable the horses accelerated their gait so that Dragutin's words were drowned in the thunder of their hoofs. As the long row of barracks came into view the men reached the end of their ride. Dmitriyevitch made a sharp turn toward headquarters while Masin hailed his orderly who lingered at the gates with a fresh mount. With a last wave of hands the officers parted and Masin changed horses, after which he and Anton headed for the inner city.

PART TWO

DRAGA

CHAPTER X

THE BRIDE

FOR the first time in her life, Draga Lunyevica felt that she had really accomplished something. Not only had she escaped the confining bonds of her family but, through an unexpected marriage, she had found a far more desirable stage whereon to enact the drama of her existence. This marriage—to a man who had access to the highest circles—surprised no one more than the girl herself.

True, she had come to Belgrade with the purely hypothetical intention of pursuing a career. Great-Aunt Anya had done it, hadn't she? And that at a time when no one had heard of a career for women! Draga was very emphatic in stressing this angle, lest she be accused of establishing a precedent. As to the exact nature of her career, she preferred to remain vague. The pretext had been offered largely as blandishment for her distraught mother and older sister, whose tearful farewells were rich in dismal prophecy. For this was an age when not even progressive England, flouncing along in Victorian furbelows, recognized female emancipation of any category other than that known as the world's most ancient profession. To the Lunyevica household Draga's flight spelled worry and disgrace. But then, the Lunyevicas did not know their Draga!

She had cherished the dream of going to the great city ever since that eventful night on the crowded square of Obrenovatz. She had guarded in her memory, as clear as an etching, the name of Mihailo Masin. The day would come when this foresight must reap a pleasing reward. If nothing more, the gallant officer might take her about and show her the town. She hoped to impress him with her helplessness and perfect confidence in his support. Though her poor mother had sobbed and pleaded when the girl ran off, she meant to imply that an intolerant parent had driven her from home. In her despair she had come to him. Perhaps he would be touched. Perhaps he would be kind. Who could tell? Perhaps for her sake he would be even a little bit foolish.

He was. Recalling her extreme youth at the time of his own lighthearted promise, he felt now in a sense responsible for her blind leap. Mihalio Masin was burdened with a conscience which became easily alarmed. This reckless girl. . . . Could he turn her loose in the glittering, sinful metropolis? He noticed that she was very pretty. No, he must do something for her.

And so it was that Draga found lodging with a respectable family who lived not far from the Masin mansion. A little way up the street there was even a school for seamstresses, where one could take lessons in cutting or fine embroidery. Not a bad idea, opined the landlady at the *pension,* what with every well-to-do family in Belgrade employing a private seamstress. There was a premium on girls who could turn out a proper leg-o'-mutton sleeve. Young women who were serious about their work and not just courting adventure (here the landlady fixed a gimlet eye on her new roomer) could save up a neat penny in no time at all. Draga thought she would have to think about it.

Thus far her dreams had materialized beautifully.

With the faithful Masin at her beck and call, she soon
became versed in the ways of the city. Daily they visited
the show-places of Belgrade, the *Teraziye* gardens, the
Kalimegdan park overlooking the confluence of Danube
and Sava, Milosh Street with its double row of shops.
Everywhere the vivacious girl attracted attention. Everywhere she, in turn, took stock of her environment and
the possibilities it might contain. For this was not all
Draga wanted. It was a good start—toward something
better.

The inflamed Mihailo's offer of marriage frankly surprised her. It came abruptly and without warning. She
had never speculated upon him as a possible husband,
nor had she thought of him in a romantic way. He was
a man of diametrically opposite temperament, at least
twice her age and, though not unattractive, without physical appeal. Naturally in one respect he far surpassed the
heavy-featured peasant swains who lingered about the old
mill on summer evenings, for his manner was urban and
marked by a quiet distinction. But her fancy was not
captivated by quiet distinction. Rather did it respond
to the vigor and dash of another she had seen, a dark
fierce *Boyar* who—her instinct told her—was not easily
won by mere woman. That other whose name—
Dragutin—was so similar to her own: had she not come
to Belgrade with the secret design to conquer him?

And now, here was Masin. He would be a kind and
generous husband, the sort of man it really behooved her
to want. She did not love him. But he offered practical
advantages. Draga Lunyevica had never been spoiled.
She knew poverty and the drabness of manual labor.
She loved the trappings of more privileged classes

and would go to any lengths in order to obtain them.
In return for jewels, silken robes and carriages it would
be simple to offer so small a thing as gratitude or even
love. Possession, she reasoned, could not but inspire
affection. Luxuries (to one who had never known them
before) carried an almost aphrodisiac lure which could
beguile, no matter how unglamorous their dispenser.

Of course, inexperienced as she was, the girl considered Masin a man of wealth. He drove in a crested
landau, didn't he? He was slated for a captaincy on
New Year's Day next, wasn't he? And, most important
of all, as Draga Masin she would rise to greater eminence
than anyone in her poor village ever aspired to. In the
spring of the year they were married.

Once she had become mistress of the house on the
Danube Quay Draga's pride expanded. The manage-
ment of so sizable a ménage (in her honor the unoccupied
portion had been reopened) proved a delight. She allied
herself cheerfully with Anton and the servant girl who
performed house duties. But her own provincial dialect
which she had not yet been able to blend with city speech
led to excessive familiarity, even disrespect, from the domestics. Hearing Draga's vernacular, Anton and the
housemaid Luba regarded the new mistress as no better
than themselves. Their informal conviviality became
embarrassing and led eventually to a studied aloofness on
the part of the annoyed bride. She ended by addressing
the servants only in her husband's presence and assuming
the airs of an inaccessible duchess when he was away.
Only thus could she keep Luba from romping into her
boudoir for an hour's chit-chat, or Anton from retailing
the sort of back stairs anecdote that necessitated a con-

fidential wink. In an earlier day Draga would have
roared lustily at such piquant morsels. But now she was
engrossed in the serious business of becoming a lady, a
process which robbed her of her sense of humor. She
found the manservant's Rabelaisian utterances quite un-
funny.

Her pursuit of culture covered various fields. First
of all she took up the study of elocution, a most fashionable pastime of that era. Daily she recited reams of
poetry for which her teacher, a retired *diseuse,* supplied
elaborately illustrative gestures. To wit: hands crossed
on bosom denoted holiness or devotion, right fist thrust
heavenward showed patriotism or heroic wrath, left hand
on heart was passionate bereavement, while feet set at
right angles (with toes pointing outward in an enterprising manner) meant going somewhere in a great hurry.
It was an absorbing art for which Draga seemed particularly fitted. She was tireless in her study, performing
ardently before the tall cheval glass in her bedroom. Nor
did all this effort lack therapeutic value, since the calis-
thenics entailed by gesturing alone provided good setting-
up exercises.

Having become proficient in the Sapphic graces Draga
turned next to music for which, on the other hand, she
had no talent whatever. Sitting at the piano picking out
scales, while a meticulous metronome clicked its doleful
measure, soon wearied her and presently she exchanged
arpeggios for the conjugation of French verbs. A certain Monsieur Simonet, who used atrocious pomade on
his hair but was otherwise very charming indeed, arrived
each noon with a syllabus of delightfully nasal Gallic
terms. Furthermore, having observed a time-worn

heraldic device carved into the lintel of the Masin doorway, he promptly addressed his pupil as *Madame La
Baronne,* an appellation which pleased Draga no end.
Henceforth she doubled her exertions to command the
vast vocabulary of the gallant Gaul.

But despite these occupations there remained long afternoons of idleness. Tired of lessons, the transplanted
country bride lolled about her boudoir, going over stereop-
ticon views of the Kremlin citadel, the Vatican libraries,
St. Sofia's Basilica in Constantinople, the Pyramid of
Cheops, a lovers' tryst, the interior of the Pasha's harem,
gold-diggers in the Klondike, a blooming cactus, and
scenes from the private life of a whale. When the novelty
of this was exhausted and other indoor diversions palled,
there were long rides in the carriage through public parks
and thoroughfares. Now and then Draga stopped to
drink fresh *yoghurt* (similar to Bulgarian sour milk) at a
sidewalk café while her eyes surveyed the passer-by. She
felt very satisfied, very important. It was the sort of
thing which she hoped to do for the rest of her life. She
belonged. She was the wife of a royal Guardsman and
as such a member of the nation's élite.

It required several months of self-deception before the
realization struck her that she was nothing of the kind,
and that—despite her finery, her fond devoted husband,
the house on the Danube with its handsome old furnish-
ings—she was a lonely village child starving for human
contacts. Hers were the lovely, if not elaborate, Masin
jewels. Hers both horse and carriage. Yet what profit was
there in these treasures, and in all her new accomplish-
ments, when Belgrade refused to accept her as its own?
Yes, she had gradually noticed. Regardless of her pretty

clothes, her knowledge, her assiduously cultivated grand manner, people left her strictly alone. No one ever came to visit and Draga knew no place to go. What advantage was there then in being an officer's wife, if the wives of fellow officers barred her from their society?

Only when her husband's generosity failed to surmount this obstacle did Draga find it hard to live up to her marriage bargain. Caresses she had lavishly bestowed for small gifts were now withheld, since her ingenuous and maladroit Mihailo neither grasped nor remedied the oversight. Instead, he seemed to be perfectly happy. Intoxicated by the joy of having Draga under his own roof, he had no need of outside interests other than his work. Would not their life together continue as one single prolonged honeymoon? Mihailo, who was never bored, failed to see why it should not.

He failed also to see that his young wife returned from her lonely excursions through town each time more heavy-hearted than the last, or that reproach was mounting within her—reproach against him and against her fate. Nostalgia, of which she would have thought herself incapable when first she dreamed of coming to the city, made cruel inroads on her sadly awakening spirit. Yes, she was homesick and ready to admit it. She yearned for the easy freedom and companionship of her village girlhood.

A brief period of excitement relieved the monotony of her days when for a while she believed herself with child. Her normal instincts reacted joyfully to this prospect. But a competent physician, Doctor Edouard Michele, blasted these hopes by the discovery of a faulty organism. Without her husband's knowledge Draga placed herself in the specialist's care. Summoning to his aid such medical science as the late nineteenth century afforded, Doctor Michele strove vainly to save her from frustration. His failure intensified her gloom.

The fact that their union remained childless was not mentioned between man and wife. Masin, recalling the difference in their ages and his own not particularly virile constitution, secretly took the blame upon himself. This view only increased his complete subjugation to Draga's will. Realizing her advantage she accepted his attitude and took care that he remained in the dark concerning her already proved sterility.

She lived on beside him, slowly falling prey to a profound discontent. In a fit of melancholy she sobbed two days for her brothers and sisters. Mihailo sent for them each in turn, little Voika coming last with her mother. Bustle and a modicum of cheer filled the house but vanished again when the visitors departed. In Draga there lingered only one desire: to push and elevate this family she once spurned, so that they, the Lunyevicas, might force their way into the inaccessible confines of Belgrade society. She could not bear her isolation any longer. She wanted her own people to be always near.

It was her plan that both her brothers should leave the mill and embark upon military careers in the capital. Her sister Sabine, whose religious fervor greatly increased after Draga's absence from home, longed to gain admittance to the Noble Convent of Vulpin in the Tyrol, where one could be devout without personal discomfort. But the Vulpin ladies were expected to bring a small dowry, a minor obstacle which heretofore had blocked Sabine's path. Draga removed it eagerly. With a sister who was a member of this most distinguished order she herself could not fail to gain prestige.

The advancement of her brothers was less simple. Masin applied in person for their enrollment in the Royal Cadet Corps, but the request was denied on the grounds that they were past the age of admission and lacked the proper preparatory training. Draga was not deceived. She knew that it was humble birth which shut her brothers out. Nikodem and Paul had to be content with regular service in the ranks and the hope of advancement by merit alone. With no war or political campaign in sight, the outlook thus afforded was bound to be discouraging.

It was in the third year of her marriage that Draga saw at last an opening which, though it might affect her family indirectly, held particular promise for her own person. Quite by chance she found herself drawn into a set of circumstances so dazzling in their implication that for months her peace of mind was gone. She had hurried, during Holy Week, to Austria for the purpose of visiting her sister Sabine at the nunnery. On returning from this pilgrimage she had stopped in Vienna where one changed from overland stage to Danube steamer. But the Hapsburg capital was still teeming with holiday bunting and Easter crowds which lined the avenues from the far canal to the very portals of the *Stefansdom*. In this turbulent and confusing atmosphere Draga Masin lost her way. With her heavy Serb diction, aided only by a smattering of Slovene, she could make nothing of the Germanic and Hungarian accents which beat about her ears. Driven almost frantic by this bedlam she ventured at last to hail a fiacre. By means of signs and the frequent reiteration of her nationality she contrived to be taken to the *Ballplatz* where the driver halted before a white building. Over its door Draga recognized a shield with the silvery arms of her country. Here was shelter, for within these walls lived Serbia's envoy to His Apostolic Majesty, the Emperor Franz Joseph. Here they spoke her tongue and she could ask her way to the Belgrade boat.

She lifted the bronze knocker and waited. After a few minutes a mild-mannered attendant led the way into a somber reception room where she explained her difficulties. During the narration of these a door opened noiselessly and the envoy himself appeared, followed by a stoutish lady whose hair, touched with gray, lay smoothly against the brim of her small hat. But it was not the woman so much as the diplomat himself who absorbed Draga's attention. For he was bowing incessantly, shaking his coattails the while he embroidered his speech with such verbal arabesques as "Exalted Sovereign" and "Your Most Gracious Majesty."

And now the attendant who had first admitted her pulled Draga's sleeve and whispered: "There goes the Queen!" With this he himself fell promptly into line, while Draga, undecided as to a proper course of action, curtsied awkwardly and stared at the amazing performance.

Then happened the most extraordinary thing of all. For the ambassador, having suddenly caught sight of the younger woman, exclaimed:

"She is here, Your Majesty—this is the lady I promised you!"

Queen Natalia, wearing the ready smile which Draga

remembered from numerous picture postcards of her, stood quite still.

"One of my own Serbian girls, of course," she murmured in throaty Slav tones, "that was my stipulation. . . . I can hire companions by the score in France, but of what use are they to me when they do not speak my language!"

"Please," gasped Draga in alarm, "I am afraid there has been some mistake—I just happened to walk in here, when——"

The diplomat's eyes grew bulbous. "What is this?" he asked fretfully, "you are not the young lady from Frau Danner's employment bureau?"

"Certainly not." Draga stiffened with pride. "I am the wife of Lieutenant Mihailo Masin who is stationed with the Royal Guards in Belgrade, and I have just visited my sister who is a nun in the Holy Order of——"

The Queen seemed disappointed and a little detached. "That is too bad," she said, turning toward the outer passage. On the threshold she hesitated and added: "You are very young to be married. You would have made a good lady-in-waiting."

The door closed behind her. In a second it was all over and Draga stood entranced, wondering if perhaps it had been only a dream. The attendant assured her it had not. He explained that Queen Natalia had hastened to Vienna in obedience to her husband's wish. King Milan, bored with exile, longed for the comforts of family life and the recovery of his lost throne. In an access of well-calculated remorse, he planned an immediate reconciliation with his wife, to be followed by negotiations with the Serbian authorities and a possible return to Belgrade before the majority of his son.

Draga's senses reeled. King Milan and his consort back at the *Konak!* And she, Draga Masin, had just relinquished the honor of becoming personal companion to the Queen! Keenly she now regretted her quick impertinent tongue.

"Did the reconciliation take place?" she asked, tense with excitement.

The man shook his head emphatically. "Oh, no," he declared, "they fell at once to quarreling and the King betook himself and his temper back to the royal lodge at Krusedol. The argument, I believe, was an old one. It concerned the exotic Princess Stourdza, a former flame of His Majesty."

Draga's heart sank. Her alert mind had already visualized glowing possibilities if she could win Mihailo over to the cause of the horrid old monarch. With her own prospects as lady-in-waiting to Queen Natalia it would hardly have been fair of him to refuse. But now——

"What will happen?" she asked with a catch in her throat.

The attendant smiled indifferently. "Nothing at all. Her Majesty returns to France in the morning. We are endeavoring to find a suitable Serbian lady to go with her as a sort of secretary-companion. It is really most unfortunate that Madame—or would Madame perhaps reconsider?"

She gazed sullenly through the window to the busy streets below. To think that here in the great Hapsburg city fate permitted such honors to fall at her feet when she was powerless to accept them. To think that she must go back to Belgrade where no one knew, where indeed she dared not even boast, that she had found favor with a dethroned queen. She must sink again into obscurity, galled by the treatment with which a snobbish clique of officers' wives would favor her. She—whom royalty had not disdained—must bow again to bourgeois prejudice. The thought made her ill.

She did not wait for the returning envoy but ran through a side exit to the street. At the next corner she obtained a *droschke* and, again with the aid of signs and proper names, managed to direct the driver to the Danube embankment. The Budapest-Belgrade-Bucharest boat did not leave until dusk. She entered the station restaurant and ordered *"eine Jause,"* the Austrian vesper bite. Wearily she forced down a few morsels of food, but the effort distressed her still further.

Her whole nature rebelled against the caprice of fate and the drabness of her own lot. It was not a Lunyevica trait to accept what seemed inevitable. The cruelty of chance, which threw opportunity across her path yet denied her the triumph of seizing it, now roused Draga's ambition. Once more, as in her earlier youth, a hunger for attainment consumed her. Was she not destined for a life of greatness? Did not the pattern of her career show bold designs?

Fiercely she brooded in the dim light of the gas jets. Her hands were trembling—as if something had just slipped from their grasp.

CHAPTER XI

MARITAL DISPUTE

MIHAILO MASIN was not elated over his wife's experiences in Vienna. He was, on the contrary, disturbed. It would not do for the report to become public that a member of his household was even remotely involved in the intrigues of the deposed monarch. Indeed, the very presence of Queen Natalia in the offices of Serbia's envoy to Austria bore a tinge of treason. Unless it could be established that the exiled lady had visited Vienna on a purely private errand, the whole episode might lead to an investigation of Belgrade's representatives abroad. Furthermore, even though Masin himself had taken no active part in the overthrow of Milan, it was today his duty as a soldier to uphold the rights of the boy-King and the Regency. No amount of persuasion on the part of his wife could sway him from this honest conviction.

Draga could not understand such loyalty to an administration which quite patently retarded all military advancement. She frequently heard her husband mention friends who railed against the deadlock which doomed them to permanently subordinate positions. In a recent gazette she had read that one Dragutin Dmitriyevitch had demanded his long deferred appointment to the rank of major or threatened to resign. The whole country's affairs hung limply on a thread of suspense, awaiting the majority of a moody and unaccountable young boy who lived within palace walls, terrorized his servitors and already played at being king.

"Remember," she observed acidly to her husband across the dinner table, "to be a lieutenant isn't so much at your age. You don't seem to realize that by allying myself with Queen Natalia I might do a great deal for you."

The reference to his age stung. Although he had just entered his forties he felt upon his shoulders far more than twice the burden of her lively years. For the first time in their marriage there was anger in his voice.

"You thought well enough of my rank," he snapped, "when I first appeared in your village. The peasant lads who wooed you then were clods in your sight, once you had met a Guardsman. As for my slow advancement— that's inevitable during the unnatural calm of a regency. Curious it may be, but nobody moves out of his seat at such a time."

His tone surprised and warned her. She was unaccustomed to opposition from one whose meekness had never failed to feed her own self-esteem.

"Of course," she pouted, blurring the issue, "if you decry my origin I can only deplore forgetting it when you pressed me to marry you."

She rose from the table and with a wounded look hurried to an adjacent sitting room. Dismayed, her husband followed. The accusation numbed him. It was unfair. He had accepted ostracism and gone into debt for Draga's sake; he had never refused her most erratic wish. But this was different. The thing for which she hankered now, with all the unreasonableness of a spoiled infant, was preposterous.

"Draga," he begged, "listen to me! You don't know

what you are saying. Haven't I been proud of you?
Haven't I vowed that my Lunyevica bride is far more
clever than the most shining princess of this or any other
realm?"

"Then why do you contradict me?"

"Contradict you?"

"Yes, when all I say is that King Milan hopes to re-
claim his vacant throne and that we shall benefit if he
succeeds."

"But darling, the throne is not vacant. Alexander will
be eighteen in less than three years' time. He will take
up the office which is theoretically already his. As for
poor ridiculous Milan, there isn't a chance!"

Her face looked very white in the shadowy darkness
of the room. Anton, the orderly, came discreetly through
the hall bearing away a tray of dishes from the dinner
table. His sudden appearance gave Masin concern.
He did not want the servants to overhear a conversation
of so delicate a nature. He motioned Draga to be silent,
but her agitation brooked no effort at restraint.

"Oh," she exclaimed, "but there is a chance and Milan
is sure to learn of it. The way people have talked about
that silly Sasha's temper, his stupid brain, his obstinacy—
to wait for his coronation is the worst thing Serbia can
do."

"Draga, watch your words."

She laughed. "When the papers openly lampoon his
insolent and overbearing conduct? You should have seen
the Slav pamphlets which circulate among our countrymen in Vienna! Right now Milan could bank on this
sentiment and plan a *coup* for the harvest season, when
the army moves south to help with the crops——"

Exasperated, Masin pushed back his chair. "A charming picture," he snorted, "the swashbuckling old rascal and his consort reopening the circus of their private lives. And you applaud the sordid spectacle! Well, let them settle their domestic problems in their own way. But politically, at least, Milan ought to know he's done for. Serbia does not want a dictator. Serbia wants no *protégé* of Austria. If Milan returns I'll be the first to fight for a republic!"

There was intensity in his voice which, Draga realized, would tolerate no compromise. Despite this she parried with a touch of malice.

"Of course, my dear, don't ask me to remember the terrible days of Milan's reign, since I was at that time a mere child——"

With furtive eyes she watched the effect of her remark and was delighted to see him bristling, as usual, on this sensitive point.

His face darkened. "Yes, yes," he muttered, "your senile husband unfortunately remembers very well. He drilled under the tyrant's henchmen and bore their insults. No, we must not bring sorrow over Serbia by aiding such a plan as this."

She sulked prettily. "That means I shall never become lady-in-waiting to a queen."

His smile was quizzical as he regarded her. "So you have actually set your heart on a fantastic illusion. I had rather hoped from the start that this whole discussion would turn out to be one of your little jokes."

There was disdain in Draga's voice as she answered. "It couldn't have been very funny, the little joke, as long as Queen Natalia in person asked if I wished to be her attendant." She meant to stagger him with this disclosure but he only shook his head.

"You baffle me," he said soberly, "one would suppose that peasant blood——"

Furiously she bit her lip. "Mihailo!"

He shrank from her rage and, for a moment, became his usual timid self. "I'm sorry," he murmured, "forgive me. But, Draga, your enthusiasm for the regal limelight puzzles me, since I, who am city bred, feel far more kinship with Serbian peasants than you, worshiping the crown."

Her fury had not subsided. She hunted for further aggravation and now veered sharply: "May I remind you that since our marriage I have ceased to be a peasant?"

He smiled indulgently. "Very well. You wear a natural pride that I, for one, find quite becoming. And now let's stop this idiotic quarreling or we shall lose our happiness." He held out his hand but she withdrew hers reproachfully.

"No?" he asked.

"Not unless you promise never again to imply that I am not a thoroughbred."

He took her in his arms impulsively. "Oh, but you are," he whispered, "and you don't know how I prize my luck. Of course that foolish Natalia would have you! She could make good use of your charm to dazzle Belgrade anew. There, am I telling the truth?"

She softened, disarmed by flattery. He stooped and tenderly kissed the lobe of her small ear.

"Now, my sweet," he said, "you are going to forget all this and prepare for Voyan. It's almost eight o'clock;

we may expect him to be here in half an hour. You don't want my young brother to find us sparring with each other on his first visit, do you?"

At the sound of Voyan's name she grew sullen. This pampered boy who had gone to expensive Russian schools and hobnobbed with grand-dukes while her own brothers served in the ranks as common dragoons, had long aroused her scorn. She deeply resented his visit.

"Don't worry," she replied stiffly, "he won't find us together at all. I am very tired and shall probably be in bed when he arrives."

Masin did not seem to comprehend. "But dear," he faltered, "Voyan has never met you! And I've told him so much about Obrenovatz, everything——"

She remained aloof. "In that case he will snub me just as your friends have done. I prefer not to give him a chance."

Masin's voice was anxious. "Not Voyan! He's the only relative I have. I was both mother and father to him through all these years; gratitude alone would make him loyal to you even before knowing what you're like. Besides, he's simple and unpretentious. Why, I believe you are far more proud than he."

She glared at him with blazing eyes. "It's easy enough to be condescending with Voyan's advantages. Yet the best you could do for my brothers was a nice start at the bottom of the military ladder. Nikodem told me only yesterday that he would just as soon go back home and raise turnips."

There was a pause during which Masin should have said something, but he was too confounded to speak. Defiantly she went on: "Well, you can convey my pro-

found regrets to your beloved Voyan and tell him I have
a severe headache."

She turned to go but found her wrist caught in an
iron grip that made her wince with pain. She did not
know he had such strength to hold her, nor had she ever
thought him capable of his present ire.

"Draga," came an ominous rumble from his throat,
"be careful what you say. I have been more than kind
to that family of yours. I placed your spinster sister
Sabine in a foreign convent and, though we cannot afford
it, I'll see that Voika attends a fashionable school. But
the boys—there I am balked. If they are to live in Serbia
they must of necessity accept their station. No amount
of bribery will get them to the top."

Draga could not resist the thrust. "Is that why Voyan
had to go to St. Petersburg?" she asked with savage irony.

His face had turned gray with anger and disgust.
"Voyan——" he began. "Damn it, Draga, you force
me to come back and harp upon the theme of blood, blood,
blood! Somewhere, far back, Voyan and I had an ancestor who was a nobleman. Do you hear? Don't ask
me what that means because I don't know. But it helps.
Only a drop of blue mingled with much wholesome merchant red, yet it seems to make a difference."

He opened the door of a liqueur cabinet and poured
himself a drink which he gulped down rapidly. Draga,
released from his grip, rubbed her wrist and regarded him
through narrowing eyes. He had poured himself another
glass without taking the slightest notice of her. This
was more than she could bear. Rushing from the room
she crossed the hallway and flounced upstairs. Masin
heard the slamming of a door. He recognized it as the

door to his wife's room and knew that she would not return. His face was torn with humiliation and pain as he sank mechanically into an armchair and continued his drinking. Somewhere in the house a clock struck the half-hour.

CHAPTER XII

Voyan's Arrival

FROM her balcony Draga could hear the approaching carriage. The sound of footsteps echoed through the house as Anton's voice announced the arrival of the young *Knese* Voyan. How they all fussed over the boy! Even Luba, the maid, ran out into the street to welcome the master's brother.

Draga sniffed scornfully behind the window draperies that concealed her from below. And now, for an instant only, she saw Voyan Masin. He was like a sword, smooth, gleaming, handsome in a cool and austere way. He wore the fur-trimmed black uniform of a military attaché. There was impatience in his movements as he leaped across the sidewalk and disappeared through the portal.

A sudden and inexplicable regret came over her. She could have shed hot tears over the conjugal rift that had just sent her rancorously upstairs. So this was Voyan. This was the brother-in-law against whom she harbored a blind and unreasonable hatred. But she hadn't known that he, or indeed anyone, could be like this.

He looked older than she expected. Although in his middle twenties, there was about him an air of complete and almost cynical maturity. In a flash she realized that Voyan, far more than his brother Mihailo, was a man of the world. To her provincial heart this thought brought a disturbing thrill. She turned from the window and went

130

quickly to her dressing table. The mirror reflected the pallor of her strangely agitated face. Should she primp and go down again, as if nothing had happened? For a moment the impulse seemed irresistible, but she fought it like a child hugging its grouch. No, she had already made her exit. To reappear would mean that she was giving in to a dictating husband. That she could never do. Dejectedly she dropped on the bed and began to remove her clothes.

Confusion reigned in the hall below. Anton puffed asthmatically under a burden of traveling bags while the girl Luba scurried back and forth between drawing room and pantry, trailing spangled *opanké* (sandals) as she ran. Meanwhile the brothers, who had not seen each other since Mihailo's marriage, exchanged formal greetings. Mihailo spoke first.

"*Zdravo,* my boy. You have been missed."

"Thanks," said the younger man in a jocular tone that was at the same time a trifle self-conscious, "I trust you have consoled yourself. After all, I've ceased to be your main interest."

"What do you mean?" Mihailo asked and knew the answer.

Voyan's expression was one of mock pathos. "You have a wife. Monogamy, they tell me, is monopoly."

The other nodded and essayed a feeble grin. "That reminds me," he mumbled uneasily, "Draga begs to be excused. She is ill."

Voyan raised cool eyebrows. He had lighted a Turkish cigarette and dropped lazily into an armchair.

Mihailo felt impelled to go on. "Yes, one of those ghastly charity bazaars kept her outdoors most of the afternoon under a merciless sun which brought on one of her headaches."

The dark eyebrows showed polite concern. "Ah, then she has headaches?"

"Yes, dreadful headaches—migraine, the French call her malady. She is forced to remain in her room for days at a time." Since he did not know how long his wife's hostility might endure Mihailo allowed a prudent margin.

Voyan's manner was correct to a fault. "I'm very sorry, sir," he said.

Relief freed the other's tense facial muscles. "So am I," he remarked lightly, "but you two will meet and make up for lost time. I daresay you will find Draga a clever and beautiful woman."

Without leaving his chair Voyan bowed from the waist. "So one hears."

Mihailo looked up. The words had sounded harmless enough. But something in his brother's voice aroused his suspicion.

"I'm afraid I didn't understand," he gulped, unable to master the doubts that beset him.

But Voyan remained bland. "Your letters, of course. I don't know when I've read more extravagant rhapsodies! However, Draga must be an exceptional person since you chose to marry her. As for the rest——"

Mihailo's throat felt parched. "Don't let me stop you," he urged.

"It's only talk, anyway."

"What sort of talk?"

"Idle gossip, I'm sure." Voyan frowned. "I really don't understand, but people say things—mostly about your giving up old friends and connections for her sake. As if there were something wrong. And then, in Cetinye, during a dinner at General Pazlov's——"

Mihailo reddened. "Yes, go on!"

"Some Serb officials were being entertained. When the Belgrade garrison was toasted someone mentioned your name. Another took it up, saying that you hadn't come to the Casino for months without, well, getting drunk. I tried to hear more, but somebody must have told them I was your brother, because they shut up like clams. It made me boil. I wanted to fight. But I was the only junior officer there and Pazlov would have had me thrown out. Besides, I realized that if tongues were already wagging, this sort of thing wouldn't help your troubles any."

"Nonsense!" Mihailo forced a defensive laugh. "I have no troubles. We simply don't give a rap for society, that's all. And just because I like an occasional stimulant the rumor spreads that I am dragged unconscious from the Casino bar? Very well. I shall drop my membership, that's what I'll do. Those scandalmongers must be taught a lesson."

Voyan cast a sidelong glance at the half-empty bottle of absinthe which stood on a near-by console. He drew a few puffs of smoke before turning, speculative and thoughtful, toward his brother. When he spoke his tone was good-natured, almost jocose.

"After what you told me about our father," he began, "I assume that you can take care of yourself. You always used to say that our lusty parent left us, if not wealth, at least a fancy liver."

Mihailo welcomed what seemed to him a digression.

"A dry and porous one," he chuckled. "That new foreign Doctor Michele who recently opened a practice here says I shall in time be cursed with a monstrous thirst. The 'Masin thirst' I call it, for we come by it naturally, my boy. Too many generations of us lived and died above these ancient cellars. . . ." He pointed a significant finger to the floor.

The younger man gave a startled exclamation. "My word, are those dungeons still in existence? I thought you had them filled up long ago."

"That was my plan. But Draga thinks them picturesque. She loves mysterious haunted places and wants to keep this old establishment the way it is. So I dropped the idea."

"That's all very well," Voyan admitted, "but I know a German professor who spends his time gauging the comparative stability of ancient and modern buildings. He hasn't much to say for medieval foundations. I don't mean to be an alarmist but, if you don't make up your mind to invest in a few tons of concrete, my wager is that you'll be crashing one of these days to the underworld below. And that won't be a bit picturesque."

Mihailo nodded, bemused. "All right, bring on your experts. You young modernists are certainly bent upon changing the world. But I warn you, if we tell Draga that dungeons are out of date, she'll be most reluctant about bidding farewell to her favorite fireside ghost."

Voyan crushed his cigarette. "The woman must have a Shakespearean imagination," he commented briefly.

It was at this point that Anton came in to close shutters for the night. With a beaming smile in the direction of the newly arrived young master he crossed to the balcony

that gave out upon the Danube. Over the river twinkled
the lights of Semlin and its symbolic Millennium Tower.
Across the river blazed the power and pride of Hungary.

Voyan followed the manservant to the windswept balustrade. "Never mind about the blinds, Anton," he ordered,
"we'll draw them later. You can take yourself to bed—if
that is what you like."

Anton relished the old familiar banter. "Unfortunately
no, sir."

"Too bad, Anton."

"*Hvala hepa* (thank you, sir)."

The man departed while Voyan remained at the window staring up at the starlit heavens. There was a long
silence during which Mihailo wandered uncertainly to the
liqueur cabinet and busied himself with his bottles. As if
from far away Voyan's voice reached him at last.

"Things won't remain like this forever," the tall young
man was saying, and his words cut sharply across the intervening space.

Mihallo looked up. "What things?" he asked blankly.

Voyan's profile was etched against the sky. "That Magyar arrogance over there," he said, indicating the far
shore. "The Serbian nation too shall have its jubilee.
And that before long. The *Narodna Obrana* will prepare
the way. . . ."

The older brother paled. "The Black Hand? . . . Voyan,
you tread on dangerous ground when you conjure up the
Karageorgevitch conspirators. Most of those fellows
were banished for life; it is treason even to speak of
them."

"I know. But a good many years have passed since
then. Up in the *Konak* our little Sasha is growing to

manhood and matters don't look so well. Unless——"

Mihailo watched his brother closely. "Yes?"

"Unless Sasha surprises everyone by not outblundering the worthless Milan, we can expect to hear from the Black Hand, that's all."

"You mean an open insurrection?"

Voyan nodded. "That is the grapevine report, making the rounds in both military and diplomatic circles."

"You have no proof, then."

There was a shrug of shoulders as Voyan finished guardedly: "Since I am not a member of secret societies, and don't know anyone who is, I can only give you the rumor at its own value."

Mihailo clenched his fists. "They can't do it," he muttered, "they wouldn't dare!"

"Why not?"

"Because Serbia must not make a spectacle of herself before the world by periodically sweeping out her royal family. The boy up there in the palace hasn't had a chance to prove his mettle. Wait, I tell you, and let him finish growing up. I'm not nearly as pessimistic as the rest of you. Give him time and he'll show us what he can do."

"He certainly ought to. A king brought up by formula was predicted as the wonder of the age. So far the reports sound dreary enough. The oversized Sasha has sent his French governess away because she caught him peeping through keyholes."

"At her? They tell me she makes a fine scarecrow!"

"No, no. Even Milan's son would have better taste than that. But he is said to show a lively interest in the boudoir activities of Father Milutin's painted paramour, the Countess Eudoxia."

Mihailo scowled. "Rubbish," he cried incensed, "the boy can't be blamed for the indiscretions of his entourage! I forbid you to repeat that story. We are officers, you and I. We wear the King's coat and are sworn to his oath. Remember that."

The brothers faced each other eye to eye.

"Very good, sir," said Voyan quietly.

But Mihailo's wrath had not subsided. "Cads and old women retail slander," he muttered.

"Sorry. What I just told you happens to be common chatter repeated at all the embassies, so I felt no compunction——"

"You mean," Mihailo corrected, "the small legation in the Black Mountains. Well, you've graduated from Montenegro. Berlin or London will prove a good change, once you earn your promotion."

Enthusiasm lighted up the other's face. "Yes, thank God. When I'm through with my apprenticeship in the Balkans I can leave that terrain to the cavorting tenor of a Viennese operetta."

He struck a match and returned to the window. Outside a shimmering mist had settled on the river. The smoke from the cigarette curled into it invisibly.

CHAPTER XIII

WINE FROM OLD CELLARS

SEVERAL days went by before Draga met her brother-in-law. At first Voyan's time had been taken up by the Foreign Office where he delivered reports and took up instructions for his future post. After that he had gone to the country with a friend whose family held an annual *zadruga* (gathering of kin) in a Croat mountain village.

During this time, which gave suspense to their eventual confrontation, an extraordinary change came over the woman Draga. Less than change, it was an unfolding of her true nature. To all appearances she seemed to be a born coquette, a creature of vanity and calculating ego, but now a different personality emerged. Mihailo found her no longer quarrelsome. Her quick tongue lost its edge almost to the point of dullness as a wistful Draga dawdled through her days. The large clear eyes, veiled suddenly in tenderness, acquired the shy depth of a faun's regard. All this was very becoming. It enhanced rather than detracted from her charm. Added to such outward manifestations, there was an inner change of mood. Once a prey to quick boredom, Draga now could sit for hours, her moist lips parted in a dreamy smile which puzzled even Anton. She seemed to breathe lightly like one who is wounded and dares not gulp the precious air. That was it. There was about her a poignant quality, as of hidden and exquisite pain.

What did she feel? It would have been difficult to explain, since she was not in the habit of analyzing her emotions. Certainly she did not think herself in love with Voyan Masin. She was true to her husband in the primly accepted fashion of that day. Her sturdy peasant notion of a fair bargain precluded any lighthearted views of marriage. Besides, she had caught a mere glimpse of Voyan through a curtained window on the night of his arrival, a view so brief that she could not thereafter reconstruct from memory a single feature of his face. Daily she tried to recall that face, yet daily she failed. Obviously, then, her transformation could have nothing to do with Voyan.

Nothing and everything. She thought of no one else but Voyan. Once before, on encountering Dmitriyevitch, a similar absorption with another being had seized her, only that time it was less engulfing and complete. Then as now she had not stopped to render account. Life had its own way of answering questions; Draga did not ask them.

The actual meeting between Voyan and his brother's wife was extremely matter-of-fact. Returning from her French lesson, Draga had heard voices from the courtyard that stretched narrowly across the rear of the house. Here, in an open space where she and Mihailo took their summer meals, the two brothers had established themselves beside a steaming samovar and a tray of assorted spirits. At sight of her they paused in their dialogue.

"Hello," cried Mihailo, "here she is. Darling, this is Voyan—my little brother Voyan."

She regarded the tall stranger and her face lighted up in an amused smile.

"Small brother," she said, "I am charmed. You must

forgive that we did not plan a better reception, but——"
She faltered. She had not thought of an explanation for
her absence on the day of his first coming.

Mihailo rallied to her aid. "Voyan understands, dear.
I told him about your illness."

Puzzled, she held out her hand. The younger man
bowed to kiss it. "I trust," he murmured, "that you are
feeling better. Our midday sun is particularly bad here in
the flatlands."

She stared at him blankly. Illness? Midday sun?
Whatever were they talking about? She certainly hoped
Mihailo had not introduced her to his relative as a neu-
rasthenic invalid. Like every healthy young animal she
scorned weakness and disease. In her rebellion against
any such implication she failed to grasp her husband's
helpful ruse.

"Oh," she said brightly, "I don't mind the Belgrade
climate at all."

Mihailo signaled over Voyan's shoulder. "But the heat
was unusual the other day, Wednesday, remember? At
the charity bazaar. I told Voyan how bravely you
stood the strain, even though you did retire early——"

She rallied. "Yes, of course," she sighed, showing
signs of belated fatigue, "but as a matter of fact, all that
fresh air has done me a world of good. Doctor Michele
says I stay indoors too much."

"I hear," Voyan remarked, "that you were brought up
in the country."

She paused for the fraction of a second, then turned
and held his gaze serenely. "My parents have an estate
on the Sava River," she said curtly. "As a girl I led a

truly ideal life. City children miss so much, don't you think?"

"Rather."

He bowed again and offered to take her wraps while Mihailo ordered Anton to fetch another tea glass. But Draga excused herself and left them. A little breathlessly she hurried upstairs.

That evening, and for many evenings thereafter, the dinner hour marked the climax of happy and thrillingly interesting days. Mihailo was beside himself with joy at his brother's visit; every moment that he could spare from duty was spent in Voyan's company. They must look up old cronies, they must take long jaunts on horseback into the wooded environs of the city, they must attend plays at the Royal Theater. Always Draga accompanied them. For her it was like a perpetual holiday. She was in a festive mood, changing costumes every few hours for the next treat on their crowded program. At night when she dropped into bed, weary with pleasure, a wave of gratitude welled up within her. All this, the friendly parties, the gay outings, and—best of all—the heavenly *soirées* at the opera, she owed to Voyan. Although he made her shy and a little afraid of him, so that in his presence she controlled her impulsive nature lest anything in her conduct offend his tastes, she felt happier when tormented by his scrutiny than at any time within her memory. She was a good wife, keeping the pledge of a loveless marriage. But because of Voyan, whom she must call her kin, that loveless marriage and the very name of Masin acquired a new meaning.

Late in June they had gone to a performance of

Cavalleria Rusticana. Emma de Roquer Calvé sang "Santuzza," a rare artistic event since stars of such magnitude were seldom available after the close of their Paris, Vienna or London seasons. At the fall of the last curtain a storm of applause rang through the house; the audience remained on its feet, cheering for twenty minutes. No one wanted to go home. Again and again the great singer appeared in the glare of footlights, to be showered with blossoms and shouts of praise.

From a plush-curtained box in the second tier Draga Masin gazed upon the magnificent scene. Drunk with excitement, she clapped her hands like a child, crying *"Bravo!"* at the top of her very sound lungs and clinging now to Mihailo's arm—now to Voyan's—lost in a transport of rapture. At last it was over and a long chain of carriages departed through the inner city. Over the clop-clop of horses' hoofs the cheers echoed upward to the skies.

It was midnight when the portals of the Masin mansion opened to admit its owners. The housemaid Luba had retired many hours ago to her attic chamber where she slept with an aged aunt. But Anton, who shared quarters with his master's horses in the commodious stable, was still about. He had lighted tall aromatic tapers in the drawing room and placed a tray of fruits on the table. After greeting the elated arrivals and inquiring with solicitude as to their further wishes he found himself dismissed for the night. Bowing noiselessly, he vanished, taking the hall lamp with him, which left the service portion of the house in darkness.

Humming a stray melody Draga paused on the stair landing.

"Adio," she said softly. "I'm afraid I can never thank you enough for so perfect an evening."

It was not clear to whom she had spoken, for her eyes, lustrous with an inner light, were fixed into space. Both men turned toward her with words of protest.

"Draga, you're not going to bed!"

"I am going to bed."

They caught up with her on the stairs. Mihailo seized her elbow. "But an occasion like this," he pressed, "calls for special celebrations."

She looked at Voyan, whose nod was an entreaty. "Your husband is right. We can't let you go."

There was a moment of hesitation during which Draga regarded the hem of her creamy lace frock. Suddenly she broke into a little gasp. "Oh, see what's happened! Someone stepped on my train——"

Twisting and wriggling about she obtained a full view of the damage. Under the strain of her exertions the delicate material ripped still further into a cascade of loose threads.

"Oh——" she cried again, this time on the verge of tears.

Mihailo's festive mood defied calamity. "Run along and change," he suggested airily. "Tomorrow you can order another dress."

Slowly she walked to her room, absorbed in thought. She loved pretty things and she had not many of them. The country child's reverence for one's best Sunday clothes was still deeply rooted within her and the wide gash in her party gown assumed therefore the proportions of a major disaster. Sadly she extricated herself

from the garment, laying it away in a drawer of her
sewing cabinet. It was all very well for Mihailo to propose ordering another dress in the morning. She knew
they could not afford even that phthisic Gabrielle who
worked so cheaply, copying expensive models of high-
class seamstresses with fashionable display rooms in town.
The Masins had horses and a carriage, even a groom to
look after them; all this because Mihailo once enlisted
under King Milan whom he now repudiated, yet whose
provision for officers in the guard regiments continued
to be a boon. But money, actual cash, was scarce. No,
she must see how she might repair the torn lace with
careful and diminutive stitches so that no one would
notice.

From below came the sound of restive voices urging
her to hurry. Still occupied with economies she wandered to a chest and took from it a wrap which she flung
about her person. Slipping her toes into soft Turkish
mules she ran out on the gallery that encircled the top
floor. She leaned against the banister, laughing down at
their impatience.

"A helpful pair you are," she scolded. "Don't you
ever give people time to think?"

They glanced upward and beheld her there on the landing. She looked very lovely. There were times when
Draga labored for effect, but this was not one of those
times. Of course, she was essentially melodramatic;
her loveliness verged always on the lurid, even when she
did not strain to achieve such a result. Thus at the
present moment the emerald satin of a casual négligée
clung to her like a cobra skin while its sheen brought out
a phosphorescence in the black pupils of her eyes. It was

in spite of this unconscious theatricality, rather than because of it, that she could arrest attention.

On noiseless feet she descended. Mihailo rushed forward, enthralled, possessive. He placed a protective arm about those unprotected shoulders and beamed at his brother:

"She is beautiful, isn't she?"

"Magnificent!" Even as he spoke, the speaker's impassivity was complete.

With a shade of exasperation Draga disengaged herself from her husband's embrace. In drawing away she knew that Voyan's eyes swiftly appraised her supple figure. He had crushed out the stub of his cigarette and was taking a step toward her. Reaching for her hand he kissed the center of its palm, sending an unaccountable shock through her. She paled.

With renewed solicitude Mihailo led her to a divan where she sank into a sea of pillows. Drawing up her heels she kicked a snug nest for herself in the silken depths. And now a long-laid-by coquetry reasserted itself.

"Draga is thirsty," she purred.

"Good," Mihailo rejoiced, turning to his brother. "You've no idea how hard it is to get her to drink."

Voyan's answer was noncommittal. "Some people need no stimulants," he said.

Mihailo began to explore the liqueur cabinet. But for his cheerful puttering among the bottles a tense silence hung over the room. After some sampling he returned at last, shaking a square flask of *Danziger Goldwasser*. The clear liquid was speckled with flakes of pure yellow metal.

"Here we are. One must drink gold to golden memories!" Although there was nothing on his mind he was proud of the little speech. It sounded well.

Voyan frowned. "A trifle weighty at this hour, don't you think?"

"All right. Name the drink and if I have it, it's yours." Mihailo flourished his bottle which tinkled brightly.

"Wine, perhaps?"

"There's a cask of Tokay, some Burgundy, a remnant of Sherry—dry Amontillado, you know."

"Splendid. Amontillado is the very thing, provided our hostess will join——"

They turned questioning eyes upon Draga who reclined lazily in the cushions.

"Draga would love it," she said in a blurred, throaty voice.

They drank, not one but several rounds. The superlative Spanish vintage, obtained long ago in trade for a carload of Macedonian grapes, spun them into discreet animation. Voyan's pronounced scruples on the subject of the "Masin thirst" seemed to have vanished, for he slapped Mihailo's back with vigor.

"Come on, old man," he urged, "we must have a toast. After all, this is an occasion. . . ."

"Is it?" Draga asked, her lids closing to a fine oriental line. She gave Voyan a searching, intimate look which he returned. But he did not answer her.

Mihailo needed no urging. He had grown a trifle uncertain on his feet. Such frank encouragement, to which he was unaccustomed since his wife condemned free bibbing, now released a wave of pent-up desires. Tossing down an empty beaker he leaned over her in fawning adoration. Draga forced a smile. She patted her husband's flushed face and pushed him into an armchair where he fell abruptly into a semi-conscious doze. At sight of Mihailo's sudden collapse Voyan came to his senses. His was the sort of constitution that sobered instantly.

"I don't recognize Mihailo," he muttered so low that the words might have been only for himself, "he was never this way before."

Draga stared up at his towering height. "What do you mean?" she asked, trying to puzzle him out, for as yet she did not understand this man.

"Weakness, flabbiness—my brother would not tolerate it in others. And now look at him. I'll never forgive myself if——"

"What?"

"If I've done something to him."

"But how could you be responsible?"

"Only a moment ago I spurred him on, knowing all the time that we Masins aren't any of us safe drinkers. I rather supposed he had told you that. Something goes wrong with our hearts——"

"I see," she murmured and her voice was like velvet, making each double meaning a caress; "then you do have to be careful."

Voyan studied her expression. When he spoke it was in a hard whisper. "Don't," he said.

She caught his hand.

"But why should you worry about your brother? Isn't he years older than you or I? Doesn't he know what's right? Besides, that thimbleful isn't enough to hurt a

lamb. . . ." She paused, waiting in vain for an answer.
A feverish glow colored her cheeks. "If anything, we
made a mistake in selection. That Spanish concoction
was wrong. We should have had champagne. Do
you hear? This is a night for champagne!"

She glided toward the edge of the couch until her
husband's slumped figure came within reach of her arms.
She shook his shoulders with unexpected vehemence.

"Darling," her throat opened shrilly, "we are all completely wilted. We must have champagne. Remember
that last bottle of *Veuve Cliquot* you promised not to
touch unless Draga asked you——?"

Slowly Mihailo came out of his stupor. He glowered
about him as if in a fog.

"Who?" he queried in a dull monotone.

She broke into hysterical laughter. "We must celebrate! Voyan, your little brother Voyan, is here, and
you're so slow to offer him the best. What is she for,
then, the Widow from France, unless we lift her cap
today?"

Into Mihailo's face came awareness, and with it a
sly grin. "Little brother," he repeated, "Widow *Cliquot*—
sure, got to have champagne!" His eyes started on a
circumspect search for the cabinet.

"We've none up here," his wife reminded him sharply.
"Anton keeps it in the cellar since the warm days are
near. You told him to yourself."

There was an interval of hesitation during which
Mihailo struggled with a new plan. Before he succeeded in mapping it out Voyan had reached his side.

"Don't be absurd," he snapped, "we're tired out and

have had enough for tonight. Let me take you to your room."

But in Mihailo's head the idea was gaining a steady and dogged impetus. "Must celebrate," he chuckled furtively, "you wait. It's a surprise!"

"You can't stop him," Draga interposed, meeting her brother-in-law's frown; "his mind is made up. Surely you know him well enough not to try."

Voyan bit his lip. "You're not going to send him downstairs in this condition. At least, let me go. I've played hide-and-seek in those cellars as long as I can remember; I still recall every corner——"

He rushed to the open doorway but was held back by the enterprising Mihailo.

"You leave me alone," the latter declared emphatically, "or I'll send you back to Montenegro."

"There," Draga gloated, "he doesn't want your help."

Voyan remained unreconciled. "The darkness——" he warned.

She laughed away his fears. "There's a night light burning in the passage. Besides, Anton is such a slow beggar that he will probably still be shuffling about. . . ."

Mihailo, meanwhile, had started on his way. At the far end of the hall he stopped to look back and wave a deprecating hand. His red face wore a happy, if fatuous grin.

Voyan did not enjoy the pigment of that face or the quality of its grin. He turned back moodily toward the room and the waiting woman.

CHAPTER XIV

The Accident

THEY were alone.

A hush descended upon the house and in it Draga's unnatural excitement was suddenly spent. She felt small and timid in the presence of the man whose smoldering eyes now rested upon her. What would he do? What did he feel? Was it hate? Ah, if he hated her——

Suddenly his voice came to her as if across a great space, and she was surprised to find no anger in it: "Mihailo has changed very much since last I saw him."

It was like a statement about the weather. Almost serene. Certainly conciliatory. She must make the most of it.

"I find him quite angelic, at times. There are few things he wouldn't do for his own kin. . . ."

"You mean, for his wife——"

"No, I don't. I mean what I say—his kin."

In spite of himself, Voyan reddened. His next words were a confession. "Mihailo once swore I was all that mattered in his life."

A far-away look came into her eyes. "Perhaps you still are."

"No, Draga. It's you who crowded me out long ago. And I don't mind. In fact, I——"

"Yes?"

"I like it."

"My being your brother's mate?"

150

"No, not that——" His answer was vehement, almost brusque. Again he frightened her with his incomprehensible change of mood. But she was beginning to understand. Not her person, but her intrusion into the sacred precincts of the Masin household—that was what he minded.

"Oh," she said slowly, feeling her throat go dry. "I think I see."

He caught the faint quaver in her voice and realized how deeply she was hurt. Hurt by what she thought she saw. Well, she was wrong—how wrong he could not even tell her!

For a moment a wild urge prompted him to drop down beside the couch and clasp her knees, burying his head in her lap. Draga, beloved . . .

The moment passed. On the rug before him stood an ivory inlaid *narghile*. Lest an unguarded gesture had already given him away, he became absorbed in the convolutions of its design. He remembered having once tried to smoke one of these Persian contraptions. Not the tobacco, but the sight of the water had made him ill. He felt ill now—in a way that was both racking and delicious.

For Draga the interval of suspense had brought composure. The best that was in her seemed to be roused by this man, and so she wished him to know only the best. Never would she let herself bore, or, what was worse, disgust him. Never should he suspect that in her mind, a thousand times over, she was already an adulteress for love of him whom she divined to be both fire and ice.

There are occasions when no gift is greater than the

gift for small talk. Women excel in it. With little words they often avert disaster. On the very brink of that abyss opening before her, and into which she longed to hurl herself, Draga turned back. She would pretend interest in a rosy speck of cloud on a safe skyline.

"You've traveled," she mused with a dreamy air of detachment. "How I envy you your experiences."

He fell in gratefully. "Oh yes," he agreed, "there's always escape in other lands and other tongues. I shall never see my fill of the earth."

She must spin the thread deftly, weaving it about his hardness so that for the space of these few stolen minutes he would vouchsafe her at least a smile. It was like begging for alms. But she could not help herself.

"All my father's people have the roving instinct," she explained, "they love to run off by themselves. All but my Uncle Misha, that is. He once got as far as Samarkand. But Aunt Yenkina, who was very ugly, always went with him."

Voyan's teeth flashed. "I don't believe it," he laughed, "it's impossible to imagine anyone connected with you who isn't beautiful."

"Oh, but Aunt Yenkina looked like an ostrich. Everyone said Uncle Misha always took her with him so he wouldn't have to kiss her good-by."

They were both laughing now. They were being absurd and they knew it. But they wanted to be absurd. For Voyan this gay sparkling Draga was yet another revelation which fascinated him the more because she embodied a racy native wit. She was like a mirror holding up to him a national trait of which one was proud. A mirror that reflected a hale spirit wherein, as a Serb, he might find a counterpart. In this, then, they were one.

It was not the banter, but rather a sudden vision of her polychrome personality that caused him to exclaim: "Superlative!"

She was ready for the *ricochet*. "Superlative is a very superlative word," she said; "after using it one does not know how to go on. For that reason the people on the Sava never say more than, 'It is a good crop,' or 'It is a pretty good crop,' so that they may keep on talking a long time."

He learned. Although goodness knew where she had learned such wisdom which was not in books. Was hers a mind that picked up clarity in transit, as it were, through life?

"Then you want us to talk—a long time," he said, underlining the words that were her own.

She had grown serious. "Yes, tell me about Russia."

Astonishment lighted up his face. "Russia—it interests you too!"

"It interests all Slavs, doesn't it?"

A quick intensity sharpened his voice. "Yes, and that's as it should be. Russia is the greatest nation in the world! Not scattered and parceled out like that merchant corporation, the British Empire, but unified, colossal, a single race with but a single breath. We, in these Balkans, have fallen away from her, becoming vassals to the conquering West. Yet our final salvation cannot lie anywhere but in Russia and the coming Pan-Slav movement."

His words were intoxicating like some incantation

from an unfamiliar world.   She sat up, her eyes fixed on
his lips.

"Draga," he went on, "if you could see Muscovy's
cities, churches, shrines and palaces!   They are unlike
anything in Europe, because each wears its proper Slav
face.   What have we from Hellespont to Adriatic Sea?
French avenues, German theaters, English trams and
omnibuses, Swiss instruction in our private schools—
nothing belongs to us, nothing is real, and so our peasants
emigrate in droves to America.   Or better still, like your
Uncle Misha, to Samarkand."

"Is Russia so different, then?"

"Russia!" he cried.   "Her bulbous domes, her *troikas,*
her solemn streets, the very air of her unending spaces—
everything looks Russian, tastes Russian, *is* Russian. . . ."

"Only the Tsar—he is not Russian."

"Yes, with great Catherine the German Romanovs
began.   But, knowing what is good for them, they
are trying to forget.   Even so, we Slavs shall have our
day!"

He stopped, flushed with excitement.   Sinking down on
the divan beside her he seized Draga's hands, pressing
them until she winced.

"Oh," she cried, but there was a thrill in her voice,
"you are hurting me!"

His grip loosened, although he did not let her go.   Instead he held the bruised fingers to his face, as if to
cool the burning skin.   And now she felt for the first
time the outline of that head, so fine in profile, with the
black hair curling stubbornly about the temples.   "Like
a young Greek god," she whispered.

With a groan that was more a sob his face sought the folds of her gown. Hungrily his arms closed about her.

"Draga——"

Her firm flesh resisted him. "I'm so sorry," she breathed, "sorry I love you."

His eyes drank in each detail of her face. It told him what he needed to know.

"My dear," he murmured.

She let him have his way. "He is beautiful like a young priest," she thought deliriously, "and ardent like a man with his first woman."

They were unable to speak, yet each knew that in this other lay fulfillment. Minutes elapsed. Shreds of time that seemed to them imperishable. Yesterday? Tomorrow? Nothing mattered but the ineffable present, this present which must be stretched beyond its own endurance, beyond desire, beyond——

"God! What was that?"

Voyan had leaped to his feet and stood listening in the center of the room. It was almost as if he had anticipated a heavy crash which came from somewhere far away and was now followed by a single long and muffled outcry. Then silence.

Draga held her breath. She too had heard the sound. Like a whip it had lashed across her consciousness.

And now she felt Voyan's stony stare. "Mihailo——" he gulped.

She shook her head, suppressing a gasp of horror. "No, no, it couldn't be. It was something, someone— on the street." With outstretched arms she ran toward him, but he warded off her embrace. There was a peculiar rasping sound in his throat.

"We both know better. That voice—it was my brother's!"

She clung to him. "No, I tell you, no———"

"Yes, damn you and me together! The cry came from below, from those dungeons you love so much." He was all hardness again.

"Voyan," she pleaded, "don't leave me———"

But he had already torn himself loose, hurling her back against the couch. In another instant he had rushed from the room.

She was alone. Shaken with dry sobbing she pulled herself up and leaned against the wall, waiting, listening. In the distance there was an echo of footsteps which drew gradually nearer. Voices seemed to come from the servant quarters and the long dark passage beyond. The lone woman held herself pale and erect. Paralyzed by fear, she dared not move.

After a while they brought him. A frantic, disheveled maid heralded the tragedy, crossing herself and screaming: "The Master, oh, the poor Master!"

Draga shivered. "What is it, Luba, tell me in the name of heaven———"

Wailing aloud, the girl dropped to her knees. "It happened on the steps, near the second turn. Oh, the good Master—we shall never see his like again."

"What happened?" She had to shake the girl to get an answer.

"The Master, he fell in the darkness———"

"Is he badly hurt, Luba?"

But the girl was incapable of coherent thought. *"Bogami,"* she lamented noisily, "it has pleased God——"

Like a wax image Draga stood. She saw Voyan and the servant Anton carrying her husband across the room to the divan. She saw a wide red gash along one side of Mihailo's twisted head. The face, drained of all color save for that thickening stream of blood, looked lifeless. While she strove desperately to grasp the truth that spread out there before her, the two men struggled over the motionless body. Luba's hysteria, meanwhile, grew. She was clutching Voyan's arm, breaking into renewed outcries:

"He must have a doctor. Oh, the poor gentle *Gospodar!*"

Voyan shook his head in dumb horror. "Too late," he said thickly, leading the distraught maid into the hall where she shifted for herself, leaving a trail of tears in her mournful wake.

As he turned in the door he beheld Draga against the wall. Coming slowly toward her he gripped the soft shoulders cruelly.

"Do you hear?" he thundered, and at the sound of his voice her face took on the opacity of chalk. "He dashed his brains out because you—we——"

She could feel the shudder that went through him as he broke off. She made a small piteous gesture, reminding him of Anton's presence. The servant's eyes, peering like a rodent's, were fixed greedily upon them.

"Is he—dead—sir?" Anton now inquired in a flat treble.

Voyan's nod was mechanical. At this Draga's poise

crumbled. Her knees gave way as she reeled against a chair. Voyan saw her fall but he did not move.

"You may go, Anton," he said bleakly.

With hunched shoulders and quivering jowls the man-servant fled from the room. Behind him the young *Knese* stooped over the body of his brother, staring into a vacant face.

"Neither she nor I," he muttered, grimly indicating the prostrate woman, "shall fail to pay for this, Mihailo!"

It was an avowal. But the dead man looked glassily upward, paying no heed.

CHAPTER XV

BIARRITZ

QUEEN NATALIA put down the letter. She looked at the Vienna postmark and puckered her brows into a perplexed frown. For the life of her she could not identify the writer, although there hovered before her mind's eye a vague memory that just verged on recognition and then danced away again like a teasing kobold. Impatiently she repeated the name, Draga Masin, who called herself a "Baroness." It conjured up nothing. Nor did the Austrian city prove a clue. Still, in that Austrian city lay the explanation and one must find it.

For two days the ex-sovereign mulled things over in her not very occupied cerebrum until at last there emerged an image. It was the image of a vivid face with slanting eyes, a pert, short nose, and a mass of blue-black curls over the narrow forehead (curls, incidentally, which any woman could discern as impermanent if very fetching). In addition, there suddenly loomed up a brief scene at the Serbian Embassy, only a few months ago, when she, Natalia, had been strangely attracted by this face. She remembered her own words:

"You are very young to be married."

The letter. One must reread the letter. In an angular and uncertain scrawl it contained the announcement that "a gentlewoman whom it pleased Her Majesty to notice during a recent chance meeting" was now disposed to accept the office of personal companion to Her Majesty, provided that doubtless much-coveted post was still available. If Queen Natalia approved, it might be helpful to arrange an interview. Baroness Masin, the letter went on, was even now *en route* to Paris for the sole purpose of placing her young sister Voika in a French school. Should such a step be desirable, Baroness Masin would gladly stop at Villa Sashino in Biarritz and pay her respects to Serbia's beloved Dowager Sovereign.

"Serbia's beloved Dowager Sovereign!" Ex-Queen Natalia was more than pleased. She discovered in her breast a positive longing for the charming company of so gifted a correspondent, and so she promptly penned an answer to that effect. The reply was posted to an obscure hotel in Vienna where the unhappy widow appeared to be seeking solace after her tragic bereavement.

Queen Natalia could not help herself: she looked upon the sudden death of Lieutenant Masin as a sad, yet fortuitous, coincidence. That inopportune individual who, such a short time back, thwarted her own happy plan was now neatly disposed of by a fate which had the loneliness of exiled royalty at heart. For it was perfectly clear that Providence itself took a hand in leading this clever Draga once more across Natalia's path. And how especially gratifying, too, in view of the fact that the jaunt to Biarritz would be combined with Baroness Masin's duties in Paris, necessitating no financial outlay on the part of the Queen! Ladies of more distinguished nomenclature had applied for the job at Villa Sashino, only to balk at Natalia's refusal to pay their railroad fare. In consequence the frugal sovereign had remained alone and would, to all intents and purposes, have continued to do so. if a Serbian Lieutenant of the Guards had not plunged headlong down the steps of his wine cellar.

Of course, Natalia wished to appear neither callous nor profane. Very likely the young widow was demolished with grief and would, for a time at least, be none too cheerful to have around. But this in itself provided an admirable foil for the older woman, since it opened up a pool of genuine sorrow wherein her own poisonous rancor might be drowned. Natalia, the abandoned wife who had lost a husband unwept (and unsepulchred), would mourn with Draga. For herein lay the grandeur of death: it brought sheer undiluted drama, honest pain! The widow knows none of the bitter gall that clouds her divorced sister's cup of sorrow.

Having dispatched her correspondence for the day Queen Natalia now rose from her writing desk and left the sanctum which was her sleeping chamber. In passing the draped canopy that enveloped her couch she caught a glimpse of a small tinted miniature which hung at the head of her bed in the place usually reserved for holy ikons. It represented the cherubic head of a small boy who seemed to have usurped the niche of the household saint and who, indeed, had given the villa its name.

"Sashino," she whispered, "my little Sasha. You too will come to me from Serbia some day!"

It was ten o'clock. In the sunny garden outside waited her young nephews and nieces, the Ghika and Bibesco children whose mothers (of Kesko and Mavro-Cordato lineage) had married the Rumanian envoys at Berlin and Paris, respectively. Both families met every year in the Basque country for the summer holidays, a circumstance which had prompted Queen Natalia to establish herself near these loyal relatives along the Atlantic Riviera. In the company of the two Ghika boys, Henri and Georges, as well as the pretty little Bibesco girls, Jeanne and Marthe, her starved mother love found a large measure of consolation. The children themselves adored her for she spoiled them inordinately.

At present, what with the prospect of Draga Masin's arrival, a new interest began to animate the household. Not only the children but their parents and neighbors must be told about the impending event. Queen Natalia's unknown lady-in-waiting became, within a few hours, the talk of the tiny seaside town. Her indubitable charms were extolled at length and with the aid of the most colorful adjectives for, barring the questionable favors of an occasional demimondaine, the exclusive royal playground on the shores of Biscay was sadly in need of a thrill.

To be sure, it would have been impossible for any human being to live up to the descriptions which preceded Draga's appearance. The male population was particularly wrought up. Beau Brummels from Biarritz to San Sebastian looked forward to a creature pulchritudinous beyond compare. In addition to the exemplary attributes with which they had already endowed her, the young lady possessed a specific halo; for, was she not crushed by a romantic (though transitory) sorrow? The idle gentlemen considered this. Their eagerness to comfort and protect the delicate flower, whom fate had cruelly trampled, bordered on a fervor not necessarily religious in character. In fact, the faun-like expectancy of these Samaritan satyrs served to antagonize the feminine world.

In Biarritz, as in Belgrade, Draga Masin was destined to find life's path a thorny one.

Three weeks after Queen Natalia's invitation a telegram announced the Baroness Masin's visit. On the morning of the appointed day the diminutive station was crowded with curious onlookers who craned exasperated necks. Everyone wanted a good view and felt entitled to a good view, for had they not all contributed their share to the sum total of the heroine's graces?

And now the much-heralded moment had come. From the railway carriage stepped a pale tired woman whose black weeds hung limply on a small body, a degree too slender for that day of opulent curves. The disappointed swains of the town retreated noticeably. This weary traveler, whose drawn cheeks showed irritating specks of coal dust, did not differ from other spotty mortals whom the train belched forth in drab little groups. She could not differ from them half as much as she belied the exquisitely fair apparition Queen Natalia had prophesied. In no time at all the crowd dispersed, leaving only the handful comprising the royal Dowager's suite. The Sashino carriages alone remained at the curb.

Draga did not mind. She who detested loneliness longed, as never before in her life, to hide away from people. It was not the tiresome journey from Paris that accounted for her drab and desolate appearance; it was what she had been through previous to her escape from scandal, suspicion, Voyan. . . . The strain of those last weeks after Mihailo's death, the days and nights in the old house with Voyan's dark accusing eyes upon her had all but sapped her marrow. She had gone literally without sleep, choked by the fear that this foolish sensitive boy would seek vengeance upon her for his brother's sudden end. As if she, Draga, could have had a hand in what was so palpably an accident! Even the coroner's jury had cleared her by a unanimous vote. But peccant tongues continued to wag.

The funeral itself had been an ordeal. Voyan addressed her at the grave in so erratic a manner that observing bystanders shook their heads significantly. Once during the obsequies his eyes had pierced hers with such intensity that she had almost cried out: "He wants me to take the blame, only to cover up his own guilt! He made love to me—you didn't know that, did you? He made love to me after sending Mihailo down to die. . . ."

But she had checked herself at the last moment. She had not found the strength to do it, or she had found the strength not to do it. Who could tell which? This much was certain: it would not have been true, any more than Voyan's unspoken reproaches were true. Perhaps her own nerves were responsible. Perhaps Voyan had no thought of pursuing her. Her tortured conscience could easily have misconstrued his natural despondency.

Of course, there had been that unpleasantness about the house. Mihailo had died intestate. That left the entire property to his widow. But the Masin mansion did not belong to Mihailo alone; it was a joint inheritance which had come down to the brothers since their father's death. Draga and Voyan now had equal rights to the establishment along the Danube Quay, and after the horrors of that tragic night each upheld these prerogatives in obstinate silence. Even the servants could sense the bitter conflict between their new master and his defiant sister-in-law. But in the end the duel had been too much for Draga.' Seeking a refuge, she had abruptly recalled her previous travels through Austria and the attendant encounter with Queen Natalia. Here was her chance! She must take it at once and flee from Belgrade. Voika's schooling in Paris would provide a convenient pretext, while the Serbian representative in Vienna might be persuaded to do the rest. Mihailo did not leave her a fortune, but she would spend what funds she had on this venture.

The outcome of her desperate gamble was Biarritz and a peaceful shelter in Queen Natalia's white villa by the sea. There was an atmosphere of safety and comfort about the French resort the like of which Draga had never experienced. Within a week of her stay the color returned to her cheeks and she was able to work up a normal appetite. She regained her buoyant energy and soon lost the pining look which had proved such a damper on the spirits of local Lotharios.

As for Queen Natalia, that lady's joy knew no bounds. In Draga's company she could relax from the annoying effort of constantly speaking French, a language full of hazards for a Balkan tongue. From morning till night the two women chattered now in Natalia's beloved Serbian, much to the dismay of the Ghika and Bibesco children who, growing up in France, were more at home with Parisian *patois*.

It was only natural that before long a conspiracy against Draga, the intruder, took form in the nursery. There was ample grievance. Heretofore Queen Natalia had been wont to lead her young visitors through the fruit orchards which spread out toward the back of her

estate. The children loved these excursions, especially
during blossom time when the perfumed groves formed
a veritable fairyland. Then there were long afternoons
on the east terrace overlooking the sea; basking in sunlight while their aunt read aloud from old story books—
the children could think of no greater delight. Yet now
they seemed to have lost this, their former cherished
prerogative. For the Queen was too engrossed in her
new companion to romp under fruit trees or weave word
pictures for little people. And so the little people took
their revenge.

They disliked Draga from the start, having sensed instinctively that in some insidious and grown-up way she
was going to supplant them in their aunt's heart. Of
course it was fickle of Aunt Natalia to allow this to
happen, but they loved Aunt Natalia and could forgive
her. Draga they would not forgive.

At first it was impossible to discover any suitable point
of attack, since the newcomer seemed to be a person of
mystery. They had to study Draga and know something
about her before they could devise an effective means
of mortifying her. Until some definite weakness came
within their ken they were content with minor tortures,
such as the pilfering of thimble and scissors from her
sewing basket or the systematic rearrangement of her
toiletries so that nothing on her shelf remained in its
proper place. Careful spying had netted the disclosure
that the widow devoured books, especially the lurid variety
of paper-backed novels peddled on the boulevards by
agents who, if encouraged, had also "art" postcards for
sale. The Ghika boys, precocious gamins despite their
dainty rearing, were set upon stealing these tomes for

their own perusal. Quite obviously, though, this constituted a major theft leading to serious conflict with the Queen and (previous misdemeanors had taught them) exile from her society. For on occasion Aunt Natalia could be stern. When the antics of the youthful barbarians overtaxed even her infinite patience she was capable of dispatching them home to their parents, without wasting so much as the flick of an eyelash. No, Draga could not be robbed of her literature. But one could upset, quite casually, the pot of mucilage that stood on her writing table. A bit of expert canalization would direct the oozing flood so that near-by objects fell within its radius. The near-by objects happened to be books. With horror and chagrin the lady-in-waiting would come upon her nightly reading matter, swimming in a sea of gum, the pages glued firmly together. An open balcony with curtains blowing bore mute and spurious testimony. The wind over Biscay was a bluff, furious playfellow. But she knew it had not been the wind.

The merciless rascals had other ways of teasing her. Sometimes they would appear with faces dipped in flour to imitate her furtive application of white rice powder. Cosmetics were frowned upon in those days. They constituted the stock in trade of *grisettes* and adventuresses. But Draga, unaware of the disapproval her little vanities aroused, sedulously explored the realm of self-improvement. To Marthe Bibesco, whose pen in later years recalled each prank played on the harassed waiting-woman, the perfume and pomade flagons on Draga's dressing table provided an enduring source of speculation and interest.

The spirit of buffoonery indulged in by the children

soon transferred itself to their elders. Many guests came
to the Villa Sashino, especially on sunny week-ends when
excursions could be planned, for the environs of Biarritz
were both picturesque and easily accessible. Not infre-
quently a large party drove across the border into Spain
to see the bull-fights at Pamplona where, some years
before, the Empress Eugénie had applauded that gory
sport. Like the unhappy Spaniard, Draga responded
passionately to the cruel spectacle which excited and galvanized her nerves. Her reaction did not go unnoticed.
Henceforth, in the placid gardens of Sashino, she was
chased by old and young over imaginary arenas, while
tennis racquets and croquet mallets were brandished at
her in the manner of fierce *banderillas*.

She was at no time quite able to analyze her true
position. As royal lady-in-waiting (even to an ex-queen)
she claimed a definite social rank. Yet, try as she might,
the titled personages with whom she came in contact
mustered a condescending jocosity rather than an ami-
cable interest in her person. With the exception of the
kindly Natalia, no one addressed Draga as "Baroness,"
even though the Masin linens flourished an antiquated
and neatly embroidered crest. She was the "Widow"
or, at the most, "Madame." If, in keeping with her
new position, she gave herself such airs as (to her mind)
befitted a lady of the court, someone was sure to laugh
aloud at Draga's expense. Her gestures, her little pretensions, her downright comical slips in etiquette, all her
brave and pathetic efforts to rise above her humble station
provided hilarious entertainment at the Balkan embassies
in Paris and Berlin for several winters.

She moved through this mocking world that refused

to take her seriously with a chill sort of insensibility.
Her healthy peasant torpor served as an impenetrable
armor. The actual daily tasks assigned to her were simple
enough and she enjoyed performing them. There was
Queen Natalia's correspondence to be gone through each
morning after breakfast. There was the sorting and
reading aloud of any press notices concerning Serbia and
the disrupted Obrenovitch household. There was the
promenade to be taken each day after the siesta hour for
the purpose of staying Natalia's hopeless obesity. And
finally, there remained the duty which Draga relished
most of all. The Queen's cupboards were stocked to
capacity with a voluminous trousseau which, due to
Milan's poaching in forbidden amorous pastures, had lost
much of its allure. The intimate lingerie of that frilly
era boasted many trimmings. For one thing, each shift,
peignoir, corset-cover and pantalette was festooned with
lengths of narrow ribbon which had to be removed before
each washing and thereafter inserted anew. But as a
wife, Natalia had become discouraged. And so, when
the first set of *passementerie* wore out, she gave no orders
for its replacement nor indeed would she clip a sum
for it off her budget. At the time of Draga's arrival
the royal nightgowns, petticoats and wrappers showed a
network of perforations running like a miniature railroad
track over the hills and dales of the Queen's frame. But
the tidy new lady-in-waiting soon took matters in hand.
From her own supply of inexpensive ribands and laces
she restored these sorry garments, tying a bow here and a
rosette there, so that in the end Natalia herself began to
take an interest. Happy hours were spent by the two wom-
en in thus re-establishing a coquettish order of things.

"Ah," the exiled Dowager would sigh, as her unaccustomed fingers plied the needle, "once upon a time my husband said I was a figure of a woman."

Draga fitted a tassel into place. "Who knows," she replied hopefully, "but that he may again?"

In short, equivocal though her position might be with Biarritz society at large, in the eyes of her employer Draga was a complete success. If there was hostility or even outright criticism on the part of others it needed little discernment to understand that such were the promptings of envy. For Draga had gone far. She was nearer the top than she had ever dared to aspire in her wildest dreams. She had left her own kind too far behind ever to turn back. What if these high-born sycophants who hovered about Natalia chose to scorn and make their sport of her: to the village of Obrenovatz she was as good as a grand-duchess! She, Draga Lunyevica, had become the confidante of a queen. . . . The mortifications that accompanied this borrowed glamour she could keep to herself. They who were now so far beneath her, village friends and kinsmen, need never know how much it hurt to hold elusive glory in one's grasp. Nor should they guess how excessive was its price.

At times, during moments of honest introspection, she wondered whether anything on earth was worth that price. Court life, either in its fullest sense or in this passing phase of exile, was at bottom servile in character. Each climb in social rank left always others higher up whose favor must be cozened by flattery and chicane. And if you reached the pinnacle itself, what then? Did not the monarchs of the world kowtow to that even greater despot, the mob?

Still other doubts beset her. A lady-in-waiting was, after all, not much. Did she possess the indispensable requisites that might lift her to further heights? Beauty and temperament were of no avail in a stilted milieu where all impulse was frozen. The triumphs which would most certainly have been her reward, had she chosen the path of the actress or courtesan, were unthinkable in the role of a mere servant to royalty. Here, in this circumscribed aristocratic setting, all her wiles, her poses, her little deceptions could only produce the worst possible effect. Yet it was here that she wished to stay.

The theater? She would be only Draga Lunyevica, a peasant girl with a gift for mimicry.

As a *grande amoureuse?* She could not claim a title even so modest as that of a Baroness Masin! Without exalted patronage love was a proletarian trade like any other. In her own case there would be those who called her the harlot of Obrenovatz, as they had called her in childhood the vixen of the Sava River mill.

No, she preferred the glitter, however false, of a regal limelight. She clung to that for which she was least fitted, the chafing, hidebound, artificial existence of a palace domestic. Even as she stitched edgings on the dowdy garments of a mistress whom reality had long passed by, so her fingers were tying together the strands of a fate not predestined for her, but wrested by sheer determination from a world quite alien to her own.

She who could stride over the ground so personally was willing to mince at dizzy altitudes along the taut streak of an aerialist's wire. However dexterous, such a march through space is always serio-comic.

CHAPTER XVI

ALEXANDER COMES OF AGE

TOWARD the middle of 1894 the boy King Alexander I of Serbia attained his majority. The occasion was celebrated by nation-wide religious services and a special meeting of the classic *Skupchina*. It was further marked by the automatic retirement of Cincar-Marko as the head of the Regent Council. He had served his country well, this unregenerate idealist. At a time of life when other men contented themselves with a disinterested spectator's seat beside the arena of political combat, the beloved Minister President had shouldered more than his share of responsibility. He had done so in good conscience and for the sake of a greater Serbia. Yet, as he walked now toward the high altar of the old Belgrade cathedral and studied the face of the young monarch whom he, Cincar, had hailed in infancy, the veteran's heart quavered.

This individual who stood before him in ceremonial robes, staring arrogantly through gold-rimmed spectacles while with gloved hand he plucked at a stubby and recalcitrant mustache, did not even remotely personify the Messiah whom Slav patriots had been taught to expect. Lolling absentmindedly through a pompous inauguration service, the son of Milan gaped with unabashed curiosity at the crowds assembled in the church. It was plain to see that he gloried in his own importance. Nor was this unnatural. Restrained until this very day

172

by the fetters of fustian tradition, Sasha had grown to manhood imbued with a hunger for human contacts.

Just as he had once gazed from nursery windows at the play of strange children outside the *Konak* gates, so he peered in wonderment today at the men and women who had come to pay homage to his person. As a child he had longed to cry out across the empty royal park that held him prisoner: "Look, I am the King! You must come here. Don't you see, a king is not allowed where you are?"

Even so he chafed now under his coronation harness and waited fretfully for the hour of freedom. He did not know, as yet, what one did with freedom. But this he knew: that all those people round about him, his people, the Serbian nation he was called upon henceforth to rule, would be very different from the dried-up bureaucrats who had shaped his destiny. They must be different! It was intolerable to visualize a whole world as hemmed in and stultifying as Sasha's own existence. Such a world would be impossible to accept.

He thought he would never tire of scrutinizing their faces. They seemed more real to him at this moment than all the realities that had made up his cloistered boyhood. In viewing these strangers he almost forgot what his guardians looked like, having seen too much of them too often. For all those faces out there, filling the apse and the aisles and the nave of the church, excited him as nothing had ever excited him before. They looked alive, he told himself, more alive that any he had been living with from day to day.

They brought back memories, too, of a distant and altogether hazy past. Anya—that was it! These people were like Anya, whom one loved, if only because her name was like the comfort of secret prayer. . . . Over there, beyond the chancel rail, he saw two women kneeling. They had fine olive skins, like Nushka. It thrilled him to look at their curved throats. . . . The men beside them had thoughtful eyes that reminded you of teacher Abramovitch.

Poor gentle Abramovitch who had caught cold years ago and coughed himself to death. Sasha missed him. Abramovitch had been the only one who knew about the things that really mattered: things that went on beyond the *Konak* walls, across the mighty Danube, in great cities or dark jungles, and overseas, in a New World called America. . . .

From the choir loft a voice rose in solemn Gregorian chanting. The worshipers bent low under the pontific accents of the court chaplain, Father Milutin. In the royal enclosure where Sasha and his retinue foregathered a woman cleared her throat. Her arm brushed accidentally against his sleeve. He did not turn or take notice of it. With a shrug of shoulders the Countess Eudoxia resumed an attitude of piety, her eyes fixed on the pages of an ivory prayer-book. Eudoxia. Would he ever forgive her? She had been the first to teach him the pangs of jealousy, childhood jealousy—more bitter than that of adult years.

The service was over. With powerful chords the organ broke into the measured strains of an ancient national anthem. Slowly a glittering assembly filed past the baldachin where, flushed with pride, stood Serbia's King. One by one they bowed: foreign dignitaries, princes of the Church, ladies of title, followed by the native gentry and, eventually, a conglomeration of commoners from merchant nabob down to humble peasant.

Sasha reviewed them all, intoxicated by their number. Unmindful of etiquette, he tapped men's shoulders and grinned disarmingly at the ladies. Once he stopped a buxom country lass whose blushes spread to the roots of her hair. Turning to his new aide-de-camp, he exclaimed:

"See, Naumovic, the servant girl Nushka looked like this!"

The incident left a queer impression. Even his lowlier subjects were baffled by such lack of majesty in their King. For years the tale had been going from mouth to mouth that Sasha's manner with subordinates was either despotic or rudely familiar. Had seclusion and the most methodic supervision failed to conquer this? Did the boy who had been molded for kingship lack even the first elements of sovereignty? Could anyone who descended to such blunt informality with his own subjects command their respect when a change of mood prompted the exercise of authority?

It all seemed strangely reminiscent of blustering and headstrong Milan. Education or environment appeared to be powerless in the face of heredity. Or had the formula been wrong? Did leadership develop from a different root which needed no hothouse methods of forcing? At all events, this restless, eager Sasha had neither the poise nor the bearing of a dignified monarch. For all his noble raiment he looked like a school boy at a country fair. Filled with misgiving and doubt, the crowds began to pour out into the great *Slaviya* Square, drifting slowly homeward.

The official session of Parliament which took place on the following day was restricted to members of the diplomatic corps and the leading government functionaries. In the presence of the outgoing Regents several new appointments were to be made. Also, and this would be the climax of the coronation ceremonies, the monarch was to read his first public manifesto.

Since the eighteen-year-old Sasha was unfamiliar with proceedings of this sort, the necessary reorganization had been planned beforehand. At a given signal Cincar-Marko would hand his sovereign a list with the names of new cabinet ministers, counselors, and heads of the diplomatic and military staffs. The list was small, for it was deemed prudent to retain as many experienced figures of the retiring administration as possible.

Among the few changes that took place two were significant. First, the General Staff announced a vacancy in its ranks. An honorary post, originally intended for a deserving but heretofore unrewarded public servant, Lieutenant of the Guards Mihailo Masin (now deceased), had remained unfilled. Despite rancorous protest from Cincar-Marko, for he continued to nurse an undying grudge, the promotion was now bestowed upon Colonel Dragutin Dmitriyevitch, who had acquired renown both as a capable disciplinarian and a strategist. The second appointment concerned a brother of the above-mentioned guardsman, namely the *Knese* Voyan Masin, whom the diplomatic coterie regarded as a most distinguished prospect.

Other assignments had been carefully noted. But to Sasha it was all a matter of supreme indifference. He read off the names in a halting monotone and seemed to experience some difficulty deciphering the script. Despite the unattractive eyeglasses, which afforded him normal vision, his old habit of squinting endured. His failing sight had gone too long undetected; even the patient efforts of teacher Abramovitch had failed to cure the boy's aversion to letters.

At last the tedious list had come to an end. There was the boom of a gong, followed by Cincar-Marko's request for complete silence. And now, from a portfolio of tooled leather, the aide-de-camp drew forth an illumined parchment.

"The manifesto, Your Majesty," he murmured with a smart click of heels and a deep bow.

Sasha stared at the document. Its text was finely etched in India ink with occasional ornate blotches of crimson and gold. These irritating blotches were symbols in the Kyrillic alphabet. They gave him a headache.

"Everyone is waiting," came a sharp whisper, "Your Majesty must read!"

The whisper subsided into a discreet mumble and now Sasha recognized the voice of Father Milutin. He must read, must he? Well, they would see about that. It seemed to Sasha at this moment that he had heard Milutin's voice once too often. Making a sudden turn toward the surprised court chaplain he dropped the parchment into his former governor's lap.

"I have experts," he announced cheerfully, "who will honor me by interpreting this lengthy text. I charge Father Milutin with the reading of it, while I make preparation for the first public act of my reign——"

A chorus of voices had arisen. Someone pounded a gavel. There were half-uttered admonitions:

"Your Majesty, that is impossible—we have no precedent for this!"

Sasha broke into a lusty guffaw. "Then I shall set a
precedent. That's simple, isn't it? And now you may
adjourn until my return from the French Riviera, where
I must visit my mother, the Dowager Queen."

The words reverberated through the vast room. There
was a moment of speechless perturbation before the tumult broke loose. What was this? King Alexander
refused to recite his manifesto and had boldly made plans
to call on his exiled mother! Did he intend to bring
Natalia Kesko back to Belgrade? Worse still, did Austria
and the treacherous Milan lurk behind all this? Outraged, the members of the assembly rose in protest.
But Sasha's small black eyes flashed back at them un-
daunted.

"I am the King," he cried gruffly. "There you have
my manifesto! And furthermore, I now decree that my
first act shall be a journey to France. Who, pray, would
stop me?"

Still robed in his coronation mantle he took a step
forward. Quiet descended upon the listeners, and with
it an instinctive awe. He had reminded them of that
which must remain unchallenged if they wished the
monarchic principle to endure. He was the King! They
had willed it so when, as a helpless lad, he had been
anointed as their future liege. If now he would not do
their bidding, but imposed upon them his own will, this
too must remain unchallenged. For today, in their sacred
cathedral, they had acclaimed him anew as Alexander the
First, King of all Serbia.

The storm had passed. Contritely they made room for

him as he prepared to depart through their midst. Somewhere in the gallery a military band started the recessional march.

Although no one was aware of it, the next few minutes proved to be the most trying of all. Scepter in hand, Sasha found himself concentrating on an almost superhuman feat, the balancing of a top-heavy crown which was several sizes too small for his own brachycephalic head. He had no sooner assumed the lead in the procession than profound regrets overcame him. What if someone should laugh? Perhaps he was going to drop his crown. If so, would they jeer and lock him up? They could prevent his going to see his mother, of course. How had he ever found the courage to say the things he had said? Right at this moment, even if it were to save his life, he could not have uttered a sound!

Today he was of age; he had come to man's estate. And what had he done? He had brazenly confronted a nation over which he was supposed to be king. But he was not that way at all! He had not shown them his true colors. For in his heart there lodged the old familiar fear, that which made up his earliest memories. Sasha—afraid of the dark.

Gingerly he stalked through the crescent-shaped hall. At its end, by some kindly magic, a door opened. Footmen hastened to lift the royal mantle, to prevent its brushing the uncarpeted curb. Outside he could hear the snorting of horses and the rumble of carriage wheels.

At last he could say good-by to the young men of his suite. He must remember their names, Naumovic, Slavyanin, Tanko and Lazar. They formed his personal bodyguard and were expected to accompany him at all hours. Well, he didn't need them. They ought to go home. He was going home too.

The nightmare had lifted. No one had laughed. No one had even dared to question his, Sasha's, authority! It was extraordinary. He had spoken his mind, in no uncertain terms, to the assembled Parliament. And Parliament had stood for it without a whimper.

Breathing a sigh of relief Sasha stepped into the waiting landau. He enjoyed the ride back to the *Konak* immensely. All the way the streets were lined with people who waved their handkerchiefs and cried *"Ziveo."* Regardless of the jeopardy in which this placed his crown, he responded with lively nods to their acclaim.

CHAPTER XVII

Mother and Son

In the early days of September Queen Natalia's capacious villa buzzed with preparations for the visit of her beloved son, King Alexander. Slender Serbian flags, in horizontal blue, white and red stripes, hung limply in the late summer heat. Residents along the Basque coast took notice. Throughout the fashionable resort district a report was spread concerning the impending festivities. Shopkeepers were roused to a prodigal output of paper garlands and other patriotic furbishings.

Biarritz, owing its earliest prestige to the French Second Empire, provided an admirable setting for royal pageantry. Since the days when Napoleon III and Eugénie periodically called a truce in their marital disputes and hied themselves to the imperial summer villa (only to return to Paris where with renewed vigor he engaged in infidelity and she in political intrigue) the famous town specialized in ermine and escutcheons. Only the *crème de la crème,* socially speaking, were wanted here. Through indirect insinuation, wistful advertisements and outright propaganda the elegant resort conveyed to idle, ailing or fugitive aristocrats that on the shores of Biscay a refuge awaited them. This was gratifying news. In endless succession and through innumerable years the crowned heads of Europe, as well as sundry Latin-American presidents, came to the famous *ville d'eau,* not only for the "cure" but for permanent residence to boot. The present prospect of welcoming a ruling monarch, rather than a deposed one, filled the local patrons with particular glee, for an occasion like this served to enhance the name of the Basque Riviera among prominent people everywhere.

At Sashino invitations and requests for private audiences began to pour in. Queen Natalia and her lady-in-waiting were kept in a state of happy turmoil which lasted from early morning until late at night. Inquiries concerning Serbian court dress and priority preoccupied the ex-Queen to such an extent that she imagined herself once more a reigning sovereign. Draga, no less agitated, blossomed out in this deceptive atmosphere of *bonhomie*. She acquired an air of Byzantine grandeur, for now she had the Biarritz ladies exactly where she wanted them. When haughty feminine visitors called, these days, they actually spoke to her. Quite abruptly she had ceased to be "Madame Masin," becoming *"la Baronne"* as if by some official edict. And all because this unknown Sasha, Queen Natalia's little boy, was set upon a reunion with his exiled mother!

It was at the height of the season (a variable term, since Biarritz shifted seasons to oblige) that the special train bearing the royal Serbian party arrived. The special train had two engines, an unheard-of extravaganza in those days. Spectators who thronged the station platform were more than rewarded by so imposing a sight. But this was not all. King Alexander traveled in style. Besides his immediate bodyguard he was accompanied by a large personnel of physicians, aides, secretaries, valets, grooms and other attendants who poured freely from first- and second-class carriages.

One glimpse at this human ballast told Queen Natalia

enough. She would never be able to accommodate them.
Villa Sashino, though capacious, was not a caravansary.
Messengers must be dispatched at once to every hostelry
in town for the purpose of preëmpting all available space
for the horde of Serbians. If any other traveler stopped
in Biarritz that night he was out of luck.

But even after quartering most of the escorts in hotels
and private lodging houses there was the problem of getting Sasha and his bodyguard settled. The Queen's prim
sense of propriety required that all the men be located on
one floor. To achieve this it was necessary to move Draga
to an upper story. Here, in the immediate proximity of
the children's nursery, she shared a cramped chamber
with her sister Voika, who had come to spend her holiday
from school.

The arrangement brought new tortures for the lady-in-
waiting. In childish solidarity Voika allied herself with
the young Ghikas and Bibescos and shamelessly laid bare
to them the most private aspects of her sister's life.
Draga's curling papers, her bustles and *chignons,* all came
up for the closest inspection. More than ever was she
made the butt of their hilarious antics.

For a time she hoped that the presence of the royal
company would distract her tormentors, since, in antici-
pation of Sasha's arrival, Queen Natalia had erred again
and prepared her household for the coming of an Apollo.
With the garrulity of doting mothers everywhere, the
Dowager had indulged in sentimental descriptions which
proved to be the very antithesis of cold fact. The children expected nothing short of Prince Charming. Sasha
fell far short of that.

To begin with, he did not wear uniform, but appeared

in the most unbecoming mufti.   The conscientious little
Marthe made a memorandum of his sartorial equipment which consisted of a flannel suit with big stripes.
On his thick, square head (characteristic of Northern
Slavs) he wore the flat straw hat which the Spaniards
call *jipi* and the Germans *Butterblume*.   It was a silly
hat, perched high upon his bristly hair and attached to
his coat button by means of a long cord.   But this was
not the worst.   Under the brim of that hat his porcine
little eyes peered at you through a pair of nose-glasses
which were secured to one ear by a length of gold chain.
The children found him unspeakably ugly.   They would
have nothing whatsoever to do with him.

Not so his good mother or, for that matter, the ladies
who made up the Biarritz élite.   To the radiant Natalia
he was still Sasha, her baby, the fulfillment of lifelong
yearning.   In her sight he was not only beautiful but
richly endowed with intellectual gifts as well.   As for
the damsels who curtsied before him, bending their hour-
glass figures to the ground, they found his ungainly
exterior enhanced no end by the alchemy of worldly
position.   What if he wore a hideous *pince-nez* and a
sprouting mustache that made him look like a cross
between an owl and a porcupine?   He was a king.   To
be sure, he commanded only an obscure third-rate country
in a rather disreputable corner of the world.   But, with
no better morsel in view, Biarritz society was determined
to make the most of him.

The only person who regarded Sasha in the light of
cool reason was Draga, the waiting-woman.   As a result,
hers was the only true estimate of his worth.   Like the
children, she had been disappointed and repelled by his

gawky appearance. Like the fluttering French ladies, she acknowledged his importance. Lastly, like his mother, she saw that he was not a man but only an impetuous oversized boy. Where each of these erred in taking just one view of him, Draga, the outsider, instantly perceived a complete picture. For, despite her efforts to attain an urban veneer, despite her opportunism which brought insincerity in its train, she possessed a primitive and fundamental sense of values. Regardless of the hollow artificiality of her present life, she was still able to pierce the outer shell of things and plumb their core. With her peasant instinct she would always sound the depths of human nature. Whether, in sounding them, she had the wisdom to benefit by that which came to her so easily was another matter. There were deficiencies in her own make-up which seemed to invite frustration. In Draga herself there existed elements that made for a constant anticlimax.

She did not actually meet Alexander until the second day after his arrival. Although she had been at the station in company with the Queen's domestic retinue, there had likewise congregated too many persons whose social precedence made lesser introductions impossible. The staff of the Villa Sashino would have to wait. A special little ceremony, during which the King would be presented to the members of his mother's household, was planned for the following morning.

It was planned but it did not take place. Instead, shortly after dawn, Queen Natalia became acquainted with some of the idiosyncrasies peculiar to her young son.

For years the pious lady had made a habit of attending early mass at the near-by shrine of Saint Cyprian. Since she enjoyed daily communion, and fasting put a keen edge on her appetite, a well-appointed breakfast table always awaited her return from matins.

In summer this table was set on an open terrace above which ran a series of balconies belonging to second-floor rooms. Before Draga had entered her service the Queen had found the breakfast hour somewhat lonely. But in the company of the young widow church peregrinations gained in sociability and zest. Draga herself seemed to incline nicely toward mysticism, a faculty essential to the fullest enjoyment of God. If, before this, Natalia had sometimes succumbed to pardonable sloth (and, on hearing the *Angelus,* turned over in her bed for an additional nap), the presence of Draga put an end to such venial transgression. The sacrament, partaken *à deux,* was in itself pleasurable. But the convivial cup of chicory imbibed thereafter capped spiritual with temporal bliss.

On the particular morning in question, the Queen and her lady-in-waiting awoke, as usual, to the chiming of early church bells. With black lace mantilla pinned over her gray hair, the portly Dowager led the way to a tiny mule-drawn wagonette. Both ladies refrained from speaking, for special precautions had been taken against disturbing the tired guests who slept in the upper chambers. Even so, several of the King's aides must have been aroused by the subdued activities below, for on returning from prayers the Queen found them rallying around her *omelette confiture.*

At sight of their hostess the four strapping officers leaped to their feet. Kissing her extended hand, they repeated their names: General Lazar, Captain Slavyanin,

Captain Tanko, Lieutenant Naumovic. They were up and about, Lazar explained, because of misleading signs of life.

"Tanko, here, noted for his gluttony, heard a tinkling of cups and saucers," added Naumovic, who was the youngest and the most aggressive.

Natalia's face spread into a huge smile. These dear attentive boys (even the General!) with their gallant little ways! My, how long it seemed since she had had a man around the house. . . .

If only Milan would reform—but there, she must not let herself get maudlin again. (He always used to accuse her: "Bah, Natalia, you are getting maudlin!") Milan was a horrid creature, and she never thought of him any more.

But her charming guests, she was neglecting them! They were famished, no doubt, although the honey jar looked as if it had provided first aid. What, no more chicory? She must order another pot.

"Where is my table bell?" she asked, searching for the silver trinket.

It was in Tanko's pocket. He produced it sheepishly and began to swing it with gusto, whereupon a breathless steward appeared with a tray of bread. Before a place could be cleared for it to be set down, the tray was empty.

"I hope," beamed the Queen, "you will enjoy our freshly baked *brioches*."

They were sure they would. Not only that, they liked the French word for a small crescent of dough. They began calling the steward Brioshenka.

"Do it again, Brioshenka," they cried in unison; "you are wonderful!"

At which the manservant departed, lowering coy Gascon eyelids.

It was altogether a very successful breakfast party. Even Draga smiled and entered into the general spirit of wassail. She was beginning to preen herself, touching a curl or patting the lace of her collar, for she felt the men's admiring glances upon her. Their unspoken insinuations brought a glow to her cheeks. It made her quite lovely to look at.

"Hosannah," exclaimed Tanko, "I, too, shall go to early prayers!"

They all burst out laughing and slapped one another's knees, while the ladies discreetly dodged the gymkhana.

It was at this moment that something appalling happened. From an upper balcony came the sound of a slamming door. Shuffling footsteps could be heard and suddenly, between two pots of flowering geraniums, a bare head was projected over the balustrade. Squinting eyes glared down resentfully and the quick silence was broken by the boom of Sasha's petulant voice:

"So . . . this is a proper reception! My gentlemen look after their bodily wants while I am left to slumber through the morning——"

He paused to glare still more peevishly at his mother, for it had been primarily a jealous impulse which aroused his rage. That she should have been willing to exclude him, Sasha, from this first collation was to his mind a profound affront. It very nearly equaled the iniquity of the Countess Eudoxia who first had made him feel the pain of playing second fiddle. As if he objected to the fun other people were having! Not at all. He objected to being left out—and it seemed to him that he was always

being left out.   As long as he could remember, even as
a small boy, Sasha had been left out of things.   And
he was very tired of it.

A pall had descended upon the gathering below.   In
the silence that followed His Majesty's angry outburst
the four officers jumped from their seats.   They stole
covert glances at the King who towered grotesquely
above them in his nightshirt.

"Your Majesty," Lazar apologized, "it was a most
regrettable error.   We were unfamiliar with the schedule
of our gracious hostess, and on discovering this extremely inviting table——"

The words did not soothe Sasha.   Quite to the contrary,
they lashed his temper into flame.

"Regardless of our location, gentlemen," he stormed,
"it is *my* schedule and not that of our current hostess
which you will do me the favor to respect!"

Having voiced these sentiments he gripped the railing
and, either by accident or intent, nudged a crock of pink
blooms off the sill.   It flew brightly through the air,
crashing into the center of the table below.   There was
a clatter of Dresden china, accompanied by a sudden
shower of hot liquids.   With a shrill scream Draga
ran from the terrace, shaking her drenched skirts.

The King stared down from the balcony, unable to
distinguish the full extent of the damage done.   His
nearsighted eyes followed the figure of a female in flight.
The scene amused him inordinately.   So he had disrupted
the pretty gathering!   Splendid.   They would know better,
hereafter, than to go about their mysterious amusements,
ignoring him.   They would learn not to plot gay parties
without Sasha.   The punitive geranium could not have

been better aimed. Delighted with his prank, the monarch burst into a roar of laughter.

"Sashino, my little one," came the tearful wail of his mother, "I promise—it will never happen again!"

Blinking at her, he exulted anew in his triumph. With a defiant gesture he gathered up his trailing gown and shuffled back to the shelter of his bedroom.

CHAPTER XVIII

A KING AT PLAY

THOUGH inauspicious, such nevertheless was the prelude to the first meeting between Alexander and Draga. When, in the course of that hapless day, the dressed monarch descended upon a distraught household he found its members walking on tiptoes. Well, at least he had impressed them. There was some satisfaction in that.

Natalia, still dabbing at her wet cheeks with a futile square of Madeira lace, awaited him sorrowfully in the privacy of her boudoir. Beside her stood the offended lady-in-waiting. Draga had changed her frock and, despite the presence of a king, assumed her haughtiest manner. Her small head with its tightly wound tresses (she was training a fashionable top-knot) remained rigid even during the brief curtsy which was her greeting. Her eyes met Sasha's gaze squarely.

He was quite taken by her. Furthermore, Queen Natalia's reproachful reference to broken chinaware and the spots on Draga's leg-o'-mutton sleeves, not to mention flounces, surprised him. For he did not recognize in his mother's attendant the rapidly departing female of a few hours before. This made matters difficult. Should one refresh his memory by recalling the morning's incidents, or was it more prudent to ignore the affair altogether? The Queen was uncertain. She looked at Draga.

The lady-in-waiting showed similar qualms, although

191

she was nearer a solution. Nothing would be gained,
she reasoned, by arousing the antagonism of so self-
willed a tyrant. Especially since it was only too apparent
that she attracted him. He stood staring at her with
undisguised admiration while his irregular teeth were
bared in an artless smile.

Queen Natalia observed her son's change of mood.
Reaching for a straw, her anxious maternal heart determined to foster his budding interest. She proffered
explanations.

"Our dear Baroness Draga," she introduced, "who
has been such a comfort to me. She came here all the
way from Belgrade where her late husband was one of
your loyal subjects."

The effect on Sasha left nothing to be desired. His
face brightened. Of all things, the dark piquant lady
was a widow—nothing in the world could be more
glamorous to a boy of eighteen. . . .

In a display of chivalry which was intended solely for
Draga's edification he stooped to kiss his mother's hand.
Next, he bowed before the Queen's companion while a
wave of crimson colored his cheeks.

"Baroness," he murmured, and his words were not
without eloquence, "I am a fortunate man." The
inference was plain.

In Draga something awoke which had lain dormant
since the early days of her loveless marriage. It was
not passion. It would take more than this unprepossessing
lad to stir a woman's blood—it would take the challenging
arrogance of a Dragutin on the moonlit square of
Obrenovatz, or the poignant unforgotten beauty of Voyan.
This Sasha? Ah, no! Emotions were not stirred by

such a one as this, with his deplorable manners and his absurdly ill-fitting clothes. . . . But that which now came to life in Draga was older than her thirst for love. It was the Lunyevica heritage—her restless, deep, inborn ambition.

Thrice it had been defeated and thrust back. First, when Belgrade would not have her. Next, when Mihailo Masin refused to sanction her interest in the return of Milan and his consort, following that accidental encounter at the Serbian Embassy in Vienna. And finally, the treatment accorded her in Biarritz where she was even now no more than servant to a deposed queen.

But this was altogether different. The King of Serbia, Alexander himself, had bowed to her. And his first utterance had been like music to her wounded ear. "Baroness——" To Serbia's monarch she was not a mere domestic, then. She was a personality who might some day become a personage. Who could tell? Biarritz might take notice and change its tune.

With one quick glance she took stock of the blushing son of Natalia Kesko; one glance told her she had found favor in his eyes. More than that, she had aroused his desire. With a bit of skillful maneuvering this interest on his part might be transformed into infatuation. Certainly the prize seemed well worth the gamble, especially since the odds were all to her advantage. He was so young (ten years her junior) and susceptible. In fact, he seemed inexperienced to the point of embarrassment. But he had the determination of a naughty child that is ready to howl and storm if crossed in the attainment of its wishes. This made her task fairly

simple.   He must want her.   She could depend upon
his temper for the rest.

The possibilities inherent in these reflections caused a
wave of excitement to surge up within her.   She felt
dizzy and begged to be excused.   In passing through the
door she rewarded Sasha with the ghost of a smile.
After she had gone he turned to his mother.

"Exquisite creature," he sighed.

Natalia, whose eyes had rested adoringly upon the
stalwart figure of her son, was roused from fond reveries.

"My Draga?" she asked absently.

"Yes.   What a name—*The Beloved*—it suits her perfectly."

The maternal eyebrows curved into a startled line.   It
had been well enough for the lady-in-waiting to banish
Sasha's glum spirits, but his present ebullition struck
Natalia as excessive.   She became casual.

"A pretty little woman whom I find quite useful,"
she dismissed the subject.   "But now you must come
with me and talk to your young cousins.   My little
charges, you remember?   They are already playing outside in the garden."

From her post at the keyhole Draga could see that
he hated to go.   A shade less graciously he now inquired
whether he had not already met the children on his
arrival the day before.   But the Queen shook her head.
Taking his arm she dragged him downstairs.

Just beyond the villa the ground sloped toward the
ocean, forming a private bathing beach.   A rail fence
shut off the two far sides, providing a safe enclosure
for the children who were at the moment engaged in
furious Indian warfare.

"There," Natalia pointed a fluttering finger, "the little darlings. I see they are about to scalp Voika."

Sasha was not attracted. Neither, for that matter, were the children. At his approach they scarcely paused in their activities, pretending not to hear their aunt's mild chiding. The good Queen was baffled. She could not understand that anyone in the world should disapprove of her Sasha. Perhaps the little ones were bashful, due to her own rather solemn presence. Well, she would go back to the house for a while, so that during her absence Sasha might get acquainted with the cousins in his own sweet way. Pleading some errand, she turned and started uphill. She would give them all a nice long chance.

It was an hour later when, in the company of her son's aides, Natalia returned. This time, although the noon sun shone brightly, the beach was hidden from view by a low cloud of dust. From somewhere within this cloud there issued a torrent of vituperation and abuse such as the queenly tympanum had never before recorded. Somebody's paternity seemed to be questioned.

"Rumanian *raya* (rubbish)!" This was undeniably the voice of Sasha.

"Stupid Serb!" The cousins lost no time in replying.

"Stinkers!!"

"Frog-egg!!"

"Oh——" gasped Natalia, reaching for her smelling salts. She would have given anything to swoon but an unmerciful destiny held her upright. Not enough that she must hear their vile language, her eyes now witnessed a truly incredible scene.

In the middle of the beach stood Sasha, her beloved Sasha, surrounded by a screaming horde of barbarians.

Although he seemed to be covered from head to foot
with sand, dampish moss, and the smelly shells of sundry
dead crabs, his attackers continued to dig into the ground
for further missiles with which to bombard him. Nor
was Sasha slow in returning their trophies, hurling them
back as fast as they came. It was a huge and lusty
brawl.

The Queen's heart threatened to stand still. Tears of
humiliation burned in her eyes, for not only was this
rowdy display in her back yard vulgar beyond description,
but the participants were actually enjoying the fray.
Even Bibi, the royal pug, took an active part. Wagging
the curved emblem that served him for a tail, Bibi
encircled the combatants, barking ferociously at shins
and knees.

As for Sasha himself, he was in fine fettle and seemed
to be having a particularly good time. With grotesque
gestures he motioned to the approaching officers, inviting
them to join the tussle. Undecided as to a proper course,
some of the men pretended to side with the children
while the others supported the sadly battered King. The
conflict threatened now to assume gigantic proportions
when, abruptly, Sasha's interest died down.

Having just intercepted a live clam with one hand
and a piece of wet jellyfish with the other, he suddenly
stopped in his tracks and with squinting eyes stared back
at the villa. For there in the distance, with white skirts
blowing in the breeze, a slender figure tripped gracefully
down the terrace toward the beach.

The children, disappointed by this interruption, followed
their enemy's gaze.

"Ooh," they cried, "it's Draga! She hides down here every afternoon to read one of her books——"

"She's early today," added one of the boys.

Voika's gypsy eyes flashed mischievously. "That's because she just started a new one called *The Weeping Corpse*. It's real long, so I guess she needs more time." The brown-skinned little girl felt no compunction about abetting the sport that was made of her sister.

The announcement was now greeted with shouts of glee. As Draga moved toward them the savage little faces grimaced knowingly. But she went her quiet way, taking no notice. Far down the beach she sought out a sheltered cave formed by a rock that jutted into the water. Here she sat down beneath a drooping, striped umbrella.

"She stays there for hours," the youthful tongues continued to jabber, "and you should hear her scream when we put a fish in her lap!"

Queen Natalia had meanwhile regained a measure of calm. She must retire to her rooms and reflect. Sasha, and everyone else for that matter, had given her enough surprises for one day. Where on earth had her innocent nephews and nieces picked up their vocabulary? And what were those books which so occupied her lady-in-waiting? From her father confessor the virtuous Queen had heard of wicked authors like Zola, who wrote lewd things on paper. For this was, after all, France—where they printed everything. Most decidedly she must have a look at Draga's books.

But all this comprised only a fraction of Natalia's worries. Her true anxiety concerned Sasha and his extraordinary behavior ever since dawn. What were these startling twists in his nature? Had he the faintest notion of what it signified to be a king? Obviously not. With her own eyes she had seen her darling Sasha disporting himself like a street urchin, and his profanity—she could not bear the recollection of his profanity.

It would never do. What did the men, her son's officers, think of their master? What would Biarritz say? She must control those children and keep them from retailing these dreadful events to their parents. She must take Sasha aside for a serious talk. Of course, one had to be careful—he was a sweet, sensitive boy and she did not want to hurt him. But he must be told, nevertheless.

With a supreme effort at self-control she summoned the five youngsters. Looking them over, she remarked in her most casual tone:

"It is almost time for luncheon. I think you will want to clean up."

Yes, they wanted a bit of cleaning both inside and out, she reflected bitterly. Clapping her hands, she shooed them toward the house.

At the same time she made the disturbing discovery that Sasha was not with them. Turning back, she saw him standing motionless on the beach, his gaze fixed on a distant rock beyond which fluttered a billowing white skirt.

"Sashino," she called to him, "we are going to have our lunch. Did you hear me, darling?"

He did. A frown knitted his brows into a bushy line. "But the Baroness, Mama—who is going to call the Baroness?" It was apparent that with only an ounce of encouragement he intended to dash on the proposed errand.

Natalia observed his expression and her own became quizzical. It struck her that Sasha's interest in the lady-in-waiting was as disquieting as his informality with the children. It proved conclusively that, as a sovereign, he did not know his place and would never be able to keep other people in theirs. Whatever had they done, back home, to this boy of hers? Was he left to his own devices, without care or guidance? Had he grown to manhood like a weed, untrained, unfettered? This was unthinkable, since royal children were surrounded by tutors and governors; they were hemmed in on every side. Even her son's letters to his mother, during all those years of separation, had been read and revised by strangers who lived his life for him. Poor Sasha. He had never really been a child. Was it to follow now that he would never be a man?

She retraced her steps and slipped one arm into his. "Don't worry about Draga," she remarked airily, "I have never known her to be late."

"But——"

"She has a watch. She will start back in good time. Besides, we do not concern ourselves with the responsibilities of those whom we employ, except in so far as these responsibilities are neglected."

Even as she spoke a slight irritation overcame her. Was it not a trifle silly for a lady-in-waiting to sit by the sea at stark midday? Especially Draga, who took such pains about her complexion and hated sunburn. What was the meaning of this? As a woman, Natalia

Kesko did not have to ask. She knew coquetry even when she did not see it.

Holding herself erect, the Queen stalked across the sand. Behind her, moody and itching with the heat, trailed Sasha. He was tired. He had no appetite. And so he would not let them hurry him.

CHAPTER XIX

THE DROWNING

LIFE at the villa had become a hectic round of activities. Daily a score or more visitors paid their respects and, when no one was coming or going, the royal company drove about the countryside on sightseeing expeditions. In this manner mornings and evenings alike were given over to social diversions, for nothing was left undone, if it offered amusement to the Serbian guests.

To be sure, it was all a terrific strain on the aging Dowager who, at fifty-two, looked back on a decade and a half of uneventful quietude. Late nights and breathless days, such as she now experienced, belonged to the long-forgotten years of her youth. Their reappearance at this late date brought wistful memories as well as physical discomfort, for Natalia was not the robust amazon she had once been. Although she enjoyed at first the illusion of a simulated court life, the very effort it required now began to dim its pleasure.

When she slipped into bed at night, footsore and weary, sudden doubts assailed her. Was anything worth such expenditure of time, money, energy? But then she thought of Sasha. A mother's instinct told her that he needed watching. He needed, above all else, to be kept busy. This was his first contact with a world which dazzled and bewildered him because he had no knowledge of people, no sense of values. She must brace herself, despite fatigue, and plunge into this maze of gala events

201

for Sasha's sake. He must be taught, by constant
example, how to distinguish, to discriminate, to choose
that which befitted his station. If she did not arrange
parties and formal obligations for him Sasha would be
quite content to romp over the country with hoodlums
who, on learning his identity, hailed him with proletarian
nonchalance whenever he went out.

It was not that Alexander showed any intrinsic democratic leanings. If he met mankind at large on its own
footing this was due merely to a morbid curiosity. He
had never known human kinship and intimacy except
during the brief span of his nursery days. Now he
felt drawn toward those whom it was easy to approach:
the plain, the simple, the lowly. Since he was conscious
at the same time of their subordination he did not hesitate
to bully or abuse, when some dark impulse prompted him
to do so. But with equals and aristocrats he felt ill
at ease. Their self-imposed restraints reminded him of
Milutin and the other disciplinarians of his lonely boyhood. Their refinements irked, since he had never learned
to master social graces. His life had been too isolated
for more than theoretic knowledge of good manners.

Toward the Biarritz ladies who clustered about him
in fawning adulation he behaved with execrable taste.
The pretty ones he pursued with embarrassing perseverance, while flatly ignoring those of lesser charm—regardless of their eminent station. And, no matter what the
occasion, he was always willing to desert them all for
the most fleeting moment in the company of Draga. To
Queen Natalia this discovery brought endless chagrin.
When she herself had extolled the virtues of her lady-in-
waiting it had been for the purpose of distracting her

son from the grief of that first unfortunate breakfast at the villa. With equal success she might well have arrested his attention by discussing her chronic lumbago or the new petunia bed near the front gate. It rankled her now that she had not been more botanical in her choice of subject matter.

She was particularly bent upon reforming Sasha, since Biarritz harbored at this time a Russian grand-duke among its transitory guests. This opened direct channels to St. Petersburg where, among the cousins and nieces of the Tsar, a future Queen of Serbia might be hoped for. Then, too, the Spanish Bourbon-Hapsburgs summered in near-by San Sebastian. Dowager Queen Cristina came to the seashore every year with her small son Alfonso who, like Sasha, was made a king too soon. But Cristina had been more fortunate than poor Natalia. The boy Alfonso led a normal life, with a mother's constant care and guidance, whereas her own Sasha had been deprived too early of even a nursemaid's familiar touch.

With the Queen of Spain came the Infantas, slightly mildewed, but marriageable nevertheless. Was it not Natalia's duty to further a possible union with one of the great dynasties of Europe? The little state of Serbia would gain incalculable prestige if wedding bells beckoned from Tsarskoë Selo or the grim Escorial.

To nurture the delicate spark of romance which as yet existed only in the Kesko imagination, it was necessary to provide the "young people" with an opportunity to get acquainted. For this purpose a series of nautical expeditions was planned, encompassing the entire length of the Basque coast. From these Draga Masin was carefully excluded. In her place Alfonso's younger sister

Eulalia functioned as Sasha's escort. Eulalia was a cheerful maid, given to convulsive laughter which revealed an alarming expanse of dental arch. Her French was mingled with Spanish phrases which Sasha could not understand. As a result, their friendship advanced slowly. While Eulalia punctuated her monologue with sudden blasts of hilarity, Sasha did little more than count her molars.

The royal outings lasted from sunup until sundown, during which time Draga was left severely alone. She did not mind. She spent the days in curl papers and oatmeal packs, welcoming the returning picnickers with saucy ringlets and a velvet complexion. Stuffy from heat and boredom, Sasha looked upon her cool loveliness with renewed desire. Having gazed for days at wind-bitten, tanned, regal collar bones, he found that Draga's orchid-like freshness exerted an even greater fascination. It all ended by his refusing point-blank to start on another safari, either by land or sea.

Natalia was nonplussed. She would be the last to deny her lady-in-waiting's charms. Even Biarritz, at first so disdainful, had come to concede these. But Biarritz none the less kept Draga in her place. For more than three years the young widow had primped and simpered, yet to no avail. She remained, despite her undisputed looks, a hired member of Queen Natalia's staff of domestics. Only Sasha, stubborn and un-sophisticated, was capable of falling prey to such artful and transparent wiles. . . . That crafty maneuver, for instance, on the day of the beach battle—when the young woman had ensconced herself behind that rock and spread out her umbrella where Sasha could not fail to see it!

The annoyed Dowager had required several days to figure this out. Finally the meaning became clear. Without uttering a word, the siren had marked her hide-out as a trysting place. Sasha's increasing disappearances from the villa eventually led to his discovery under the flippant stripes of Draga's parasol. Huddled together in the sand, the King and the sly vixen read vapid novels or stared into the scarlet sunset, while the royal retinue and local gentry wove the ugly thread of gossip.

Quite noticeably Natalia's manner toward her lady-in-waiting changed. A frigid tone informed Draga that she was rapidly falling out of favor. Odd tasks, like mending and useless fancywork, were assigned to her. Their purpose was only too apparent. She would be kept indoors during the remainder of the royal visit. Except on rare occasions, the beach was barred. Draga obeyed without a murmur, smiling a little to herself.

The change left Sasha disconcerted for a while. But he soon got around this too. It did not take him long to learn, through Voika, the exact location of Draga's room. To go there without logical excuse was, of course, not feasible. But there were other ways of reaching his beloved.

Although with less frequency, the Ghika and Bibesco children still came on boisterous visits to the villa. One of their favorite games, while on the premises, involved a race to the upper stories and through a trap door that led onto the roof (forbidden territory, since tramping over the shingles brought down layers of plaster from ceilings within). It was an easy matter to provoke this spirited pastime. At the barest suggestion the youthful contestants scampered upstairs, with Sasha bounding playfully behind. On Draga's floor, while they raced madly on, he stopped to knock softly on her door. She opened and stepped out into the hall. In an instant his arms locked about her, crushing her to him. She uttered a little scream and struggled to free herself. At the sound of her voice the children at the far end of the hall gave up the chase and turned back to investigate. Hiding behind a linen shelf which was piled high with freshly ironed clothes, they spied through the semi-darkness. What they saw and heard would never be forgotten, for they all kept childish diaries and they all would write this down.

"He kissed her," whispered Henri, the oldest Ghika boy, after a long silence.

"With that nasty mustache?" asked Voika, screwing up her nose in disgust.

The rest nudged her to be quiet. At the other end of the corridor the man and woman clung to each other in a desperate embrace. And now Sasha's voice rose roughly, as if in challenge to the unknown:

"I will make you Queen, my dearest!"

Draga did not answer. In the dim glow of a skylight the children saw her lift a white still face until her eyes met those of the man. With her eyes she seemed to be reading again the pledge his lips had just spoken, for now her own lips curved into a smile. Then, slowly, she turned from him and slipped back into her room. With heavy, deliberate steps the King of Serbia went downstairs.

No time was lost before the children, elated by what they had witnessed, descended those same stairs. They were bursting with news and a normal desire to stun the world. Only the circumstance that Queen Natalia happened to be entertaining her musical coterie prevented their breaking into the drawing room and spreading the lurid details of their discovery.

On the following morning, before the gloating conspirators had a chance to explode their bomb, something else interfered. Sasha had been up since dawn, hoping to catch a moment with Draga before she went to church. But Queen Natalia had given up her matutinal devotions in an effort to make up for lost sleep, and the lady-in-waiting had no permission to go out alone.

Foiled, the anxious lover cast about for a different plan. Knowing that Draga must supervise the children's swimming lessons that day, he too decided to take a dip. Attired in jaunty trunks and leaning on the arm of his *baigneur* (a Basque sailor, in whose trust lay His Majesty's oceanic safety) Sasha marched down to the beach. His dark hairy body by no means afforded an edifying spectacle. Squinting in the sunlight, he approached the water's edge with shy, gingerly hops, peering everywhere for Draga. Unable to see more than a few paces ahead, he pushed toward the rocky promontory where her parasol ought to be swaying in its customary place. He wished now that he had brought along his *pince-nez,* for it seemed that he would never find her. Growing hot, he decided at last to swim.

It so happened that the rocky region of the beach surrounding Draga's favorite spot was unsafe for bathing because of a treacherous undercurrent. Spectators from the safely roped-off portion of the children's beach gave repeated cries of warning. The *baigneur* likewise placed a restraining hand on the King's arm. But Sasha could not tolerate interference. Objections only served to make him more dogged in his resolution, whatever it might be. He had today decided to take his dip within sight of Draga's striped umbrella, and no one would keep him from doing so.

Once in the water, he emitted triumphant shouts of glee. Refreshed by the briny waves, he bounced up and down amid the breakers, cutting a caper or two. Presently he began to duck his bather. The latter, a powerful peasant type, could easily have resisted but was prevented by his subordinate position from countering the royal will. He went down good-naturedly each time the splashing King repeated his prank.

Sasha enjoyed himself. It seemed to him that he had caught the sound of Draga's voice among the persons who, with warning protests, had gathered at the shore and waved frantic signals to him. He must speak to her before she got away. He must tell her that he had lain awake all night, making plans for their happiness. . . . Pressing forward, he attempted to swim ashore when a chill undertow whirled him swiftly about. An inrolling breaker covered his head and he gave a choked cry for help. The bather, still snuffing water after His Majesty's facetious gambols, blinked stupidly about. Panic-stricken, the gulping Sasha drew near. He clasped wild arms about the Spaniard's throat and both men went down together. A moment later one of them emerged, his eyes bulging with terror.

"Help!" he roared in guttural Serbian.

The cry whipped spectators to action. Several officers threw off their shakos and plunged into the ocean. After a mad struggle they groped their way back, dragging the limp unconscious form of Sasha between them. Another trip was made for the ill-fated *baigneur*. But the sea had taken its toll. Not until dusk of the following day did the waves relinquish his battered and bloated corpse.

In an upstairs room at the villa Sasha lay delirious on his soaked bed. At intervals small spurts of slimy water burst from his lungs. At such times he groaned with pain. Then again he lay silent for hours.

Queen Natalia knelt at his side in anguish. Her heart was bowed low with despair. She had been down to the cottage of the sailor's kin and made what small amends money could make—(there was a broken woman, heavy with child)—and now she prayed for the recovery of her son. Once during her ceaseless supplication his hand reached out and touched her head. The bluish lips moved in an effort to speak and, as he lay there with his eyes half-closed, those semi-conscious lips inflicted the deepest wound Natalia Kesko had yet endured. While his fingers played with her graying hair, she heard him whisper:

"Draga—my darling Draga!"

The unhappy mother rose to her feet and went downstairs. In the library she found her lady-in-waiting standing near an open window staring at the beach where in the moonlight could be seen the fading traces left by the sailor's body. Silently a rising tide was beginning to obliterate the shallow marks, covering their outlines with a film of glistening sand.

The two women faced each other. There was no need for words, so perfect was their understanding. The one had taken everything from the other—that was all.

"When are you leaving?" asked the mother in a voice that sounded quite dead.

The younger woman smiled boldly. "Tonight," she
answered, "and when next you hear from me, Madame,
I shall be Queen!"

Natalia Kesko's face froze. It remained frozen when,
two days later, her sister Marietta Ghika reported the
shocking story of the kiss, as witnessed by that lady's
resourceful offspring. What, after all, was a kiss? A
frivolous trifle, quickly bestowed, more quickly forgotten.
Natalia did not care about that kiss. . . . She cared
about something that was far worse. For she knew
that into the small firm palm of Draga Masin's hand
Sasha had placed his future.

In another fortnight he too would go back to Serbia,
out of her life forever. He would hate her because
she, his mother, had driven Draga away. She was
intercepting, even now, all communications which came
to the villa, lest the scheming adventuress inform Sasha
of her whereabouts. This, at least, was a mother's
privilege. While he lived in Natalia Kesko's house he
must remain inaccessible to Natalia's dismissed lady-in-
waiting. Later, after leaving this roof, he might do as
he pleased.

They would find each other again, those two. And
she, who had made a last absurd effort to keep them
apart, would lose him utterly.

When she lost him before, she had waited for him to
grow up. This time, she knew, it would be useless even
to wait.

CHAPTER XX

Return to Belgrade

In driving Draga from her home the Dowager Queen unwittingly played into the lovers' hands. Since Alexander would have been obliged sooner or later to return to his duties in Belgrade, was it not foolish to set free the woman from whose clutches he needed to be saved? Natalia wondered. Would it not have been more politic to tolerate the mild flirtation that went on under her own maternal nose, meanwhile accelerating her inflammable boy's departure and keeping his lady-love thereafter under the strictest supervision? Instead, what had she done? In an outburst of choler she had released her lady-in-waiting from whatever obligations might have prevailed in binding Draga to Biarritz. She had set the huntress on the trail of an all-too-willing prey.

These thoughts tormented Natalia now, while she scanned with avid interest each news dispatch from Belgrade. Under every headline which announced her son's return to his capital she looked for the name of the widow Masin. But for the moment, at any rate, the ex-Queen's attendant and her royal lover did not seem to be reunited.

In point of fact, Draga had gone straight to Paris where Voika's new school term opened. She had stopped at an obscure hostelry and waited for some reply to the messages which she had posted at intervals since her precipitous departure. That they would most certainly be intercepted she could fairly count on, but there was nothing else for her to do. She had not exchanged a single word with Sasha since that afternoon in the upstairs hall when, too impulsively perhaps, he had exclaimed that he would make her his queen. She had no guaranty that in her present plight he would come to her rescue. She had only his kiss. Like Queen Natalia she was well aware that, more often than not, a kiss proved to be a pastime rather than a pledge. This was especially true of royal osculation.

Then, too, Sasha was only an overgrown child with a child's inconsistent whims and fancies. Since she had gone away without bidding him farewell he might trundle off to Serbia in high dudgeon and promptly pay homage to some other female in his entourage. Draga did not overrate her powers of seduction. She knew it required little skill to turn the head of an eighteen-year-old novice in the field of love. The important thing was to entrench herself in his life as soon as possible, before the foolish lad had a chance to forget her. She must hurry at once to Belgrade.

This brought up a difficult point. She had left the house on the Danube Quay without thought of ever occupying it again. Her brother Nikodem had promised to negotiate the sale of her part of the property, sending the proceeds to Draga's bank in Paris. But Nikodem had failed in his efforts. Apart from Voyan Masin (who could not be approached) no one was interested in purchasing an incomplete establishment, half of which belonged to someone else. In consequence, the Paris bank where Draga kept her dwindling funds showed no new entry. With Voika's schooling paid for, it was unwise to remain any longer in the expensive city on the Seine. She must leave France where she had neither home nor friends. She must gamble with fate anew and play for the highest stake. She must win Sasha.

During her long journey on the Orient Express she pored, like Queen Natalia, over the news sheets reporting Alexander's arrival in his capital. Since her French was limited (she spoke it with a peculiar and ingratiating singsong) she could gather only the most salient facts. In Vienna, at last, Serbian papers confirmed what she had managed to glean from Gallic captions. The King had been at home for a week and her own arrival could not have been better planned. Sasha was already engaged, she read, in reorganizing the personnel at his palace. Who could tell? Here might be the very opening she wanted. Confidently she put down the paper and drowsed through the last lap of her journey. When next she opened her eyes the towers of Belgrade were just coming into view.

Half an hour later she stood before the carved portal of her dead husband's home, unable to lift the iron knocker. It was a heavy gauntlet, rusty with age, which had never moved well on its hinges. The house seemed to be in complete darkness, despite the early November dusk. Mihailo had always kept a light burning on the stairs, she remembered suddenly, but Mihailo would not be awaiting her now. For a moment she regretted not having notified Nikodem and Paul of her coming. Still, Draga had preferred to have no witnesses when she and Voyan met again. The thought that her brother-in-law might not be at home had never occurred to her.

Using both hands, she tried again to raise the knocker. Her wrists began to ache, but the iron gauntlet did not

give way.   It was then that her eyes caught sight of a
small white button fitted neatly into the door-frame.   Not
really—an electric bell in Belgrade!   She could hardly
believe it.   Why, Paris itself was only beginning to
popularize this amazing marvel, one of the incredible
wonders of an incredible mechanical age which had just
dawned upon the world.

Forgetting the misgiving that gripped her, she stood
on her toes and pressed a gloved finger on the ivory
dot.   It moved under her touch and through the time-
eaten panels she heard a shrill jingle followed, a minute
later, by padded footsteps.   With a familiar clanking
sound the inner bolt was lifted and through a narrow gap
appeared the head of Anton.   His eyes popped open.   He
had recognized the small figure that waited outside under
the glare of the street lantern.

"Luba," he cried back over his shoulder, "quick,
quick—it's the *Gospodina!*"

Bowing excitedly, he motioned Draga to enter.   As she
stepped over the threshold the door swung shut with a
slow thud.   A trapped feeling came over her.

"Good evening, Anton," she said, if only to reassure
herself with the sound of her own voice, "is—is your
master at home?"

The servant shook his head.   Holding a burning taper
before her he pointed the way upstairs.

"Begging your forgiveness," he mumbled as they
ascended the creaking steps, "for my wearing the oldest
opanké under God's heaven, but what with sore feet—
and no one ever coming to the house anyway—a man
falls into bad habits."   He chuckled uneasily as he gazed
down at his slippered toes.

Draga stopped in surprise. "What do you mean, Anton? Isn't the young *Knese* living here?"

"Not for some time he hasn't been. We thought as everybody knew about his going to Greece in the service of the King."

The tenseness on Draga's face relaxed. She resumed the climb upstairs, her fingers gripping the banister as though she must be certain of support.

"Of course," she remarked casually, "I, too, have been gone a long time. But tell me, what is your master's present office?"

Anton assumed an important air. "Right hand to our representative at Athens, a very high post."

"Splendid."

"It is said that he will be in line for a similar rank at the Embassy in St. Petersburg, and that before very long."

"I am glad to hear it, Anton."

"Yes, the young *Knese* was always clever and bound to make his mark. There's only one thing worrying me——"

Draga held her breath. "What is that?"

"He's not the same. Not the gay one he used to be. Ever since——"

She made a nervous gesture. "That's quite natural. We're not any of us the same, I suspect. What about it?"

The servant's face wore a troubled frown. "Oh, nothing, I guess. Only, the Master, he talks and acts like there must be a burden on him. And then, he is always alone. Won't let anyone come near. When he goes away to foreign parts he makes me promise I'll allow no one into this house but——"

"Go on——" Her throat felt dry.

"But the *Gospodina*. He says these walls are meant for him and her alone. Luba and I began to think he might be joking about a young wife. But I guess the Master, he won't ever marry. Young girls are too scared of him! It's you, the Mistress he means——"

They had reached the darkness of the upper hall. With slow, habitual movements Anton groped for the lamp.

"Has he ever spoken of—my return?" she asked hoarsely.

There was a little puff from the petrol-soaked wick. "That he has. The *Gospodina* would come back, he said, just as certain as there's blood in that cellar. . . ."

She broke into a thin laugh. "How charming. So Voyan has come to believe in spooks!"

Anton was regulating the flame. "Not ghosts and such like," he commented, "the Master just believes what's there—blood."

Draga closed her fist and turned toward the sputtering light. Its yellowish glow gave her a feeling of comfort. She did not think she could ever stand the dark again. A faint odor of burning oil permeated the musty atmosphere of the upstairs hall, bringing a trifling thought to mind.

"Anton," she asked in a matter-of-fact tone, "must you continue using that old lamp with the same smoking wick that annoyed everybody so? I thought that was an electric bell I rang downstairs. What about lights?"

A beaming smile spread over the servant's face. "Electricity it was! But we got no further than that.

My cousin who works in Budapest, he brought me the button and some wires. Together we figured it out."

"Why, you're quite an inventor."

He blushed happily. "Oh, well," he admitted, "it's easy if you got a scientific mind. But you got to have that, my cousin says, or else a book with directions where you can read how it's done. We got a book like that and tried to make lights too, but they didn't work."

"That is a shame."

"Such pretty lights they were, too," Anton continued with a note of regret, "only they wouldn't work. My cousin, he says the rich people in Budapest all have electric lamps and telephones nowadays. They telephone to the Opera and someone holds the receiver so they can hear the music."

Highly pleased with himself, Anton was about to elaborate on a more technical scale when a swift patter of steps approached from the dark staircase. It was the housemaid Luba clad in night clothes and bonnet. She apologized volubly for not appearing sooner, since at the moment of Draga's arrival the servant quarters had been locked up for the night and Luba herself was preparing for bed.

Anton, whose dissertations had been interrupted by the girl, now turned and berated her smartly for her tardiness. At this Draga was unable to conceal her astonishment. Luba had always been a spirited minx who would stand for no domineering from anyone. Her current docility was baffling, if not uncanny.

"That's all right," Anton volunteered in answer to a silent question. "Luba and I got married after everybody went away. It was too lonesome around here."

The bride of three winters shuffled through a door into Draga's boudoir and set about making up the bed. In a few minutes she emerged, carrying an empty water pitcher.

Anton, meanwhile, took orders for the morning. The bath stove would be fired early. Breakfast was to be served, according to custom, in the upper gallery just off the bedrooms. Yes, the view over the Danube was as beautiful as ever. How long did the Mistress intend to stay? Had she come back for good?

Draga stared blankly into space. She did not know the answer. The stillness of the big house made her shiver. She dreaded this first night alone in her old room. But there was nothing to fear! Voyan was gone. . . . And those two trustworthy souls, Anton and Luba, kept watch below. No one could be any safer, she told herself. Yet it was closing in upon her even now—the dark cold horror of these walls. Something threatened to choke her, holding her captive in this haunted spot. She could hear Voyan's words:

"The *Gospodina* and I—we belong. . . . These walls are meant for us alone!"

The manservant was standing before her, still waiting for a reply. What was it? Oh, yes. Did she plan to stay? Her breath came in short gasps.

"No," she whispered, "I won't stay here. Not a day longer than necessary. You may go now. Tell Luba to sleep on the couch in my dressing room. I am not used to being alone."

Anton's face remained impassive. Joining his padded heels in military fashion, he bowed. Then, noiselessly, he vanished down the well of stairs.

CHAPTER XXI

TIME OF WAITING

SHE lingered in that house for weeks that stretched into a month, a year. Then she lost count. It was a time of patience, solitude, terror and slow, dogged triumph.

Her path was made difficult by a mesh of intrigue which hampered her movements from every side. To begin with, all access to the *Konak* had been barred. Immediately on her return to Serbia she had called at the palace only to find that conspiracy was already in full swing against her. It was easy to surmise what must have happened. Queen Natalia, although she no longer counted as a force in her former capital, had sent a motherly warning. This warning, since it dealt with the subject of a king's ridiculous infatuation, dared not be ignored. Besides, there were corroborating statements from other informants who claimed to be eye-witnesses of Sasha's folly. Their testimony served to strengthen the radical measures which must be devised for the monarch's protection.

During the week preceding Draga's arrival the indefatigable Milutin had obtained from His Majesty's officers a detailed description of the notorious widow. Instantly, following Natalia's example at Biarritz, a sharp eye was kept on the royal mails and every message from the ex-lady-in-waiting seized. The myopic king remained unsuspecting, even when confronted by blatant mutilation of his personal envelopes.

219

For his own part, the enamored Sasha engaged in desperate attempts to locate the lady of his choice. After Draga's flight from the villa he had raged and fretted, but to no avail. The thought of hurting him so deeply pained her, but the Dowager Queen was adamant. She had made considerable progress in her matrimonial negotiations with the Russian grand-duke; to have her son's brilliant prospects brought to nought by a nondescript love-affair would never do. For once she would not relent.

On the very day that the court train pulled into Belgrade Sasha had opened his quest. With naïve trust in his absolutism, he had confided to the members of his retinue that Draga Masin must be found at all costs. If other methods failed, scouts would have to be sent out in search of her. This guilelessness on the monarch's part made his defeat all the more simple. A pretense at combing the city proved futile and, since the lost damozel appeared to be a poor correspondent as well, the lovesick Sasha was left to ponder the fickleness of woman.

Although he had banished the unsavory Countess Eudoxia from the palace and sent his former drill master Gorlice to a distant province, there was still Milutin. The erstwhile royal governor had of his own accord renounced his duties at the *Konak* and accepted the far more influential post of Metropolitan over the diocese of Belgrade, which assured him the highest privileges. He could, for example, confer at all times with His Majesty, without appearing to dictate any royal course of action. It was Milutin who first interpreted Draga's prolonged silence as a sign that her affection for the King had cooled.

Slowly the drug crept into Sasha's soul, causing him to slacken in his ardent pursuit.

Even so, he did not give up hope entirely. The spell of this blighted romance lodged more deeply in his heart than anyone suspected. His rapture had been uninhibited and complete. With the intensity of a spoiled child he coveted Draga. No substitute would sway him from her. All attempts to divert his attention toward light-hearted amusements failed, for he would not attend command performances of the ballet any more than he consented to visit foreign courts with their flock of marriageable princesses on parade. He locked himself up in his palace and grieved. Obstinacy rather than passion lent zest to his grief.

Like a spider in her web, Draga Masin waited. The uneven struggle promised nothing but defeat, yet pride impelled her to offer resistance. She had never given herself to Sasha, Natalia's assumption notwithstanding. She did not love him (any more than she had loved Mihailo Masin)—this foolish boy who was a king. But there was a crown in the offing and, in spite of all the doubts besetting her, she still believed that Sasha meant her to wear it.

Twice she had seen him at a distance driving through city streets, waving listlessly to the crowds that lined the avenue of the Montenegrins or stopping to enjoy the view from the wide *Kalimegdan* place which overlooked the confluence of Sava and Danube. Both times she had detected a wan expression on his face. He loved her still! He was not even man enough to conceal his weakness, but sat there in his carriage, confronting the world with a glum pout on his lips.

Draga came home, after this discovery, beside herself with joy. She knew now that her tenacity would be rewarded. She must hold herself in readiness and wait her chance. She must continue to scheme and calculate until an opportunity presented itself for their meeting.

If only she had money! But months of waiting, idle, in that dreary prison on the Danube Quay, had almost swallowed up her funds. Long ago she had been forced to send Voika home to her mother. Keeping a horse and carriage was out of the question; this she recognized as her greatest handicap. For, even if she were to approach the royal procession during some popular holiday, on foot no one would take any notice of her. Her clothes had become too worn and shabby. Sasha would never think of looking for her among stampeding pedestrians on the sidewalk. He had no inkling of her poverty.

For a while she obtained help from her brothers. Their army pay was meager, but in view of her queenly prospects both Nikodem and Paul brought out every farthing they could spare. Then a despicable thing happened. By order of Colonel Dragutin Dmitriyevitch, in charge of the Belgrade garrison, the Lunyevica brothers were tried for a minor infraction and cashiered. This was a severe blow. The young men went grumbling up the Sava in search of farm work, while from her mother Draga received sound reproof. Ambition, the simple Mara wrote, often exceeded the bounds of reason. Draga must be insane to nurse delusions of grandeur which brought wretchedness not only to herself but her innocent kin in the bargain.

The woman in the empty Masin mansion gnawed her lips. She accepted the reprimand. She cringed under Paul's odium, Nikodem's ridicule. But her fighting spirit awoke at the reappearance of her original enemy—Dragutin. She understood the thrust, aimed at her through her brothers. Again this man opposed her with cunning and insult. Nothing could hold her now!

She lived on in stoical determination. From her balcony she gazed for hours at the narrow street, knowing only too well that she would never see a regal cortège pass her door. Of late King Alexander's public appearances were growing more rare. A rumor made the rounds that the monarch had fallen prey to melancholia.

Draga spent weeks pacing the boulevards until the soles of her feet blistered. Always she returned weary and disappointed to her dismal abode. Unable to pay the houseman and his wife, she refused their services and attended to her few wants in person. Luba retired to the servant realm below stairs where Anton lolled in the capacity of caretaker, plying a small trade on the side. The gaunt woman who dwelt alone in the upper regions worried them little. She was a queer one, she was. But Anton had been charged by the *Knese* Voyan to watch over the premises. And that he did. So long as she brought no trespassers, the Mistress would find Anton easy going. He did not mean to interfere.

Unmindful of time or circumstance, Draga Masin passed her thirty-first birthday. She had acquired a spinsterish appearance. Having dropped mourning in Biarritz and favored gaily colored frocks, she now went back to black. It was economical. Her shoes, once made to order by the town's best cobbler, were now fashioned of coarse and durable material. They were designed for much walking.

She had given up curl papers; their noisy rustling at night frightened her. In fact, it was darkness—stealthy and silent—that knew this strong woman in her zero hour. Night alone saw Draga tremble! She hardly slept at all. Her nerves were keyed to an insufferable pitch, so that the moaning of the wind outside her window filled even the twilight with specters.

She kept a tallow light beside her bed but was unable to read. Her customary fare of books now stood her in bad stead. Those tales of horror once so avidly absorbed had a boomerang propensity of haunting her lone hours. They intensified fear instead of abating it. Gray phantoms out of *Marquis de Sade* and *Monte Cristo* hovered before her in the company of a tall Basque sailor or the blurred shape of a Guardsman——

"Mihailo," she cried out at such times, "I didn't do it—I swear to you that you went down of your own accord!"

The shade veered gently toward her and she heard the whisperings of conscience:

"You sent me, Draga, though you saw I was in no condition to go. . . ."

Long before dawn the agonized woman would stir about. She lingered fussily over a frugal breakfast. Tea, and a dry roll snatched from a table in some sidewalk café the night before, made up her morning meal. She had learned this trick years ago, before her days of want. In Vienna and Budapest it was a familiar phenomenon. Even well-dressed ladies, who stepped from elegant car-

riages and paid for refreshments, helped themselves openly
to the ever present bread basket. Some, more finicky
than others, spread butter on the pilfered pasty before
slipping it into their reticules. No one stopped them. If
remonstrations were made, they would sit down and eat
the offending bun right before your eyes, thus overriding
any objection. Bread was free, wasn't it? You could
take all you wanted, so long as you paid for your coffee.

Despite her exhaustive use of this public prerogative,
Draga went hungry most of the time. But to suffer
privations suited her sense of drama, her histrionic nerves.
She enjoyed acting a part, and the idea of seeking work
never occurred to her. Employment would restrict her
freedom, when it was so imperative that she roam the
streets, day and night if necessary. How else could she
attain her end? How else was she to meet Sasha? No,
she preferred to count her remaining dinars and to
squeeze from them the utmost sustenance. Like a miser
she hoarded the dwindling treasure that must tide her
over—what merciless number of years? Work! The
mere thought of work was preposterous. A future
Queen of Serbia could not jeopardize her position by
seeking remunerative labor. She must not demean herself. The secret betrothed of Alexander Obrenovitch could
not hire out her services to a subject of her royal fiancé!
Then indeed would Sasha have cause to disdain her—if
she ever forgot herself so far.

A kind of fanaticism burned within her. She seemed
unaware of her wasting body, the premature withering
of her beauty. Hollow-cheeked, yet with a strange light
in her oblique eyes, she sat in her eerie chamber. Through
the murk cast by a dingy tallow lamp her distorted shadow

was thrown against the wall. It did not look like Draga Lunyevica, the little village flirt. Instead, it showed the bleak outlines of Skuld, the third Norn sister, spinning her finite thread.

PART THREE

VOYAN

CHAPTER XXII

Confrontation

THE dour ordeal which she so willingly inflicted upon herself carried its own antidote. The very monotony of her existence began, in time, to dull its poignant edge. Even solitude becomes companionable. Soon there were days (sometimes a whole week) when she forgot to go out. Now and then the purpose upon which she focused her unrelieved concentration showed a curious tendency to become a blank. She found, and the phenomenon alarmed her but faintly, that she did not know for certain what Sasha looked like. She couldn't always remember his name! Like Mihailo, her husband, he was fading into that limbo of indifferent beings whose natures never really touched her own and whose memory will-power alone could keep alive. But power of will, expended as relentlessly as hers had been, led in the end to a kind of mental inertia. Draga's living hours lapsed gradually into a twilight state. She felt herself moving through a nebulous period in which there could be neither joy nor pain. And it was now that Voyan Masin returned at last to Serbia.

She had never forgotten Voyan. Hate, fear, longing surged up in her breast at the sound of his name. She saw his form as clearly now as on that first night when he passed beneath her balcony. She knew each line of the keen profile, each shadow on that guarded face. And, though he had rejected her overtures, she rejoiced in

229

the knowledge that he was bound to her by their common guilt.

Voyan arrived without prelude or warning. He stood suddenly in the dim upstairs hall and looked into her startled eyes. She held his gaze, withstanding his scrutiny of her pathetic appearance. While Anton shuffled obsequiously about, dusting the unused flight of rooms belonging to the *Knese* and placing luggage on a rack, Voyan stared at the wraith-like silhouette of his sister-in-law. Her bloodless face was framed by flat strands of dull black hair. Offset by her drab dress he saw the wax-like transparency of her hands, their uncared-for nails broken and stained.

She realized slowly that he must be drawing a mental picture of the Draga he had known, for the space of a few days, in the shadow of these very walls. He had not, then, forgotten that—but for a monstrous mishap—he might indeed have loved her!

She watched his eyes. He too had changed. But it seemed to her that he was now more handsome. Maturity had hardened the soft line of cheek and brow. His face was thinner, more intense. Only his hair, wavy and wild, swept back from the temples in the old defiant fashion.

Draga took a step forward, her lips parted in a vague smile. He did not respond by a single gesture. Instead, he pulled himself up rigidly and spoke a formal greeting.

"So you are here, my—sister."

She paled at the irony of his address. "Does my presence surprise you?"

"No, I can't say that it does. Except, perhaps, that I expected you to return even sooner than you did."

"Then you knew of my homecoming," she asked bewildered, "yet you never tried to——"

"Certainly." His voice was quite cold. "Anton and I carry on a desultory correspondence. He keeps me informed, in his own quaint style, of important events that take place while I am gone."

A shadow of derision swept across her mouth. "You considered my return important?"

He nodded. "I was curious to know how long you thought you could run away."

She met the challenge. "If I came back, it was not for the reason you imply. Criminals return to the scene of their crime, but I've done nothing wrong. Nothing—actually. . . . In France, I never thought about your morbid accusations. They dropped away from me like ugly scales. I was happy there. Do you hear? Happy!"

"How pleasant," he commented blandly. "But if you were so happy, may I ask why you did return?"

She realized suddenly how little he knew of her life. The Biarritz episode, her years of service in Queen Natalia's employ, Sasha's courtship—Voyan had no idea of all this. He was unaware that she had, after all, become a person of importance, a *femme fatale* discussed by an international press. Didn't he ever read the papers? But no, he could not have guessed. Her name had been deleted from reports that linked King Alexander's honor with an adventuress. Although the rumor of Sasha's entanglement spread widely, the identity of Draga had been hushed up by the *Glavnyaca* (secret police).

Nevertheless, these reflections restored to her a measure of poise. "Then you don't know——" she murmured mysteriously, while a sense of security stole over her.

His eyebrows met in a puzzled frown. "I told Anton to expect you, and you came. What more is there to know?"

She controlled a wild impulse to laugh. She had returned for Sasha, not dead Mihailo! What did she care about the incubus that haunted Voyan's imagination? What did she want with the spook of memory that dwelled in this house? Ah, no! It was a living present, not a mortal past, that had brought her back. Despite herself, she broke into soundless laughter which would not be repressed. Her shoulders shook with mirth, as at some hidden joke.

Voyan's stupefaction grew. "Anton made no mention——" he began, but broke off uncertainly.

Her assurance was now complete. "And is Anton the only one with whom you have communicated in all these years?"

"On unofficial topics, yes."

"No friends?"

"No friends."

"Of course, you didn't run across my name in the diplomatic pouch."

His mouth twitched into a wry smile. "Hardly. I think you are willing to concede that your movements don't figure in official correspondence. Or am I mistaken?"

"Perhaps."

He was more baffled than ever. Observing her closely, he studied the white oval face with minute care. What lay behind that mask of hers? He found himself weakening under the old spell of her nearness. A strangely tender note crept into his voice as he spoke once more.

"You've changed, Draga. You've suffered! I know, because I too have had no peace. There was always that blind force driving me back——"

She did not seem to be listening. Her mind was far away.

"Like you, Draga," he insisted, "I knew that I must come back."

"What for?" she asked dully.

"I don't know. To face things, I guess. To try to blot them out by tearing down this terrible old house——"

"Yes," she gasped, electrified by his words, "that would help!"

He caught the eagerness in her voice. "It might be a solution," he went on, "for both of us, I mean. Maybe we could start again."

"Could we?" She was afraid of the thrill that vibrated in her throat. But Voyan could not restrain himself longer.

"It can be done and it must be done. What happened here lies over you and me like a curse. It is making you grow old before your time and causing me to flee from my own shadow. . . ."

"What do you want, Voyan?" she asked faintly.

His face was bleak. "On my person depends the survival of an honored race. I am the last Masin——"

"Yes?"

"Long ago, I put marriage out of my mind. But now——"

"What will you do, Voyan?"

"I have an audience, today, with His Majesty, Alexander. I shall submit my report from Athens and after that lay down my foreign credentials. There is nothing

on my record to bar me from an appointment right here.
I don't want to leave Serbia again."

At the sound of these words Draga swayed forward
and caught herself on the arm of a chair. She could not
believe her ears; she had not heard right. . . . The
King. . . . Voyan was going from this room, from her
very presence, to Sasha! No, she must be dreaming.
Hadn't he just spoken of their beginning again, making
a fresh start? She and Voyan—together.

But now Sasha would find her! He would remember
the name, of course. He would ask if this *Knese* Masin
might perchance be related to a Baroness Draga? And
Voyan, unsuspecting Voyan, would be instrumental in
putting the King of Serbia on her track. . . . A dizziness
came over her. She had never thought of such an
eventuality. It was almost grotesque.

Voyan seemed deeply touched by her confusion. Although he was schooled in self-control, her evident agitation unmanned him. He knew he had been harsh with
her, and unjust. They had both been cruel to each other—
because of that bond of guilt between them. For they
both knew that, even if Mihailo had lived, they had
already sinned against him. Yet memory could be—must
be—blotted out. It was still possible to make amends. She
was no longer the fair voluptuous Draga of her youth;
but was he the peerless *magnifico* of those gay and gallant
days? Had they not both been crushed by the same blow?
Surely it followed then that this must be the end of suffering. If remorse counted for anything, their debt
was amply paid. Could there be need of further martyrdom?

He reached out for her hand and held it gently. "It's

noon," he said, "and I must not be late. Tell me, Draga, if you want me to go?"

Her black centerless pupils fixed upon him with a lost look. Something inside her wept. He was the last of his line, he had said. And he wanted her—to perpetuate that line. But she was barren. She must not deceive him.

"I am due at the *Konak* before one," Voyan repeated. "If, in going there, I am doing something for you—as well as for myself—I shall think it a fortunate errand."

She was roused from painful reverie. Her lashes concealed a moist glint. "Yes," she whispered, "you can do much for me. I never dreamed, Voyan, that after all these years it would be you who must come to my aid."

Once more, as he had done so long ago, she felt him kiss the palm of her hand. A moment later he had vanished.

She stood in silence, letting the tumult of mixed passions sweep over her. Then, abruptly, she hastened to her bedroom. From trunks and cupboards she gathered what was left of her finery (a sadly depleted assortment, at best). On the covered shelf beneath her washstand stood a pair of dusty high-heeled slippers she had bought in Paris years before. Their thin soles rendered them unfit for such heavy walking as had been her habit in more recent times. They looked small and inadequate; she doubted whether she could get them on her swollen feet.

Tossing the shoes on her bed, she turned to the mirror. Its blue metallic surface reflected the spare outlines of her figure, and it seemed to Draga that she had not seen herself for decades. She scanned the face confronting her in the glass as though it belonged to a stranger. Despite neglect it still showed vestiges of beauty. Nothing could

mar the odalisque design of her eyes or the shapely curve
of her mouth. Lack of indulgence in any but the scantiest
foods had lent to her skin a purity too often sacrificed on
the altar of plenty. Her anæmic pallor at times gave a
parchment hue to her cheeks, but at this moment a pink
glow of excitement suffused the petal-like whiteness.
Luckily she had exhausted her stock of chalky rice powder; its application would have transformed her thin
delicate face into a cadaverous mask.

There was not much she could do for her hair. Once
she had dressed it in the style of Saharet, the dancer,
whose frivolous locks delighted audiences no less than the
phenomenal *pirouettes* to which she was addicted. But the
Draga of these hermit years gave little thought to coiffures. She had formed the habit of parting her hair in
the middle, keeping the sides brushed closely over her ears
after the manner of the famed Cléo de Mérode. This was
purely a matter of convenience, not vanity. Yet, although
Draga did not realize it, such simplicity of style was very
becoming to her. Unlike her skin, however, the lack of
sheen on her hair bore witness to deficiencies in a diet too
Spartan for continued well-being. The tide was turning in
the nick of time; another year of such privations would
have left her abused organism unfit for further struggle.
Even now the deceptive color in her cheeks exacted action
from a heart unequal to the strain. Before continuing her
festive toilet, Draga dropped listlessly amid the medley of
clothes strewn over her bed.

She must have slept for hours. When she awoke the
sun shone low in the western heavens. Its mellow haze
filled the room and warmed her cool pulses. She rose

from dreams of Voyan and a happiness too painful to
bear thinking about—when awake.

Still in a daze, she brewed herself a cup of tea, peering
anxiously at the queer pattern left by the leaves. She must
save them and go to a gypsy to have her fortune read.
She must——

A clock struck five. The distant chimes pierced through
her consciousness like sharp clean blades. She must hurry.
She must be groomed and dressed. Voyan had been at the
palace since noon; his audience terminated hours ago.
How could she have wasted all this time?

Setting down the cup, she slipped off her dress. The
Paris shoes lay perkily among the bedclothes. She stooped
over and tried them on. Yes, they pinched. She had expected that. It was one of the laws of the universe—
something would always pinch. Nothing was perfect. If
you were offered everything the world could offer, you
still would have to make a choice. That was where the
pinch came in.

Drawing her cramped toes together, she took a few
steps. No, it would not be easy. But she could manage.
She had managed before. Turning back to the mirror,
she proceeded with her dressing.

CHAPTER XXIII

ROYAL INTERVIEW

KING ALEXANDER enjoyed the business of government. Ever since he had discovered that high and low, from the most influential minister down to the meanest peasant, must obey his dictum—regardless of their personal views—he thought it rather fun to exercise his dictum. Without much effort or cogitation he had observed that a whole army of men, guided by strategists and leaders, bowed none the less to that ultimate authority—the Crown. But he, Sasha, was the Crown!

Power gave him pleasure. As a result, he meddled actively in affairs private and public, regardless of their remote connection with the palace. He visited schools and, recalling his own early distaste for lessons, declared that the children needed longer recess. He attended parade maneuvers and exasperated his officers by taking personal command. His drill methods, haphazard and frolicsome rather than corrective, so confused the troops that several days were required to discipline the men back into shape.

He wished more holidays and thought some of changing the calendar. Following his father's example, he catered to Austrian habits of etiquette or diplomacy and exchanged many courtesies with the Hofburg in Vienna. The Court at St. Petersburg he ignored altogether, knowing that it was unfriendly to his house. It was doubtful whether he could have acquired a Romanov bride, but the fact that Sasha did not even aspire to one chagrined the

238

Tsar. Altogether, he fell into line with a Teutonic Balkan policy, content to sustain a balance of power among the small nations of his peninsula. He was totally indifferent to the aggressive aims of Pan-Slavism.

Nor would he be swayed an inch from this standpoint. Vaguely he understood the goal of the Greater Slavs. They sought the gradual eclipse of Greek and Roman races, the exile of the European Turk, the liberation of brother peoples now under Austro-Hungarian rule (Croats, Slovenes, Bosnians, Herzegovines, Dalmatians) and, finally, the establishment of an empire—such as the world had not yet witnessed—along the shores of the sacred Danube.

Quite frankly, Sasha was intimidated by these pretentious ambitions. To begin with, he failed to see how the weaker Slav peoples—now controlled by Austria—would be any better off after Russia sucked them back into her dark maternal womb. Did not the Trans-Caucasians, and those limp Crimeans, raise a constant clamor against Tsarist oppression? Besides, he simply did not believe that the Pan-Slav illusion could be carried out; at least, not without drawing all Europe into the conflict. And even if Illyrism (as the Pan-Slavs called their noble dream) were to succeed, he did not favor the stress and misery such a struggle would entail.

Not that his sympathy was enlisted by the hypothetic plight of either Greek or Turk in the event of Serbian expansion. He hadn't really reasoned things out that far. It was merely that the glory of Genghis Khan, Timur, or even Emperor Dushan, scarcely touched him. To follow the path of these heroes seemed hardly safe, and held, for Sasha, not the slightest attraction. The slaughter of neighborly races was as distasteful to him as the risk of his own perpendicular suspension from an enemy gibbet, while others reaped the dubious profit of his victories.

No, Sasha's ideas of kingship ran to quiet housewifely patterns. He intended to be undisputed master of his realm, guiding the state along the stolid patriarchial rules of his own fireside. Within his palace he would be Cæsar. A quaint, domestic Julius, to be sure—but Cæsar just the same. He had no desire to endanger the stability of his tiny kingdom by turning over the reins of government to a group of reckless Utopists. If he lacked the intellectual faculty of appraising their magnificent excursions into political science, he lacked also the mathematical detachment with which great statesmen compute the measure of bloodshed necessary for national achievement.

It was for this reason that he wished to have a hand in all foreign dealings, no matter how insignificant their nature. It was because of this that Voyan Masin, returning with routine reports from Athens, was scheduled to appear, not in the Foreign Office, but at the royal palace where the King in person would listen to his decoded texts. And it was on so slight a circumstance as this that, in the end, the fate of Sasha and a future Triple Kingdom of the Yugoslavs came to hinge.

A solemn lackey spoke the name. Alexander, seated at his desk, pored over a large portfolio and seemingly took no cognizance of the introduction. Had he not heard?

He had heard perfectly. But unbelief clutched at his vitals, paralyzing every reaction. He had lived too long with that name, whispering it in his sleep, listening to its intermittent tattoo upon his waking consciousness. He could not trust himself. He could not believe that he had heard right.

Now someone stood in the doorway and bowed. Sasha looked up into the face of a tall young *Boyar* who repeated a curt formula:

"Masin. At Your Majesty's command."

This time it could not be hallucination. Even if the voice were an imaginary echo, the young man in the doorway was real enough. Sasha leaned back in his chair.

"You are the attaché from Greece?" he asked cautiously.

There was a military click of heels. "Yes, Your Majesty."

"I am afraid I did not quite catch your name," continued the monarch with an admirable show of indifference.

"Voyan, by royal grant *Knese* Masin," was the answer.

A pause. Not a shadow of doubt. . . . Sasha restrained a violent impulse to ply the stranger with questions, for he had learned to hide his feelings. They were not alone in the vast audience chamber. Too many ears were cocked in his direction; it would never do to expose himself at this point and thereby lose whatever advantage might be gained from so rare a coincidence. He had been defeated too cruelly, before this, in his long search for Draga. If they were to discover that he still nurtured the hope of finding her, new obstacles would be thrown in his path. Besides, he might be wrong. Possibly this man had no connection with her at all; the name could be a mere accident. If he gave himself away by appearing too anxious he would only invite the loss of future clues.

With furtive eyes he skimmed the persons of his retinue. The head of General Lazar veered in absentminded contemplation toward an open window. A few paces beyond sat Tanko, Naumovic and Slavyanin, sharing the General's interest in the great outdoors. It was impossible to read their thoughts, assuming that they had any. It was impossible to infer from their expressions whether, indeed, they were awake. But Sasha would take no chances. Although he knew of no concrete action which heretofore had thwarted his discovery of Draga's whereabouts, instinct told him that such action had taken place. Instinct warned him now to be more circumspect.

The details of the royal interview followed an accustomed plan. The monarch precipitated nothing. He heard, interrogated, passed comment. He took possession of all documents, pending further analysis. At the close of the conference he begged the visitor for a moment in private. It was about some signatures which must go back to Athens by return courier.

At a table in a secluded antechamber Alexander scribbled a minor order, the execution of which complicated consular activities in Greece by just another superfluous twist. It was the sort of disposition contrived by the chancelleries of every land for the useless confusion of its citizens abroad. Having contributed this macaronic bit to the world's exhaustive supply of red tape, Sasha looked up abruptly.

"Your name, sir," he pretended to muse aloud, "is familiar. I believe there was once a Masin in my ranks. Fine chap, good officer! Let me see, his Christian name was—er——"

Voyan flushed darkly. "Mihailo, Your Majesty," he murmured, "Lieutenant in the Royal Guards."

Sasha's face had grown tense. "Right, I remember now. Quite a loss, you understand." There was an interval of speculation. "A relative of yours, I take it?"

"My brother, Sire."

"Ah!" The King sat silent for a moment. He was placing the Greek note in an envelope and imprinting thereon the Royal Seal. The procedure was obviously an unaccustomed one, for Sasha's hands were clumsy. The result, after he had finished manipulating the melted wax, looked decidedly amateurish.

"Will that be all, Your Majesty?"

Sasha reflected. "I am always interested in the welfare of bereaved dependents," he put in at last; "your brother—did he leave any children?"

Voyan hesitated. "Only his widow, Your Majesty."

"I see. You have, no doubt, kept track of her and looked after her wants?"

It was the other who paused significantly. "I regret to say——" he began, yet broke off again miserably.

Sasha found it difficult to exercise further control. "What do you mean?" he flashed.

"She left Serbia, Your Majesty. During her absence I received my appointment in Greece."

"Well—go on!"

"Upon her return——"

"Ah, then she has returned . . . ?"

Voyan nodded. "She went to my brother's former residence near the pontoon bridge along the Danube Quay, where I have just found her." He smiled, as though to himself. "Naturally, from now on I intend to provide whatever she may need."

Alexander had risen from his chair.

"That will do," he announced with sudden vehemence, "we shall see about your further obligations. After all, it would not be fair to shackle a young man like you with a sister-in-law's support, would it?"

Voyan brightened. "But I shall be only too glad to help her," he exclaimed with noticeable warmth. "She has suffered privations, Your Majesty. And that through my unwarranted ignorance. My brother had left what seemed ample provision, but she must have spent it faster than he could foresee——"

Almost jovially, Alexander tapped the other's shoulder.

"Never mind, my friend. You probably have a family of your own and can spare nothing of your income."

"I am not married, Sire. I had hoped——"

The monarch frowned. "Not married, eh? Well, you should be. What's your age?"

"Thirty-four in September. Perhaps by that time, if Your Majesty will accept my credentials and permit me to hold office here in Belgrade, I shall no longer be a bachelor."

But Sasha had been gripped by a knowing, gnawing suspicion. Intuitively, with that sixth sense which errs so seldom, he perceived that before him stood his most dangerous rival.

"Impossible, my dear *Knese,*" he said slowly, while his eyes narrowed into a cunning line, "Serbia needs men of your particular sort. Needs them abroad. I couldn't think of letting talent such as yours rot at home."

Voyan bowed. "Your Majesty chooses to flatter a poor servant."

"Nothing of the sort. I mean to give credit where credit is due. We want keen minds in our dealings with

Russia. We have just the job you deserve, waiting for you at St. Petersburg."

"But, Your Majesty, that would be too great an honor," Voyan gasped.

"Let us not lose words about it," Sasha interrupted him, "I want no false modesty. If I say Russia, to Russia you go!"

"It is because of my sister-in-law, Draga," Voyan cried desperately, "that I must refuse——"

Again Sasha's eyes narrowed. So he had been absolutely right in his surmise. This man was in love with her, he would fight to keep her, he would defy even his King! Prudence, he told himself, caution. One false move and all might be lost.

"Your sister-in-law?" he queried, raising astonished eyebrows. "I thought I had reassured you on that score. She will be cared for, let me repeat that promise."

"But——"

"The Crown owes her a debt, as indeed it owes a debt to your heroic brother who died in the service of the Fatherland."

The other paled. "It was an—accident," he stammered reluctantly. "Mihailo did not die while on duty."

"Well, well, nevertheless, there is always a debt toward those who serve the flag, no matter how they die. I shall take particular care of the unfortunate widow whom your brother left behind. You say she is in Belgrade at the moment?"

"She has been, Sire, for some time."

It was Sasha's turn to pale. "For some time!" he repeated, dumfounded. "And not once——"

He checked himself, feeling Voyan's eyes fixed upon

him in curious scrutiny. Both men were uncomfortable in each other's presence.

"As I have said," Sasha resumed, "we must make up for the negligence of the Serbian Government. You may betake yourself to St. Petersburg without further concern. Pray trust me to make reparations for the shameful wrong inflicted upon your—er—relative."

Voyan was roiled by his own helplessness. "There was never any doubt of Your Majesty's intentions," he protested.

Sasha ignored this. "Meanwhile," he finished, "please await my immediate instructions in regard to your appointment at Staff Headquarters. Good day, *Knese Masin*."

The monarch saluted and stepped quickly from the room, leaving the other speechless. Stunned by this astounding outcome of his interview, Voyan Masin steadied himself against the edge of the table. He could not grasp the reality of what had just transpired. It was not, it could not be true! Only a few months ago the Russian post had represented the very pinnacle of his ambition. Yet now, after the sovereign himself conferred upon him this supreme distinction, Voyan no longer wanted it. He cared nothing about his career, whether abroad or at home. He wanted nothing but a chance to work, at anything—no matter what. He wanted to earn money, enough money to provide a decent living for Draga. Not luxury. He didn't think she valued luxury, having done with only the barest necessities of life for so long.

It was wrong for the government to interfere at this late date. Draga would not want the state's charity now. Voyan was here. He had promised to look after her.

Which was what he should have done years ago, from the very beginning of this burning passion that had bound them together since the first instant of their meeting.

But the King? How could this sudden impulse of royal benefaction be stopped? And what about Voyan's appointment? How could he turn down the monarch's gracious "award" without offending, nay, giving grave insult?

Something was terribly wrong, distorted out of all proportion. Voyan's services, thus far, did not merit such magnanimity on the sovereign's part. Nor had Mihailo's military career been sufficiently spectacular to warrant the special mercies which the Court itself now would heap upon his widow. Decidedly, something must be wrong.

Pulling himself together, Voyan Masin rushed from the palace. His head was throbbing with a multitude of bizarre ideas. Reaching the street, he turned northward across the *Slaviya* Square which faced the ancient offices of the General Staff. Whatever awaited him there he did not know. He could only guess. One thing alone was certain. For reasons of his own, King Alexander wanted him, Voyan Masin, out of Belgrade. What could there be in a king's life that exacted the price of a subject's happiness?

Out of Belgrade. Out of the way—that was it! Out of the way, for reasons of his own. It was Voyan's task, a task he set himself methodically, to find out what those reasons were. For, whatever they might be to Sasha, to Voyan they could spell only doom.

CHAPTER XXIV

THE BETROTHAL

IT WAS at this stage of Draga's seclusion that Sasha found her. He had not recognized her on the sunbaked streets, as she once hoped. Nor did he implore her to rise from the dust and step into his carriage before a flabbergasted populace. This cherished vision had been laid to rest with other disappointments life had taught her to accept. Her path and Sasha's crossed when Draga sometimes felt she had almost ceased to care.

Even so, her growing indifference was superficial, at war with her will, brought on by the lethargy of her wasting body. When fulfillment came it would find her ready. It was only a matter of seconds before the realization of impending climax whipped her ambition to its original peak. This had happened during her short meeting with Voyan. Her brother-in-law's scheduled visit to the palace completely restored Draga's sense of values and aroused her unfailing opportunism. Although she had weakened and quivered with delight at the prospect of happiness with Voyan, she knew that he must not marry her. After his departure she had gone to her room and dressed for Sasha. Her choice had been made. It was as simple as that.

Shortly after five o'clock that afternoon she hovered behind closed shutters, waiting. The minutes she now spent peering down the quiet deserted street dragged more slowly than the years that lay behind her. Now that the

248

most decisive moment of her life had arrived she was
quite unable to master her impatience. What if she were
wrong after all? What if he did not come? But no, she
knew better than that. She felt it now more strongly than
ever—those drab interminable days and nights had not
been wasted. He *must* come! With every ounce of
strength that was still in her she willed it so.

At half past five a carriage turned into the street. A
pair of white plumed steeds pranced at the head of it and
two men in livery sat on the box. The woman in the
recesses of the upper balcony felt her knees shaking. From
her hiding place she stared down, her face pressed against
the glass pane. A heavy-set figure stepped hurriedly
across the sidewalk. Now there came the screech of
Anton's bell and a moment later the portals opened to
admit an exalted stranger.

She ran half-way down the stairs to meet him. In the
mellow light of dusk her attenuated features were softened, so that the smile which now parted her lips recap-
tured a past sweetness. She paused and turned to dismiss
the gaping servant. Then, softly, she whispered:

"Sasha!"

The King of Serbia stood before her in scarlet hussar's
uniform. On his chest sparkled the insignia of his lofty
station. On his brow rested the sheep-skinned *kalpak*
which he now removed with cramped awkward movements, tucking the unwieldly head-gear under one elbow.

She found herself gazing into a pair of familiar black
eyes squinting behind their even more familiar gold-
rimmed spectacles. He had changed very little, this Sasha
who stood here before her. A trifle stout. His gait lacked
elasticity. But she could not remember that he had ever

been particularly gracile. There was still the same doglike devotion on his face, the same bewildered candor with which in years gone by he had regarded Draga. At a single glance she knew that she had never lost him. His attitude alone revealed far more than his halting tongue could utter.

He stooped to press trembling lips upon her hand. The kiss was not Voyan's kiss.

"My darling," he sighed, "at last!"

Transfixed, his eyes rested upon her and she realized that he saw her as of old. Even the smooth severity of her hair did not alter for him the picture of a Draga he had loved in Biarritz. His infatuation had remained undimmed despite the course of time. She marveled at such fervor. How had he withstood the snares of sirens, ever on the scent of royal game? For it was evident that neither cocottes nor husband-chasing princesses had succeeded in luring him from her.

Gently she clasped his fingers between her own and led him to a curtained ottoman. In the shadows the twisted story of their tribulations poured from the lips of each in turn.

To Alexander it seemed incredible, preposterous, that she had lived so close to him during their timeless separation. In Draga this fact gave rise to rancor and bitterness. She flayed. She accused. She did not attempt to conceal her resentment. If she spoke it was to impress upon Sasha how grossly he had been deceived by those who shared his confidence. Her words were designed to implant thoughts of retribution. She intended to kindle the fires of vengeance.

As he listened, Sasha's own suspicions were intensified.

He began to recall certain evasive answers, confusing hints and downright false clues through which his search for Draga had been handicapped. Now that he had found her, now that Draga was in his grasp, he would redeem his promise in the face of every opposition. He would prove to his enemies that their chicanery had availed them nothing. He would make this woman his wife. He would make her Queen! That must be his answer to all who had cheated and conspired against him. Serbia would see who was her master.

Little beads of perspiration broke out on his forehead as he devised plans for the future. Feverish with excitement, Draga clung to him. These were the words she had waited for. This was her goal—the Crown!

Like children they sat and plotted, seizing upon one course of action only to relinquish it in favor of the next. At last the hour of parting neared. But before it struck the dice had fallen and for Draga a prize loomed close. With dry vestal lips she returned the warm kiss of her future bridegroom. Stiffly, since the ways of love had grown strange to her unyielding body, she bade farewell to her royal fiancé.

The news of the King's engagement spread rapidly. Local and foreign press seized upon the topic, exploiting its sensational character to the utmost. Photographers clustered about, first at the *Konak,* then before the rambling mansion of the Masins. The lair of Prince Charming and his Sleeping Beauty's retreat were offered to a smirking public as the newest fad in romantic settings. Caricatures showed Draga in her bower waiting for the clumsy lover who, binoculars in hand, was yet unable to spot her. Brochures recounting the royal romance sold out as soon as they appeared. On ink-smeared pages the story of this odd clandestine love-affair was told in so many renditions as to become unrecognizable even to the protagonists themselves. Some authors went so far as to avow that Draga had been kidnapped from the Basque coast by the impetuous Alexander who, lest a raging populace visit its wrath upon her, held her for years as a virtual prisoner in his palace. Still others went to the opposite extreme. They painted Draga as a national heroine, chosen by the people themselves to be their anointed queen.

Although these events were of no particular consequence abroad, it happened that in Vienna they created profound dismay. For the announcement of Sasha's extraordinary decision came at a time when the Austrian Court faced a small scandal of its own. This scandal involved the Archduke Franz Ferdinand, heir to the throne and nephew of the Emperor Franz Joseph. Franzi, as the Archduke was called, had found access of late to the Bohemian castle of his relative, the Archduchess Isabella, under the worthy pretext of courting one of that lady's sextet of daughters. How great, then, the subsequent éclat—when His Imperial Highness revealed that the object of his desire was none other than the humble Countess Sofia Chotek, employed as the sextet's governess! Vituperation and contempt rained down upon the lovers who, unabashed, sought Franz Joseph's consent to their marriage. The Hapsburg clan would never condone young Franzi's choice. And entrenched behind the House of Hapsburg stood public opinion at large.

But the news from Belgrade—where a ruling king planned to take for his bride a mere commoner (of peasant origin!)—served to sway popular sympathy in favor of Sofia Chotek. After all, the Austrian Crown Prince was wooing the daughter of an impoverished aristocrat, not a suburban barmaid. Besides, if you took one look at Isabella's sextet, you could not blame Franzi much. The lovely Countess Chotek had charms which far outweighed the ultramarine corpuscles in the veins of her charges.

Of course, Sasha's amorous dilemma in no way altered the attitude of the Hofburg. Emperor Franz Joseph had never thought well of the Obrenos. If he gave shelter to the expatriate Milan, this was primarily a matter of courtesy. Fallen monarchs everywhere had access to the guest rooms of more prosperous "cousins," whether they were related by blood or purely professional ties. One never knew when such favors might be returned.

Austria's political support of Sasha (and of the Regency which had lasted through his minority) was something else again. It was dictated by policy alone. Years ago the two Danube states, sharing a common boundary, had joined hands against the Turk. There was a practical angle to Sasha's mild flirtation with the Ballplatz in Vienna, for it behooved both countries to get along. Austria, in turn, had reason to prefer the placid and generally innocuous Obrenos to the defiant Karageorgevitch vandals who set their entire hopes on Mother Russia. It would never do to encourage the Black Georges who, with the Tsar's aid, would drive the Hapsburgs from their Balkan playground. Franz Joseph was well aware of this and other angles to the Pan-Slav movement.

From a personal standpoint, however, the Austrian

Emperor could not suppress a fastidious sniff. On reading a report of Draga's impending coronation, His Apostolic Majesty exclaimed:

"That Sasha—he must be a consummate idiot! Such willfulness is dearly paid for. . . ."

Meanwhile the enamored Franz Ferdinand availed himself of a king's example. Vienna, he noticed, had wired congratulations to Belgrade. Was it not inconsistent, then, further to impede the Archduke's own marriage? Approval of a low-born Draga Masin made imperative the recognition of a patrician Countess Chotek whose ancestors figured nobly in the history of Prague.

Foolish though the argument might seem to him, Franz Joseph saw the fairness of it. He relented. But he did not relent gracefully. He did so with far-reaching reservations. The Archduke's union must be morganatic in form and fact. Any issue of this marriage would be barred permanently from the succession. Let Serbia hail a proletarian queen—the Countess Chotek must forego all hope of sharing her husband's future throne.

In Belgrade, at this time, the telegrams came pouring in. Regardless of their private opinions, the sovereigns throughout Europe must needs bestow felicitations upon a newly betrothed brother-in-ermine. If, individually and collectively, they all despised that ridiculous Sasha whose Biarritz antics a few years ago had aroused their mirth, they could not voice such sentiments on paper. Instead, the messages delivered at the *Konak* were couched in lavish parlance. They conveyed to the elated recipient a truly gratifying demonstration of fraternal pleasure and good will.

Sasha beamed. He wished that Draga might be living

even now at the palace, so that together they might read this deluge of testimonials. Polite approval (perhaps too polite?) dripped from each line. If only Draga——

But no, his courage did not reach quite that far. They were still unwed. Public opinion, after all, must not be outraged. Until Serbia at large, and the capital in particular, grew reconciled to the idea of his *mésalliance* Draga had best remain in her wonted obscurity. He would place guards about the Masin house for her protection and patiently wait for the hour when it would be safe for her to emerge.

He now made daily trips to the Danube Quay where, anxious and restless, she awaited him. Together they gloated over the congratulatory wires, extracting a degree of comfort from them. With such encomiums (made public in the principal journals of the realm) the country's sentiment would soon revert completely in their favor. Draga's recognition in foreign parts assured her of acclaim at home, even if that acclaim was slow in coming.

She dressed better nowadays. By royal order a fashionable *couturier* replenished her wardrobe, while from a famous caterer choice victuals found their way to her frugal table. At first such delicacies made her ill. She had gone too long without even moderately ample fare. But now she gained in strength and coloring. Soon the hollowness disappeared from her cheeks, while her healthy constitution overcame the ravages of abuse.

There were moments when all this pampering failed, however, to blot a dread misgiving from her mind. She had not seen Voyan since that first day of his return from Greece. Sasha had told her of the audience and of Voyan's appointment to a Russian post, but no one knew whether or not he had obeyed instructions and departed. The King himself had ordered Voyan's luggage to be transferred to headquarters with the express command that there be no delay. Had Voyan defied this command? Did he perhaps believe that she had tricked him? But it was all so obviously the work of fate. Things happened because some hidden power decreed that they must happen. She could no more have prevented Voyan from going to Sasha than Sasha could be stopped from coming to her, once her whereabouts had been made known.

For a while such sophistries allayed her doubts, but soon a new fear pressed in upon her. Did Voyan think she belonged to him? Was he jealous of Sasha and the honors a king could bestow? Would he lie in hiding somewhere, waiting to strike out in mad revenge? Love . . . Voyan had been the closest she would ever come to love. She dared not think about him that way. It was ruinous, unnerving. It brought her nothing, whereas Sasha brought—a crown. . . .

With unfeigned gratitude she accepted the bodyguard that was placed about the house. Despite its reassuring presence she began to lock her rooms at night. Against Voyan? Yes, against Voyan. He might return and demand a reckoning before she scaled the heights, before she wore across her brow the circlet of a queen. Ah, no—this must not happen! Nothing must happen now, when she was but a step from the throne. She had gone far. Draga Lunyevica—Draga Masin—Draga Obrenovitch! A commoner, a baroness, a queen! No, Voyan must not interfere again. From worm, through chrysalis, to moth—she must achieve her final permutation.

CHAPTER XXV

Voyan's Last Visit

In a private room behind the bar of the *Café Moskva*, which faced the *Teraziye* gardens, two men were drinking wine. One of them wore a colonel's lavish uniform while the other was clad in the more somber garb of a military attaché. They drank in silence, brooding over their half-emptied goblets. Occasionally a waiter opened the door to inquire after their wants. At such times gay strains of gypsy music strayed from the sidewalk orchestra into this remote corner, and one of the guests drew his wide cloak more carefully about him.

"Don't worry," admonished the other. He was a powerful man whose black mustache was lined with gray.

"But I do worry," said the younger of the two, without relaxing.

"No one would think of looking for you here. Besides, Voyan, you've been away so long that even the steward at the Casino had trouble recognizing you yesterday."

Voyan Masin shook his head. "They are after me," he muttered grimly, "and you know it. There's been ample time for St. Petersburg to report that I have not arrived. His Majesty will be interested to find out why."

"Well, if the worst comes to the worst, you will be safe on my riverboat. I happen to be itching for a cruise myself."

257

"No, Dragutin. I've already abused your hospitality too long."

The officer touched his companion's shoulder. "Never mind that," he said earnestly, "you are to stay with me as long as is necessary. Up to now your presence on the streets was a matter of little concern. But since you believe the answer from Russia is here, we must be more watchful. After tonight I would suggest that you retire from circulation for a while."

"But I can't stand this situation much longer," Voyan chafed. "Why don't we go ahead and do something? How long are you going to wait?"

Dragutin filled the glasses. "The plan is complete down to the last detail," he announced calmly. "If you are ready we can start."

"And our helpers?"

"I can count on my men at a moment's notice."

"Good."

"Your task, Voyan, is the only ticklish one."

The younger man bit his lip. "Yes, I realize that. And I'm not sure I can go through with it."

Dragutin frowned. "You mean—you are afraid?" he asked.

"Afraid," the other groaned, "that I shall not be able to keep my hands off her unholy throat!"

"In that case I must have your oath. The woman is to remain unharmed."

Voyan laughed hoarsely. "Very well, I give you my word. If I should fail to keep it, there can be only one explanation—namely, that at sight of her I lost my reason."

"See that you don't," Dragutin warned. There was

a stern undertone in his voice. "Ours is a political organization, Voyan, not a *vendetta* society."

"I know. But——"

"Personal grievances don't concern the state. You were not selected for this deed so that you might visit your private revenge upon an enemy, but merely because the house where Draga Masin lives remains accessible to you alone."

"That calls for a question mark, my friend."

"Yes, I agree. Ordinarily, the cordon of guards ought not to stand in your way. But since you are supposed to be in Russia, someone may ask for explanations."

"In which case?"

Dragutin's jaw was rigid. "You mustn't let it come to that. You carry a key, don't you? Surely there's some way of slipping into your own home without attracting too much attention. Besides——"

"Yes?"

"I doubt very much that you are being hunted—yet. Your faith in our bureau of communications is touching and exaggerated. My own opinion would be that they haven't thought about you at all. That saphead Sasha has been too busy planning his bride's trousseau. Anyway, that's the gamble we are taking."

"I see. And if I am caught, Dragutin, have you thought of that?"

The officer lighted a thin Macedonian cigarette. "If you are caught you keep your mouth shut. Nothing will happen. The Brotherhood is pledged to save you."

"But I am not even a member of——"

"The Black Hand will count you as a member after you have proved your mettle."

Voyan rose, pushing back his chair. "It may be," he smiled cynically, "that as a burglar I shall be a rank failure. I never thought that entering my own house would require such acrobatics. However, I'll chance it."

"Our purpose, Voyan, is well worth your personal risk. Remember, we must stop this marriage. It's bad enough that we have tolerated a worthless dynasty to the point of granting these Obrenos a second chance. We simply aggravate our national doldrums by submitting to the petticoat rule of an adventuress."

Voyan's fists tightened until the knuckles showed white. "No, by all the saints," he muttered under his breath, "it must not be! I'll go now, this minute, and finish her——"

He had rushed to the door, but Dragutin restrained him with a firm grip. "Just a moment," he snapped. "Our little show needs proper staging. I must have time to give the signal, or we shall have a nice confusion."

Voyan ran nervous fingers through his hair. "Of course—have all the instructions been rehearsed?"

"Perfectly. Three men will wait for you down by the river, a block away from the house. If, as I hope, Draga listens to your arguments, all you need to do is leave with her."

"In plain view of the soldiers?"

"If they happen to be looking, yes."

"But——"

"You stroll down toward the stream. A boat will be concealed behind the landing steps."

"Her going out at such an hour will seem suspicious," Voyan put in doubtfully.

"Strolling in the moonlight with a relative? After the cloistered life she has been leading no one need cavil with that, surely. The lady must have some fresh air, that's all."

The younger man scowled hopelessly. "I still prefer the other method. As I know Draga, she is certain to resist."

"Well, you are prepared for that emergency——"

Voyan nodded and tapped a small flask that protruded from his breast pocket. "A drop of chloroform will do."

The other agreed. "In the event you—er—must use this, a closed carriage will wait at the rear cellar exit which, apparently, has been left unguarded. Someone is there to help you. You are sure you can carry the woman that far?"

"She's only a shadow," Voyan murmured. "With two fingers I could——"

Dragutin caught the glint in his eye. "Disobedience to the code of the Black Hand carries a heavy penalty," he said sharply. "I trust, Masin, that you understand?"

Voyan bowed.

"Very well," the officer continued, "I shall send out the password. One hour before midnight, then, on the bank of the river. Your own rendezvous with the woman is thirty minutes earlier."

He saluted and turned toward the French doors that led to the restaurant garden. Voyan, lingering behind, slipped quietly through a darkened hallway and reached the street by a side exit.

A short time later the old portal of the Masin mansion creaked on its hinges. As Dragutin Dmitriyevitch had surmised, the guards had no specific information about Voyan. A pair of querulous sentries who insisted upon his identification were satisfied when Anton, beside himself with joy, greeted the young master.

Draga had not yet retired. She sat reading before a fire in the great hall, for autumn evenings had turned cool and the thick walls of the house were quick to absorb the chill.

At sound of the door she put down her book and felt a shiver travel down the length of her spine. Who could this be? Who came to her at such an hour of the night? Footsteps approached. She stood up suddenly and veered about, facing the man who at this moment stepped across the threshold.

"You!" she gasped in her best Sarah Bernhardt manner.

He remained silent. Her throat grew parched, making her voice sound thick and strangled as in chapter five of Monsieur Simonet's manual on elocution.

"What is it you want?" she burst out. "Don't you know that the King forbids me to have visitors?"

A deprecating sneer flashed across his face. "So your bodyguard informed me, but I succeeded in convincing the fellows that a man is not a guest when he produces the key to his own home."

She watched every one of his movements and felt fear clutching at her heart. "Why did you come?" she asked dully. "I thought you had left Belgrade a week ago."

"That's what people are supposed to think," he replied, "in royal circles, that is. But I couldn't make up my mind to go without——"

Ah, here it was, the peril she had dreaded for the

past six nights. If only she had warned Sasha against this! He was so trusting. He did not know Voyan.

"Without what——?" she repeated in a voice that was almost toneless.

His words were fraught with ridicule. "Without taking leave of you, my dear."

His manner thoroughly alarmed her. He seemed now to have caught sight of her elaborate dress, her generally improved appearance. An ominous wave of crimson spread over his face. For a moment he resembled some wild creature about to charge. But almost immediately an inner force exercised its control and he relaxed, taking a few desultory steps toward her. She retreated.

"I have come," he said quietly, "to make you a serious offer."

Draga misunderstood. "But I meant to tell you all along," she stammered, "about my—my engagement to Sasha. If only I had known that you, that we——"

He waved his hand in a gesture of disgust. "This has nothing whatever to do with us," he broke in vehemently, "I am not concerned with your emotional life."

She winced at the thrust. "Neither am I interested in any sort of proposals," she parried.

His voice was hard. "You will do well, Draga, to consider this one. It happens to be the wish of your countrymen, the entire Serbian nation."

She burst into a high shrill laugh. "Since when are you the spokesman of the Serbian nation?" she demanded.

"I was sent here, Draga, by the Pan-Slav Brotherhood, the powerful Black Hand. If you ignore what I tell you, you are doomed, and I as well, for having failed in my mission."

"The Black Hand!" she breathed in horror.

"You have heard of it?"

She nodded. "What—what is it they want of me?"

"I am to persuade you to renounce the King's suit. You must refuse to become Queen of Serbia."

"And if I do?"

"A villa on the Island of Lacroma, as well as an attractive appanage, will be assured you." He was seized by a vague nausea while enumerating these inducements. The urge to leap upon her and destroy that treacherous mask she wore became almost ungovernable. That he should have to stand here, bribing her, was gross indignity. Was she not talked of on the streets as Sasha's mistress? He found it hard to be even civil.

She had listened. And now she clapped her hands in vast amusement. This was too good! They were asking her to give up a throne in exchange for a cottage by the sea. She was to turn down a royal husband in favor of a prim monthly stipend, a neat household allowance. What else did the considerate Brotherhood desire? Had the Serbian people any further wishes?

Short ripples of laughter shook her frame as she echoed the words: "Renounce the King's suit! Never—do you hear? Never!"

Voyan's face turned slowly to a deathly pallor. "Draga, this is your last chance. Come with me willingly, or I shall use force."

Her mirth had given way to anger. "Come with you?" she shrieked, withdrawing from him as he advanced upon her step by step. "Are you mad? I'll deliver you myself to the King's men, that's how far I'll come with you!"

She glowered at him through narrow eyes and crept furtively toward the door that led into her bedroom. Consumed with sudden hatred and rage, he sprang across the intervening space and gripped her frail shoulders.

"Strumpet!" he roared. "You'll settle this, and earlier accounts, at one clean reckoning——"

With both fists he held her, digging his fingers into her throat. She gave a scream that rang through the building and reverberated thinly down the street. An instant clamor of voices was set up below, accompanied by blows against the wooden portals. With chattering teeth, the bewildered Anton rushed from his lodge and drew the bolt. A second later he was knocked down by an onslaught of armed men.

Blindly Voyan still gripped the struggling woman. His frenzied consciousness harbored but a single thought. He must wipe out the affront suffered by his house and his own manhood. He must obliterate the shackles that had bound his brother Mihailo, and Voyan himself, to this perverted creature.

It was the shuffle of heavy feet along the main stairway that brought him to his senses. He dared not be caught here. It would spell disaster, not for him alone, but for the loyal comrades who waited outside. He released the panting Draga and veered about in search of an escape. Rushing through the vestibule he crossed the gallery and let himself down a swaying trellis to the ground floor. Without pausing he gained the dining room and took the narrow passage leading to the wine vaults. It was the same passage along which, many years ago, Mihailo had staggered to his death.

In a few moments Voyan reached the end and groped
for the rusty bar that held a small trap door in place.
His fingers slipped in a mass of crumbling mortar before
he was able to get a firm hold. He pulled. The door
would not move. Beating frantically against the worm-
eaten panels he felt his hands bruised by sharp metal
projections. Only now did the appalling truth dawn upon
him. The cellar had been walled shut! Even if he had
succeeded in drugging the woman, he could not have fled
with her unconscious body except through a window, or
the guarded front entrance. Dragutin's conjectures had
been wrong. The rear exit of the house remained un-
watched for the simple reason that there was no longer
a rear exit.

One last desperate thrust against the masonry con-
vinced him. He must turn back. Draga's own conscience
doubtless had dictated this measure. She could not face
the spot which to this day bore silent witness to her
guilt. Her guilt! Once more he saw her only as his
brother's murderess and nothing more. How grimly
sardonic that she should have devised, in this same secret
passage, a *cul de sac* which now must trap another Masin
who stood in her path. . . .

Aware of his predicament, Voyan retraced his steps.
As he stumbled forward through the darkness he suddenly heard her voice. She was directing the men. Now
they were on his track, for someone held a torch into the
passage. He faced the yellowish glare. There was a
gruff command and in another second two swordsmen
tore him from his hiding place.

In the lighted hall he caught sight of Draga, wild
and disheveled. She spat at him while a smoldering

iridescence flared up in her eyes.   Under the flicker of
the torch she looked like a witch.

"There he is," she gasped through the gullet he had
choked only so short a while ago.   "Take him away.   Let
him wait for the Queen of Serbia to settle accounts in
her own fashion!"

Voyan was buffeted toward the front stairs.   As he
descended the short stoop that led to the street a dry
cackle reached his ears.   He did not have to turn to
know that Draga was amused.

CHAPTER XXVI

THE WEDDING

ON AUGUST 5, 1900, King Alexander I of Serbia celebrated his nuptials at the royal palace in Belgrade.

The date struck Draga as fortuitous. It fell in the first year of a new century, at the start of another age. This opening ran parallel with the beginning in her own life of a fresh and glorious chapter. A believer in signs, she had long ago interpreted the strange patterns of destiny in keeping with her plans. No writing on the wall could daunt her, for she spelled it out to suit suitable ends.

Take, for example, Sasha's prolonged search and final discovery of her. Had it not all wound up at the precise moment when the broom of time swept out the ashes of another hundred years? Their meeting in that dying dusk of 1899 was nothing short of horoscopic. Fate, the supreme stage manager, had purposely delayed the rising of her star in order to create a fitting climax. The twentieth century, no less, should witness as its first major event the bridal procession of Queen Draga.

As it happened, there was no bridal procession. Although a cathedral ceremony had at first been planned, the idea was suddenly discarded. At the last minute Sasha had felt misgivings. Too many hymeneal feasts had been marred, in the long history of monarchies, by bombs and other lethal offerings hurled into the path of stubborn kings and their unwanted consorts. Sasha

268

lacked the urge to expose himself to similar dangers. The wedding, in both its civil and religious form, took place within the protective walls of the old *Konak*. All guests who attended were obliged to show proper credentials before their admission to the important act.

During the same month an analogous event created a sensation in the neighboring empire of the Hapsburgs. Here the Archduke Franz Ferdinand's marriage to the Countess Chotek was being performed at the home of the bridegroom's stepmother, the Infanta Maria Teresa da Portugal, who was a Braganza of liberal leanings. The Prague ceremony was preceded by a bitter scene in Vienna. On June twenty-eighth, Franzi had been summoned to the Hofburg, where, in the presence of the Emperor, the Prince-Archbishop, two Cardinals, Hungary's Prime Minister, as well as the assembled members of the imperial family, a formidable text was read.

It was the renunciation, not for himself, but for his wife and possible issue. In hortative Latin there followed a terse, laconic order:

"Subscribe, Francisco Ferdinande!" ("Sign, Francis Ferdinand!")

Between lighted tapers that rose on either side of a crucifix the parchment had been spread out. Raising two fingers of his right hand over the Holy Scriptures, the Archduke inclined his head. He took up the pen and spoke the oath to its inclement finish:

"This, my marriage, is a morganatic one. It shall now, and forever after, be regarded as such. . . ."

It was like writing with your own blood. Desolation filled his heart, as the future monarch signed away the heritage of his unborn children and forfeited their claims to the throne. Yet this the lover must do to win the bride of his choice.

June twenty-eighth . . . St. Vitus Day, the great feast of *Vidovdan* in the Eastern Church. Fourteen years later, to the hour, almost to the minute, Franz Ferdinand would meet his Sarajevo! St. Vitus, Serbia's holiday, would find him and the beloved woman at his side slumped over in a gore-spattered motorcar. Their slaughter by a Pan-Slav zealot would be prelude to a holocaust, the first World War. . . .

Unaware of that harrowing future, Franzi signed. Just as unwitting and romantic, his uncle, Maximilian, had once tossed Europe over for a throne in Mexico. Behind both men stood women stronger than their husbands.

At Castle Konopisht, Sofia (now elevated to the rank of Duchess Hohenberg) waited. She could afford to wait. Serene and comprehending, she possessed intelligence as well as beauty. Inquisitive minds like hers were very apt to make discoveries, especially when cornered. Cornered now, Sofia studied Hapsburg canons and the law that governed sworn pledges. Even before becoming Franzi's wife she had found a way to comfort him.

"The oath is illegal," she whispered, "and can, when the time is ripe, be broken."

"How do you know, Sofia?"

"I have been reading your books. It is there, in black and white, that a pledge involving non-existent beings is not considered valid. For me alone you have done this thing, but they—our little ones—need not suffer."

He marveled at her wisdom. "You are certain of that?"

"Absolutely. Besides, while you were signing, the Hungarian *Primas* nudged me and said that in Budapest they would never recognize it."

Franz Ferdinand smiled. "Those peppery Magyars, always running counter to Vienna. I believe they do it for the fun of the thing."

"They think it unfair, the younger Kossuth told me, to discriminate so against a woman. At any rate, even if I am never empress, you and your first-born son should wear the crown!"

She was right. But for the present they must hold their tongue. Who could tell? The day might not be far off when the scepter fell into his hand. The hour would come for him to prove that he had sworn under duress. Also, there still remained that technical loophole: remarriage, after an official annulment of his morganatic union. He might divorce Sofia. Once he was emperor, who could prevent him from selecting her anew? He would be a law unto himself, free to choose his mate. No amount of prejudice could then bar Sofia from the throne.

He kissed her tenderly. In his soul a vow, more sacred than that which his tongue had been forced to utter, took form. Together they would share the stigma and humiliation which were henceforth their lot. At court balls they would walk apart. He must follow in the Emperor's wake, leading a Princess of the Blood, while she, at the end of the long train of Archduchesses and lesser nobles, remained alone and unattended. They would not even dance together, lest this be trespassing against

the rigorous code. But they could always escape to
Konopisht, their secluded estate in Bohemia, where the
surrounding country was a vale of roses rivaling the
famed Bulgarian fields that held the precious attar. Here
they would live in peace and raise their children. Here
they were to each other what some day they would become
to the world at large—lovers who had had the courage
to break with a decadent, ingrown and incestuous tradition. Equals they would be in the human hierarchy, as
they were equals now in love.

In distant Belgrade King Alexander was not faced with
such vicissitudes. If members of the Court and Serbian
society in general had objected to the royal marriage, no
one openly voiced disapproval. If haughty dowagers
would snub the new Queen they were obliged to do so
in the privacy of their hearts. For in public none could
afford to be absent from the bowing, curtsying parade
which passed in review before the throne.

Draga herself was blissfully unaware of criticism.
She had arrived, and for her this was all that mattered.
With the smugness of the uneducated, she was content
to number her outward achievements, wasting no time
on profitless regrets. Perhaps she was unpopular? That
question left her indifferent. If people resented her
advancement, it was only natural. The peasants of the
Sava region turned green with envy when a neighbor's
sow farrowed a round dozen piglets. Did that make the
swineherd bilious? Not likely. He grinned and gloated
over his good fortune. Draga had remained, funda-
mentally, part of the rustic Sava folk. Her logic was
astute, practical, coarse in substance. She was a confirmed
realist, dealing in tangible facts.

Since she was a queen, she strutted. Always fond
of dress, she now gave full rein to her passion for
ornament. Belgrade jewelers enjoyed a little boom in
business as it became known that she could not resist
their baubles. Her fingers were garroted with rings while
the pierced lobes of her ears became stretched by the
weight of costly pendants.

Again she changed her fashion in hair-dressing. A
French *coiffeuse* came daily to the palace to crimp the
queenly tresses and pile them in a sort of coronet atop
Draga's head. This was the style that had been so
becoming to Elisabeth of Austria (recluse wife of
Emperor Franz Joseph) who had died, not long ago, at
the hands of an assassin. Elisabeth's beauty secrets
interested Draga; her tragic end did not. That the
loved Hapsburg sovereign, herself a descendant of kings,
should not escape the poisoned fangs of anarchy failed
to perturb the *parvenu* Queen. In Draga's complacent
mind such cataclysms were reserved for others; they had
not the slightest bearing on the course of her own destiny.

If triumph had made her arrogant, success now
threatened to make her fat. Lolling about in unaccustomed luxury, Draga indulged her palate. She not
only had her first breakfast—*le petit déjeuner*—of hot
chocolate and wafers in bed, but imbibed a second more
substantial ration around eleven o'clock, still propped
amid her pillows. With but little encouragement she
would have introduced social "at homes" in the perfumed
precincts of her boudoir, much after the manner of
eighteenth century Bourbons in France. Curtain
diplomacy, under the guise of a convivial Viennese
Kaffeeklatsch, held a distinct attraction for her.

Needless to say, Sasha himself was the most radiant of bridegrooms. Loneliness, the curse of his childhood and youth, had faded away until it was almost forgotten. Now that Draga dwelled at his side, each day held exquisite surprises and each night brought more endearing delights. Inexperienced as a lover, he reveled in his wife's lukewarm caresses and deemed himself the happiest of men. In his overwhelming gratitude he showered her with presents. After their brief honeymoon along the shores of the Adriatic, Draga had set her heart on owning a yacht. The Queen of England's pleasure craft, *Victoria and Albert,* cruised at that time in Mediterranean waters and caught her fancy. Had not the poetic Empress of Austria sailed on such a ship, the while she took her sunbaths on an upper deck enclosed with glass? Draga had visions of herself, alluringly disrobed under a proper awning (she favored solar rays in theory only), while from afar came the rumble of pursuing pirate ships. The thought of herself, a Serbian Cleopatra, in such romantic peril afforded unending pleasure. From day to day she was able, Penelope fashion, to unravel this fabric of her own creation and to spin it anew, adding always another installment.

Of course, the acquisition of a yacht in a country without seacoast was no easy matter. Parliament was adamant in refusing to grant the necessary appropriation. If the King wished to gratify his wife's extravagant whim he must dig into his own pocket, for the nation's treasury could not serve such silly ends. Sasha accepted the reproof and dug. He placed an order with a foreign shipbuilder in Fiume.

After the yacht had been finished it was found that

marble baths, canopied sun decks, and a score of other appurtenances without which Draga refused to accept her pretty plaything, far exceeded the original price set upon it. To draw such a sum from his own purse would leave the King's finances sorely crippled. Although generous to a degree, Sasha was still the son of parsimonious Natalia Kesko. He did not care to squander his inheritance. A serious quandary now arose which cost him many sleepless nights. Credit being unknown, the yacht would not be delivered unless paid in full. At last, with Draga's aid, he hit upon a bright idea.

For some years, Belgrade had been setting aside in its city coffers a reserve fund intended for a canalization project which would modernize the Serbian capital and place it on a par with every first-rate European community. Since the arrival of electricity and other improvements, the canalization scheme had received particular impetus, augmenting the fund to impressive proportions. This sum, lying idly in the treasury, was more than adequate for the payment of the yacht.

Without a qualm Alexander resolved to do something about it. By royal edict he canceled the engineering contracts and postponed Belgrade plumbing until some future time when "that sort of thing got beyond the experimental stage." Late in January of the new year, England's aged Queen lay dying, blinded with cataracts and rendered inarticulate by a brain disease called aphasia. As the obituaries went forth from Osborne to encircle the globe, Draga Obrenovitch obtained her coveted toy. Happily, the price had amounted to something less than the canalization budget, so that a trifling balance could be returned to form a nucleus for another fund. If Sasha had only known, he might have had the outmoded *Victoria and Albert* at a bargain.

Strangely, after its acquisition the yacht did not prove a source of undiluted joy. To begin with, it had no port. Its skipper, not knowing where to leave the boat, had to keep it on the run. This brought up a geographic angle no one had thought of before. After a maiden voyage around blue Balkan waters Draga encountered, wherever she dropped anchor, a different language buzzing against her ear. No linguist herself, she found polyglot natives a bore. Yet if she avoided the babel of strange harbors and ventured out to sea, she fell prey to a malady which the ship's medico diagnosed as *mal de mer*. While she languished nauseated in an uncomfortable deck chair, not even the prospect of a pirate schooner on the horizon could brighten her outlook. In fact, faced with it day by day, she found the ocean tiresome and disappointing. The tangy smell of brine soon irritated her. Only a few months after the launching, the royal pleasure boat entered retirement. A dock was rented in the harbor of Ragusa where the proud vessel sank into oblivion, her barnacled sides rehearsing brave dreams of having once put out to sea.

It was a bad spell of seasickness which put another notion into Draga's head. She believed herself pregnant. This possibility was more vital to her now than ever, for on this score alone did she fear public opinion. . At home among her village kin, the sterile woman with whom whole generations went to their grave became an outcast. Draga was primitive enough to accept this viewpoint as a fundamental law of existence.

She had been told she was barren. Only because of

this had she turned from Voyan. But what if Doctor Michele had been wrong? What if the Queen of Serbia were not found wanting? The Crown would have an heir and Sasha, her husband, would not be the last of his line! After all, Sasha had a right to expect a son from her. Besides, if she remained childless her enemies would use this circumstance as a weapon against her. Well, they were defeated now! She would bring forth a Child of Serbia. She, Draga Lunyevica, would be mother of a future king.

The glad news was published in all the papers. Cables were sent around the world, heralding the advent of a prospective heir. Here and there, sentimentalists relented in their harsh judgment of the Queen. After all, this changed matters. Maternity ennobled. It even hallowed. The lowliest Magdalen became a Madonna if she got herself with child.

From near-by towns and remote provinces came trinkets, toys, hand-woven garments, for the little princeling. In country churches and at roadside shrines prayers were mumbled and pious benedictions implored in his behalf. And then the happy legend was shattered. The palace physician, Doctor Demosthen Nikolayevitch, disclosed the error. Like his colleague of earlier years, the Court practitioner ascertained Draga's incurable sterility.

Promptly she exacted from him a promise to guard the baneful secret. Not even Sasha was to know. For strategy must help where nature had failed.

Methodically she set out to surmount her bitter defeat. With the utmost discretion an impoverished peasant girl was ferreted out, who, for a substantial fee, agreed to relinquish the fruit of her shame (due to be born within the proper span of time). With trickery as well as a touching display of boudoir modesty, Draga was able to carry out her subterfuge under the very eyes of an unsuspecting spouse.

The period of gestation was almost over when again an ironic fate blasted her hopes. The derelict whose nameless child was to be rocked in the royal cradle went suddenly on an alcoholic spree. On recovering consciousness she found herself in a public ward of the *Charité* Hospital. A nun informed her tenderly that God, in His unbounded mercy, had called unto Himself the innocent victim of her carnal lust, by the expedient of an undeservedly painless miscarriage. At which, contrary to the more usual reaction, a loud wail broke from the sick girl's lips. But this was impossible! It couldn't be. This infant belonged to the Queen of Serbia! It had been sold for many dinars. Her Majesty would never forgive. . . .

The lamentation increased and was echoed through the hospice, up and down the corridors, out into the street. Disturbed by these revelations the pious sister ran for help. The sobbing patient was placed in a padded cell and held for observation. But her subsequent behavior gave no evidence of mental derangement and she was released, after vain efforts had been made to quell the spreading rumors concerning her strange story. Meanwhile a private messenger reported the incident to the Queen. Dejectedly Draga laid aside her histrionic trappings and fell ill with an honest case of nervous prostration.

Outside the palace the ugly tale made quick headway. Foreign correspondents carried the Belgrade nursery myth across the Continent. Vitriolic sketches appeared in *Simplizissimus, Le Rire, Kladderadatsch* and *Punch*. With unveiled sarcasm the local press discussed what looked like a prophetic angle of the affair. If Serbia's Queen could bear no issue, King Alexander would perforce be the last of the Obrenos! The *Cerny* Georges and their scattered following would do well to take notice, for the proletarian impostor who called herself a queen had quite patently cooked her own goose. Not only had she forced herself to prominence that did not befit her, but she did not hesitate to violate the sanctity of marriage by smuggling an unborn bastard into the place of a legitimate heir. If such things were to be, and dynasties exercised no selection, it might become any fool's privilege to rise up and proclaim himself the leader of his people. If this were tolerated, anyone might elbow his way upward, through treachery, abuse, graft, until by sheer astuteness he reached the top. But ermine and purple had a place in human values. Monarchies were patriarchal. A dynastic strain was tested and, if deemed unworthy, discarded. Yet, once chosen and anointed, it became a thing revered and honored as the symbol of the state. Failing in this, as the House of Obrenovitch was failing, the common clay of common men defiled royal robes and majesty came toppling from its eminence.

Far and wide the scandal spread, yet Sasha failed to take the slightest notice. He saw no papers, gazettes or private dispatches. He grasped no insinuations, heard no gossip. Draga was suffering. Nothing else mattered. He lingered at her bedside during the night, holding anxious watch. From the discreet allusions of Doctor Demosthen he learned that, for the present, there would

be no visit from the stork.   Even now his simple credulity
prevailed and he consoled the frustrated woman with
euphemisms.   What did it matter?   They had each other!
She must hurry up and get well.   There was all the time
in the world for the gratification of her maternal instincts.   He, for one, felt in no hurry to be bothered
with the responsibility and care of offspring.

His kindness considerably hastened Draga's recovery.
Unable to gauge the full extent of her predicament, or
how much Sasha knew, she had at first simulated a more
serious collapse than was really the case.   But with her
husband's cheerful acceptance of the situation her nervous
breakdown rapidly faded into a routine performance of
feminine hysteria.   She had a pleasant rest in bed, away
from public mockery and venom.   In time the wave of
obloquy would die down.   After that, and not a day
sooner, she would reappear at her husband's side: wrapped
in pristine dignity, a sovereign regardless. . . .

CHAPTER XXVII

THE SECRET CHAMBER OF THE OATH

AMID these preoccupations, which continued far into the second year of Draga's marriage, the fate of Voyan Masin was forgotten.

After his capture on that ill-starred visit to the Danube Quay he had been thrown into chains at the guardhouse. Later, in view of his high station, he was removed to the bastion outside the city where he was held under military guard until the time of his trial. Considering the seriousness of his offense, it appeared almost certain that he would be court-martialed. But a puzzling retardment now arose. The Queen, at whose instigation Voyan had been detained, repeatedly postponed the case. Since she reserved for herself the privilege of a hearing, the trial could not be opened until Her Majesty's consent had been obtained.

From week to week, month to month, the unhappy young man sat in his cell, staring gloomily across the river to the cupolas of Semlin. The Hungarian citadel, blazing its myriad lights across the plains, filled him with despair. The pride with which those Magyars flaunted the emblem of their thousand-year-old realm made his Serbian heart rebel. He hated the very outlines of that Millennium Tower with its fluted perimeter of electric bulbs. It did not awe him. For Slavs, too, had an ancient past. Since the far days of the Roman Emperor Heraclius they had peopled the Byzantine provinces of

Moesia. Contemporaries of the Hun Ethele (Attilla) they had been, and previous—by three hundred years—to that Arpád worshiped now in Budapest! This very prison, cut deep into the *Kalimegdan* hill, was the work of Roman slaves. Its intertwining spiral stairs were carved out of the rock by captives who heard one another hammering, yet never met. On dungeon walls the seepage of Danube waters painted a tale of forgotten terror and conquest. Yes, Serbia too could build millennium towers and make the world respect her classic lineage. But not as matters stood today. A house divided and a country misruled, with these one could not make history.

Throughout his imprisonment Voyan had been kept well informed on the course of events at the palace. As commander of the garrison, Dragutin Dmitriyevitch had done all he could for the captive's comfort. He had found it particularly simple to ease Voyan's lot as soon as the latter arrived at the fort and came under army jurisdiction in place of police control. Thus the prisoner was allowed to leave his *oubliette* in order to exercise along the buttressed walls. Daily he paced the ramparts. Also, he had ceased to be completely isolated, for friends and former comrades visited him regularly. They brought books, tobacco and other aids to counteract the unwholesome monotony of his existence.

In all this Voyan recognized the silent acknowledgment of the Black Hand. Even though he had blundered and failed in his mission, the secret organization meant to stand by him. The reason was plain. Throughout a most severe grilling at police headquarters, the authorities had not been able to extract from Voyan the slightest revelation concerning the Brotherhood. The prisoner

implicated no one. He claimed to have acted upon motives
of personal revenge. He knew of no society that conspired against the Crown.

In point of fact, he knew very little about Dragutin, or
indeed, the latter's connection with the Black Hand.
Dmitriyevitch drew no one into his confidence, yet Voyan
felt instinctively that in this powerful man Serbia would
find her liberator. He believed Dragutin to be a patriot
of honest and unselfish principles, a paladin who placed
the welfare of the state before all else. If this was so,
he, Voyan, would not talk out of school. No harm must
come to this Dragutin; no obstacles were to fall across
his path. If necessary, Voyan would die rather than
betray the Black Hand and defeat the holy Pan-Slav
cause.

He steadfastly refused to speak. In the end his stubborn silence began to look like ignorance. Gradually his
jailers relaxed their grip, keeping a casual vigil over the
Queen's prisoner. Soon it was hinted about that he might
eventually regain his freedom.

Among Voyan's constant visitors was a former school-
mate, Sergei Slavyanin, now a member of the King's
personal suite. Slavyanin was a dry individual of no
particular distinction, but eminently sane in his point of
view. He bore a striking resemblance to Voyan's dead
brother, Mihailo, even as regarded the elder Masin's
reticence. All the more significant, then, were the facts
which Slavyanin now divulged.

Of late, Sergei reported, the Queen sought to advance
various members of her own family. Her brothers,
Nikodem and Paul, had been appointed to official rank
in the Guard Regiment and it was bruited about that

she thought of them as possible successors to the throne.
During a concert in the *Teraziye* park, Captain Tanko
had stood beside her as she greeted the younger brother,
Paul:

"Good evening, Prince!"

Everyone within hearing distance had glared in disapproval at the swaggering buck whom accident had made
the brother of a queen. Quite openly, people grumbled
and expressed their resentment. These Lunyevicas must
be curbed before their cupidity led too far. Once they
were firmly entrenched, like ticks on cattle, heaven knew
how Serbia would rid herself of the plague.

It was Slavyanin, too, who brought Voyan the news
that he had lost his home and property. By order of
Queen Draga the Masin house had been opened and
remodeled for the use of her kin. Only a week ago the
delighted Mara and her youngest daughter Voika had
moved in from the country. An old creature named
Anya, related to the Lunyevicas and said to have been
a member of King Milan's domestic staff, had been buried
just before these events took place. Strange stories were
told about the woman Anya. Witnessing the wedding of
her grandniece to the present King of Serbia, she had
raised a mighty scene about the vaulting aspirations of
her family and retired forthwith to her native village of
Provo. In her honest peasant soul Anya would never
forgive Draga. From Provo she periodically sent forth
baneful predictions, foreboding evil to the land in general
and the House of the Obrenos in particular. Far and
wide her oracle was gaining fame. Even after death,
the militant old woman cast a spell over the populace.
Her prophecies lodged in the minds of simple folk. If

Anya, the King's nurse, foretold a dismal future—dismal that future would be.

Voyan was not interested in such portents. He was concerned with Draga's action about the house. This confiscation of his property and assets, for the court had seized all sources of income, left him virtually a pauper. Even if he were now to be released, he had no place to go. He would be cast adrift, perhaps unable to regain a foothold.

This was precisely what Draga wanted. Although it had been her firm intention to put Voyan to death, she dared not carry out the plan. There loomed darkly over her the shadow of Dragutin, who, her spies reported, interested himself in the prisoner. With public sentiment still outraged by the purchase of the royal yacht, as well as the Queen's recent puerperal comedy, it was unsafe to carry her feud too far. Very good. If Voyan was to live, let him exist—and nothing more. Dmitriyevitch had once thrown Nikodem and Paul upon their own resources, leaving them penniless and idle to roam the countryside. The same would now happen to Dragutin's protégé.

Yes, let Voyan go loose and seek a calling. He had learned nothing in his youth save the craft of diplomats and dress-parade puppets. But today the Army and Diplomatic Corps were closed to him; she had obtained from Sasha the necessary ban. Give him a real chance, instead. It would be truly amusing to hear of the *Knese* Voyan, once attaché at Athens, plying a cobbler's trade or waiting on tables! Perhaps he had some hidden talent? He might tramp the length of the river bank playing the fiddle with some gypsy orchestra. Draga would see him and clap her little hands in praise, praise for a pretty polka or a mediocre *kolo*. She might even ask for a special *kolo,* that old national dance of Slavs. She might request the *Draga-Kolo,* with the whole orchestra on its feet! Bravo! If Voyan Masin was to be freed, he would go free on her own terms.

On Easter Sunday of the year 1902 the King's annual list of pardons included Voyan's name. Alone, the prisoner walked from the crenellated battlements of the fort toward the highway that led into town. Before him stretched golden hills, bluish vineyards and the sleepy hamlets of this fertile Danube basin. He looked about with tired eyes. All this, the soil, the river, even the wild forest would bring tenfold blessings to him who had learned how to use his hands. For such a one the earth gave forth its fruit, the stream carried his load, the woodlands offered shelter. He stared for a long time at a coal barge gliding down the mighty Danube on its route to Bucharest. A flaxen-haired Slovak skipper stood at the bow bellowing commands. He wore a torn shirt, but his face looked ruddy and jocund. He was happy. He belonged. This was his post and he held it, envious of no man. Voyan kept his eyes on the floating collier until it disappeared in the distance. He felt intensely miserable. With weary and uncertain steps he continued on his way.

Behind the *Slaviya,* in the shadow of the cathedral, someone waited. Voyan stopped short and gazed into a stolid face hitherto unknown to him. A low voice murmured:

"Lieutenant Naumovic, in the service of His Majesty."

At this, Voyan retreated abruptly. "I was being expected," he said uneasily, "by——" He broke off again, alarmed.

The other grinned. "Don't worry," he whispered, "I'm the man."

"But——"

Naumovic peered furtively about. "It's all right. I was sent here by the Black Hand. Does that convince you?"

"Yes——" Voyan agreed, although he could not disguise his amazement, "but I still don't understand. Your name—I have heard of a Lieutenant Naumovic at the palace."

The man nodded. "Exactly. In the royal suite! But you will find, my friend, that most of Belgrade's better-known citizens have joined the Pan-Slav Brotherhood."

Voyan was appalled. "Even the King's own body-guard!" he gasped. "It seems rather terrible, doesn't it?"

The other shrugged complaisant shoulders. "Are you ready?"

"Of course. Where is the meeting place?"

Naumovic grew suddenly noncommittal. "You are to follow," he said, "without questions."

They walked on in silence for a while, taking the narrow lane behind the sacristy of the church. Through winding ghetto streets they came to the old Turkish city. Under a portico which was covered by a rank growth of ivy Naumovic paused to knock softly. A panel in the door opened and through the aperture a voice could be heard.

"Password!"

Naumovic leaned forward and whispered something,

after which they were admitted. Behind them a lock clicked sharply while the porter's mumbled words directed the two arrivals.

"Apis, the Master, is waiting in the Room of the Oath."

Naumovic seemed to understand. Without hesitation he guided Voyan down a dark passage. At its end a heavy curtain parted and there was a muffled sound of voices. The two men stepped across the threshold of a bleak candlelit chamber, in the middle of which was a square table draped with black cloth. On the table stood four gleaming candelabra. Beyond, grouped in a semi-circle, seven tall figures awaited the visitors. All seven were robed in black, with monastic cowls drawn over their faces.

Again Naumovic uttered what seemed to be the password. The man in the center uncovered his forehead and eyes.

"Apis greets you," he said in a deep voice. "Are you prepared to take the vows of the Black Brotherhood?"

Voyan gave a sudden start. "Dragutin!" he cried in surprise, rushing toward the speaker.

Dmitriyevitch remained aloof, as though he had not recognized the other. "I am Apis," he spoke once more, "friend to no one, since I am the friend of all."

"But you never told me," Voyan insisted. "I have a right to know what all this hocus-pocus is supposed to mean."

The voice answered: "That you will learn."

"Well?" Voyan's nerves were taut. He had spent too many hours of lonely torture to enjoy this game of hide-and-seek.

"I am the Black Hand," Dragutin said slowly. "I am the Serbian cause. If someone killed me, I would return—like Apis, sacred bull of the Egyptians—always in another form. So, in this manner, is the Pan-Slav cause deathless! Will you join our ranks, neophyte?"

Fervor grew on Voyan's face. Even as the words fell, his troubled spirit sensed that here was the only anchor left to him, the fellowship of Belgrade's secret patriots. Like these hooded comrades, he would be obliged henceforth to work in darkness. Like the invisible legion behind them, he must lead a double life—a current one, and that of the future—the life of a Greater Serbia. Marked by the law which had only today released him, he was an outcast already. But the Black Hand would ennoble his plight. It would fight his battle, in that it doomed the Queen. A spark of hope flared up within him and burst into quick flame. It was the hope of wreaking vengeance upon Draga.

The piercing eyes of Apis scrutinized him. With a vague shudder Voyan gazed about the room. It did not seem quite believable that here, within these crumbling walls, the fate of dynasties could be decided. The whole setting smacked somehow of spurious melodrama. Even more incredible was the fact that he, Voyan, should find himself in such a place. The Masins had always been a loyal race, loyal to whatsoever ruled them. They sponsored neither change nor insurrection. Yet here he was, and he felt somehow proud at this discovery—the only rebel of his clan. The apostate! He straightened abruptly and faced the half-circle of men.

"I am ready," he said, almost fiercely.

There was a stir among the cloaked figures. As if in

response to some mysterious signal, the cowls were thrown back and Voyan looked into the faces of the Black Hand leaders. He recognized them, one and all. Here were personages prominent in the political strata of the capital. If Voyan had dreaded a possible alliance with social derelicts and outlaws, the assortment of respected citizens confronting him now banished all qualms. Here was eloquent proof that the Black Hand did not represent a band of nihilistic terrorists. It was a league of patriots as honorable as the *Skupchina* itself.

A smile of satisfaction lighted up his pale features. He raised two fingers in obedience to a gesture from Apis. With clear exultant voice he spoke the oath and accepted the pledge of the Pan-Slav Brethren.

CHAPTER XXVIII

LETTERS

THE winter of 1902 brought a disturbing factor into the life of Alexander and Draga. It was the anonymous letter, the *"Mene tekel upharsin"* of all dynasties.

At intervals, two and three weeks apart, the King received communications baffling in substance and signed always by the same cryptic symbol—the silhouette of a gauntlet. At first he made no mention of these missives, tearing them up before Draga took notice. But soon the Queen herself was made the recipient of similar notes. For her the peculiar signature held no mystery. She recognized the Black Hand of which Voyan Masin had once spoken, and she knew that trouble was afoot.

The recurring messages addressed to King and Queen were neither fearsome nor insulting. Rather were they couched in urbane language. Politely they counseled the ruling Obrenovitch to lay down his robes of kingship and surrender the throne to a candidate named by popular election. As an alternative, in the event that Alexander did not wish to abdicate, it was proposed that he divorce the Queen and send her from the country. Reasons given were limited to the throne's lack of a legitimate heir and Draga's consistent interference in government affairs. A refusal to comply with the above requests, in either one or the other form, would bring upon the dynasty untold regrets.

"It's a threat!" Sasha exclaimed in alarm. "Someone

291

is plotting against our lives. Perhaps we should invite these—er—persons to a conference?"

Draga snorted. "How are you going to know whom to invite? What are their names?"

His distress grew. "We might post a public notice to the effect that fair criticism is not unwelcome. We must placate——"

"Placate!" She twisted her lips into a pitying, derisive smile. "You are so easily frightened, my Sasha."

"This may be serious," he insisted.

"How serious? You alone can determine that. No one would dare to lay a hand on us. Think for a moment, you are the King, the highest power in the land!"

"Yes, but——"

"Avail yourself of that power. Ignore these absurd demands and find out by whom the letters were written. Arrest all who appear in the least suspicious—I can think of a few right at this moment—and let a firing squad make examples of them. That will do more good than your weak-kneed conferences."

He blinked uncertainly. "Nevertheless," he began, "there is a distinct proposal for some sort of mediation. A man named Apis offers to explain just why my subjects are dissatisfied. The least I can do is to listen."

She lost all patience with him. Despite his violent temper he had no pride, no confidence in himself or his authority. How right they were to consider him incompetent! He trembled before a piece of paper and actually planned to let a subordinate dictate his policies of government. Even as he had succumbed to her, Draga, who without birthright or influential patronage had forced him to make her a queen, so he succumbed to everyone

who daunted him by putting on a bold front. Obstinate
and obstreperous as he was about his picayune caprices,
a major crisis found him unnerved. Ah, no, he would
not fight her battles for her. He was little Sasha still,
afraid of the dark. . . .

She ordered him to surrender all future notes for her
personal inspection. She would employ a squad of secret
service men to track down their source and bring to
justice all who could be implicated in this vile crime.
Singlehanded she would cope with those who, her instinct
knew, were Draga Lunyevica's enemies rather than
Alexander's.

Here and there her agents picked up suspicious characters who could not satisfactorily explain their activities.
After a summary trial these wretches were led to prison
and never heard from again. Not one of them was a
member of the Pan-Slav Brotherhood, yet not one of
them could be saved by the Black Hand lest the attempt
reveal the identity of the real conspirators. The only
tribute accorded those unwitting martyrs was the recording of each name upon a roster hung behind velvet
draperies in the Room of the Oath. Immortality was
thus assured to many a hoodlum whose antecedents
scarcely corresponded to the select company in which his
epitaph went henceforth through the ages.

It was Draga's strategy, so feminine in its dogged
perseverance, which defeated the Black Hand's effort to
bring about a peaceful change. As yet, none of the
conspirators schemed against the King's safety or that
of his wife. The intimation of unpleasantness attendant
upon the monarch's refusal implied at the most a possible
demonstration and the ignominy of a public appeal, in

the face of which Alexander would be compelled to abdicate.

The warning missives sent periodically through the royal mails had been scrawled by Voyan Masin, the former diplomat. It had been the *Knese* Masin who, as a nobleman, felt that Alexander's plight must not be made too opprobrious. After all, he was the King. Even a cashiered dynast must be accorded the civilities that befitted his station. Alexander Obrenovitch had, regardless of his faults, been to the purple born. Of Draga, the usurper, Voyan did not permit himself to think. The letters penned to her were letters to the Queen of Serbia, not the hoyden of the Sava River mill. The monarch's downfall must not be rendered needlessly poignant by further humiliation in the person of his wife. Enough malevolence had already followed that ill-chosen partnership. Let the insatiable creature be queen for a day. . . . The loss of crown and scepter would be a stinging thorn in her flesh until the very hour of death. Voyan could well afford to be lenient. No punishment was more galling to Draga than to be hurled from her eminence back into the ranks of common mortals. For Voyan knew that there is no snobbery greater than that of the social climber.

It was only after the Queen had struck back with radical measures of persecution that the tone toward her was altered. The anonymous envelopes bore henceforth the address "Madame," a term offensive to her since those far-off Biarritz days when she had stubbornly introduced herself as Baroness Masin. One final message was directed to her along the new lines, causing her to smart under its veiled invective. Abdication, the text ran, would not be requested of her for, to Serbians and the world at large, she never had been a full-fledged queen. Her farcical mummeries were at an end since it was a well-known corollary that "royal concubines must follow their lamentable masters into exile."

No further messages were received at the *Konak* after this one. Voyan had relished each fine stroke of the stiletto-like pen with which he inscribed it, using printed characters to disguise his handwriting. Apis, who read every letter before sealing it with the official symbol, smiled grimly as he stamped this last.

"She won't like it," he chuckled wryly, "she won't like it a bit. As a young wench she all but scratched my eyes out for rebuking her in front of the assembled yokelry of her native dung pile."

"She was always high-spirited," Voyan mused. "I suppose something might really have been made of her."

The other nodded. "That seems to have been her own opinion, too. She lost no time in accomplishing her purpose, I say."

"I wasn't thinking of it in that way," Voyan broke in. "She has overreached herself all along the line, from the very start. Her growth was never organic, always forced, always twisted. And therefore evil. But it might have been otherwise."

Apis stared gloomily ahead. "This is no time for conjectures, my boy. We can't engage in seraphic visions of what might have been. Serbia is in the clutches of a selfish and unscrupulous shrew."

"Don't forget her nearsighted husband."

"Yes, myopic in a figurative as well as a literal sense. It's he who carries out her dangerous designs. That

Sasha made a poor enough sovereign, to begin with, but we might in time have chiseled away his worst faults and pinned him down to parliamentary rule. However, the woman has changed all that."

Voyan frowned. "I personally doubt that he would ever have bowed to the *Skupchina.*"

"But he did bow!" There was a slight irritation in the other's voice. "It worked when we refused the appropriation for the yacht, remember?"

"Right. Slavyanin told me about that. I can see poor Sasha, crestfallen and meek, being told that the state couldn't share such an expense."

"After he returned to the palace," Dragutin muttered, "she took him in hand and turned the trick. As fast as Parliament could bully him out of his own power she bullied him back in again. I tell you, the streets of Belgrade will be paved as soon as Madame Draga has no more use for the municipal funds."

The two men fell silent, contemplating a hopeless future. Mechanically, Apis now opened an iron coffer from which he drew a scroll of parchment. Without glancing at its text he reached for a burning candle. There was a sudden puff followed by licking flames. A pungent odor filled the room.

Voyan looked up startled. "What are you doing," he cried, pointing to the smoking parchment, "I thought you had saved this up for the last?"

Dragutin's lips tightened. "This is the last," he said slowly. "I am destroying the text of Alexander's abdication, drawn up by the Council of the Black Hand and intended for the King's signature——"

"But I don't understand," Voyan faltered.

The older man regarded him through narrowing lashes. "I don't think," he murmured in a low tense voice, "that the last of the Obrenos is going to abdicate."

A little mound of ashes gathered on the table top.

CHAPTER XXIX

Interlude in Vienna

On the eve of the first Thursday after Trinity the Austrian capital prepared for its traditional Feast of the Eucharist.

Each year, from far and wide, the representatives of the empire gathered in Vienna to join the colorful processions held in honor of Corpus Christi Day. Gala trappings were refurbished for the occasion. Lancers from Galicia, the Honvéd Hussars of Hungary, the Dragoon and Cuirassier Regiments of Bosnia, Herzegovina and the Banat, all assembled in the Hapsburg city to betoken the loyalty of their respective provinces to His Apostolic Majesty, the Emperor-King.

Tomorrow Austria's nobles, the Court, the high clergy, as well as every soldier in the realm, would march in an unending pageant over the *Graben,* the *Ring,* and the world's gayest boulevard—the *Kärntnerstrasse*—to the Gothic cathedral of *Sankt Stefan.* Here they would halt for benedictions bestowed by the Prince-Archbishop who waited in a cloud of incense at the entrance to the magnificent church. Then they would move on, giving place to ever new cohorts of chosen manhood: handsome, tall Croats, rakish Dalmatians, blue-eyed Swabians from the lower Danube, proud Slovenes and sinewy Bohemian horsemen. They would pass in separate entities, each speaking an individual tongue, cherishing peculiar traditions, harboring personal grievances and hopes. Yet in

298

this panorama of small nations held together under a common crown, the symbol of empire radiated anew and proclaimed the goal of super-nationalism. Here was the heritage bequeathed by that ancient hegemony, the Holy Roman Empire of pre-Hohenstaufen days. The Hapsburg realm, a brotherhood of weaker peoples bowing to one central federalized seat of government, held its own in a period of increasingly destructive national self-consciousness.

How long would this be so? No one could tell. Already a note of discord had been struck by a frequently applied term, the Dual-Monarchy. The Hungarians caused it by their stubborn demand to be given preference over the remaining constituents. Austria-Hungary was a title that pleased vain Magyar ears, but one which deeply offended the vast Slavic population that acknowledged Hapsburg rule. Empire, not Dual-Monarchy, must be the motto. Equality must be vouchsafed to Czech descendants of Good King Wenceslas, even as it was being granted to the rebellious sons of Arpád. For Austria's provinces were interdependent for the most essential necessities of life—grain, lumber, cattle. The spark of insurrection, too easily fanned into flame, would serve only to split the massive Hapsburg domain into a series of squabbling sovereign nations whose self-esteem must compensate for the utter deficiencies to be encountered on the plane of material subsistence.

Franz Joseph knew this. His long life represented a constant struggle to keep the balance between warring factions. Only Hungary's strength forced him to be crowned at Budapest, without repeating the ceremony at Prague.

"After my death," he once said to the Empress Eugénie of France, "all this will foolishly fall apart."

"But why?" the widow of Napoleon III queried in disapproval, for she had once dreamed empire dreams herself.

"Because," Franz Joseph concluded hopelessly, "it seems that everybody wants his own way, and when I am dead I cannot protect them any longer from getting it."

Good Friday numbered always among the happier moments in the troubled monarch's life. Like his subjects, His Majesty prepared himself a day in advance by attending confession and fasting since early dawn. Much time was given over to a careful review of the address with which it was Franz Joseph's custom to preface the opening of High Mass. For years he had rehearsed that brief text while standing bareheaded among the prelates of the Church. Years of triumph, and defeat, and deepest human sorrow. Thrice he had been too numbed with pain to speak: after the suicide of his only son, Rudolf; after the murder of Elisabeth, his wife; and during the ghastly end of "the handsomest Archduke" Otto (brother to Franz Ferdinand, the present heir). That other tragedy, the execution of Maximilian at Querétaro, had found him more stout of heart. For he had been a younger man, unused to ill fortune, in the days of the adventurous Archduke Maxl.

After the Corpus Christi schedule had been reviewed in every detail the remainder of the afternoon was given over to private audiences. Franz Joseph's antechamber was always crowded. Today there waited the sycophant Court Chamberlain Prince Montenuovo, the Hungarian patriot Julius Andrássy, Count Hoyos, Count Paar, Count Bom-

belles (once secretary to Maximilian), and finally the
Minister of the Exterior, Count Goluchovski. All were
admitted in turn. Montenuovo, who had favors to cozen
in Prague, argued against the order of tomorrow's procession. According to custom, the scarlet Honvéds were
the first to follow in the wake of the Emperor's Grenadiers. Always those Magyars! Did not His Majesty
think it wise to alter this practice? The Bosnians were
equally deserving troops and in their picturesque garb
would appear stunning in the van. Besides, there were
the Bohemians, to whom Montenuovo was particularly
partial, since they had offered him a hunting lodge.
Surely the Bohemians could be counted as Franz Joseph's
most loyal subjects. . . .

The Emperor reflected and murmured an oft-repeated
answer. "We do not discriminate against anyone, my
dear Prince. The provinces are listed according to size
and population. Hungary is our greatest jewel, the empire's granary. Hungary feeds us. From the Magyars
we exact the highest taxes and recruit the largest number
of troops. The Honvéds, I daresay, should march before
even my own bodyguard, the Grenadiers!"

Montenuovo was dismissed. The others followed in
quick succession, cutting short their interviews for His
Majesty looked tired. It was Minister Goluchovski, however, who protracted his visit to uncommon length. Goluchovski brought strange news from Serbia.

Franz Joseph made no attempt to conceal his annoy-
ance. Of late all dispatches from Belgrade had been
excessively distasteful. The unpopular Queen and her
escapades were the subject of several current Viennese
operettas, much to the detriment of the Hofburg Theater's

customary fare. The Emperor, who was a faithful de-
votee of the muses, did not enjoy caricatures of royal
conduct even when—as in the case of the unspeakable
Obrenos—there was ample provocation for this sort of
thing.

"I am not much interested," he announced succinctly,
"in gossip from Illyria."

Goluchovski wiped his bald pate with a fine linen
handkerchief. "But Your Majesty," he expostulated,
"this is a different matter."

"Very different, I hope."

"The Russian Ambassador just called up by telephone,
only half an hour ago, to read me a code message from
His Excellency, Ivan Tcharikov, who is the Tsar's representative in Belgrade."

"Ah," Franz Joseph's curiosity was aroused. "The
Russians—what have they to say to us?"

"Herr Tcharikov," the Minister continued, "has noticed some very suspicious activities around the royal
palace in the Serbian capital."

"Herr Tcharikov is an amateur detective?" A faint
twitch of amusement curled about the Emperor's lips.

"No, Sire, not at all."

"Well?"

"His Excellency made the discoveries without going
out of His Excellency's way. By that I mean——"

"Go on, Goluchovski, do explain what it is you mean."

"The Russian Embassy, as Your Majesty knows, is
located exactly across the square from the Belgrade
Konak. The main balcony looks out upon the palace gardens, permitting a clear view of whatever goes on beyond
the royal gates."

"Very convenient. And what has the busy Ambassador seen?"

Goluchovski arched alarmed eyebrows. "Late this afternoon, Sire, Their Majesties left the *Konak* to attend a public concert which would not be over before dark."

"Herr Tcharikov, did he likewise attend this concert?"

"No, Herr Tcharikov has a cold."

Franz Joseph gazed out into the night that cloaked Vienna. Where, he wondered, had this crowded day slipped to? And why couldn't the tiresome visitor get on with his story? It was long past supper-time now.

"What happened, Goluchovski?"

"A most irregular occurrence, Your Majesty. Even before dusk had quite fallen several hooded figures were seen conferring with the gatekeeper who, after some altercation, admitted them into the guardhouse."

The Emperor's eyes closed wearily. "I think your friend Tcharikov is needlessly excited over what may be no more than ordinary routine. From my own window I can daily witness mystifying scenes which, I am later told, have to do with my valet's purchase of a zither, or the forthcoming nuptials of the third majordomo's niece."

There was a note of genuine anxiety in Goluchovski's voice. "But in the guardhouse something seemed to be wrong. Panayatovic, who heads the *Konak* watch, appeared in the doorway with waving arms. A moment later he fell backward, as if——"

"Yes?" the Emperor put in impatiently.

"As if someone had struck him from behind."

Franz Joseph's face darkened. "I trust the Russian Ambassador communicated with Belgrade police," he said. "That would be more effective than dispatching code messages to Vienna."

Minister Goluchovski nodded. "That he did, Sire. But at the *Glavnyaca* Headquarters he was told that the Prefect was lying down in his private office, overcome by a sudden spell of dizziness. His Excellency of course did not wish to precipitate a false alarm, deciding instead to seek counsel both here and in St. Petersburg."

The Emperor's frown thickened into a scowl. "Unpleasant, Goluchovski," he muttered, "damned unpleasant. It puts us in a particularly ugly position."

"Very true, Your Majesty."

"We are to say how Serbia's dynasty is to protect itself. Yet, if I sent a detachment of troops to Alexander's aid tonight, the Tsar would oblige me before morning with a virtual declaration of war. On the other hand, if Russia interferes, our position in the Balkans becomes untenable—since Serbia's future policy would be controlled by forces across the Volga."

The other assented in mute accord. Franz Joseph was right. It happened to be a devilish fine issue to decide. Irregularities at the *Konak* most certainly did not call for foreign meddling which the Belgrade Government would have every reason to resent. But passive indifference seemed equally unsound, for lately there had sprung up throughout the lower Danube Valley a rumor of perilous things afoot in Slavdom. No one knew anything concrete, but people murmured about secret societies and some fanatic's pledge concerning a new order. This, it was easy to guess, boded no good for Alexander Obrenovitch or his hated wife. It also provided no happy outlook for Austria's Balkan interests, especially if the Karageorgevitch clan returned to power.

That the Black Georges had begun to stir in their mountain fastnesses was no longer a matter of conjecture; it was a certainty. Almost any day the fiery Prince Peter might descend and obliterate his erstwhile defeat at the hands of Milan's whelp, the child Sasha. London and Paris newspapers frankly identified the elderly head of the Karageorgevitch tribe with Belgrade's desperate *maffia* gang, the famous Black Hand.

These things being known, was it either prudent or humane for a neighboring government to ignore what seemed an unmistakable signal of distress? What, on the other hand, would be the attitude of the rest of Europe if Austria, uninvited, set herself up as Serbia's arbiter? Such were the questions that troubled Franz Joseph until the small hours of a night he was destined to remember for many years to come. Only a decade later the Court at Belgrade viewed with similar misgivings the visit of an undesired Hapsburg Crown Prince and his morganatic consort to the old Slav provinces of Bosnia and Herzegovina. The city of Sarajevo was known to be dotted with Serb patriots, some of whom were potential assassins. Yet neither military nor civil authorities raised a finger to prevent Franz Ferdinand and Sofia Chotek from walking into the path of death.

Stooped over his writing desk, the Emperor played with an ivory paper weight.

"The Tcharikov report," he murmured significantly, "may prove to be erroneous. If it is not, and something leads me to feel pessimistic in the matter, our hands are

still tied.   Nevertheless, I wish King Alexander to be
given immediate shelter within our own boundaries in
the event of—er—a revolution."

"Does Your Majesty plan to hold Krusedol in readiness?"

The monarch nodded.   "Old Milan ended his days in
comparative contentment at the little *Schloss*.   You may
give orders to reopen the place."

The Minister bowed solemnly and took up his silk hat.
With diffident steps he crossed the thick carpet and dis-
appeared through the door to the anteroom.   Franz
Joseph was alone.

CHAPTER XXX

THE QUEEN'S DETECTIVE

THE garden of the *Café Takovo* near the Officers' Casino in Belgrade was crowded with an unusually lively throng. From deserted Milosh Street, just beyond the iron gates, a thin echo of gypsy music could be heard. It was long past midnight. In the distance shone the empty whiteness of the *Slaviya* Square, surrounded by a shadowy fringe of chestnut trees. The *Slaviya* and the sidewalks and the avenues all were empty. But in the *Takovo* gardens they had not enough tables or benches to go round. It was odd. Yes, it was decidedly strange.

The Queen's private detective, hovering in the darkness just outside the restaurant door, peered cautiously through the morning-glory vine that encircled the grating. He could barely distinguish the voices that rose occasionally on the far terrace, but here and there he spotted a familiar face. What could be the occasion for such roistering celebrations? Almost the entire regiment of Royal Guards, with orderlies and mascots, seemed to have assembled here. Officers and men sat in open conviviality around crowded tables from which dripped pools of carelessly spilled wine.

The man beyond the gates took a quick mental review of summer holidays. This was the eleventh of June in the year 1903. St. Barnaby's in the Christian Church; the Devil only knew what it might be to the Moslem. . . .

Perhaps it was some sort of political anniversary? The

307

detective, a man of practical education, had only the most cursory knowledge of history. He knew about sundry battles with those rascals, the Bulgarians:

"For barbarians, yes, barbarians
are in war-time the Bulgarians!"

And then there was always Serbia's liberation from the Sultan's yoke, a handy bit of information whenever you hadn't known the correct answer to some query in school. Teachers never failed to respond to this bromide. But every urchin, and the Queen's detective too, realized that these things had not happened in the middle of June. The Army camped during midsummer and helped bring in the harvest; most Balkan disputes were postponed until this necessary task was done.

All the more reason, then, to keep an eye on the crowd which had concentrated in this single spot. The *Takovo* resort was not known to be a favorite military hangout. Why, then, this obviously prearranged meeting? It was imperative to find an answer.

For six months now the Queen's agents had combed the town, ferreting out signs of conspiracy. Countless idlers and ne'er-do-wells vanished from the streets of the capital, never to return. Belgrade had grown quiet in that time. When Alexander and his wife drove through the boulevards barely a handful of school children gathered to cry feeble *"Ziveos."* The town had learned to mind its business and avoid the royal displeasure. Everyone knew that Draga's henchmen were about, watching, spying, waiting. . . .

Tonight's commotion was most unusual. Earlier this

evening the King and Queen, together with the diplomatic coterie and other notables, had gathered around the pavilion in the cathedral square to attend a band concert. Her Majesty, onlookers observed, was elegantly robed in ivory satin under a wrap trimmed with white astrakhan lamb. Never had she appeared more dazzling. For she was one of those extraordinary women who could look hideous one day and ravishing the next. Tonight her beauty was at its ripest, with the lush sinister quality of full-blown lotus blossoms.

At the close of the musical divertissement the royal carriages had driven straight to the palace while the small crowd dispersed. It was at this point that the secret agent had observed two members of the King's suite who lagged behind and strolled in leisurely fashion down a side street. A lantern disclosed the large-boned Bosnian features of Captain Tanko and the lean face of Naumovic, the young lieutenant who for two summers had been ravaged by Malta fever.

Swiftly the detective had followed them, catching now and then a scrap of their conversation. The officers discussed a subject which of late was in everyone's mouth. It concerned the growing impudence of the Queen's brothers, especially her favorite, Paul. Tonight this insufferable prig had detected a shade of disrespect in the curt salute with which Captain Tanko greeted him. The occasion lent itself marvelously for an effective reproof. In the presence of superiors and subordinates alike, the offending officer was halted, as the dapper Lunyevica snapped a command. Captain Vladimir Tanko, on whose gold-braided tunic blazed the Order of the White Eagle, was forced to stand at attention for ten full minutes, saluting the brother-in-law of Serbia's King. In stony silence Tanko endured the incomparable affront. All color vanished from his cheeks as he told of the experience, hours later, groaning through tightly drawn lips:

"Soon, soon, Apis!"

At sound of that name the secret service man had quickened his step, but now the officers entered the *Takovo* grounds and were lost from view. Through random openings in the surrounding hedge other familiar figures could be seen, apparently waiting for something. Once the agent thought he recognized the elusive *Knese* Voyan Masin walking across the restaurant terrace, but he must have been mistaken. The Queen's former prisoner, whose description was in the hands of every police agent, would not show himself so publicly. It was no secret that Draga had given orders for his renewed arrest.

Music filled the air, drowning out conversation. Somewhere a lone troubadour drew polychrome fugues from the single string of a *gusla* and broke into song. Voices joined in the ribald couplet of a Czecho-Slovak lay:

> *"Má roztomilá Barusko,*
> *vem mê sebou na luzko. . . ."*

Although no linguist, the plain-clothes man was nevertheless able to gather from these lines that "with a beautiful charmer, the bed is warmer."

But now Her Majesty's spy was completely mystified, for in the center of the clearing there appeared the figure of a staff officer. By the epaulettes one could easily recognize the dress uniform of a colonel. The spectator gasped. This was the great Dragutin Dmitriyevitch! If *he* was here there could be nothing wrong, for Dmitriyevitch—a model soldier and veteran of three campaigns— was the Serbian General Staff in person. . . .

Baffling things continued to happen. The heroic Dragutin tossed a coin to the orchestra while his voice droned:

"Czigány, play us a *kolo!"*

The gypsy leader lifted his baton. Now the cry went from table to table:

"Gentlemen, take your positions for the Queen's dance, the *Draga-Kolo!"*

A mass of human figures milled about until from this confusion there emerged a circle of stamping men. The band struck up a slow melancholy measure which increased gradually to a mad crescendo, while the dancers kept time. Gravely the enormous wheel was set in motion, yet it did not leave the spot—two steps to the left, two steps to the right, while arms intertwined to form a living chain. Rhythmically the circle swayed back and forth to the tune of the ancient Slav ritual. This was *kolo*: the male dance, the peasant dance, the soldier dance.

Again the lone troubadour began to sing. For there were words to every measure, words in praise of whomsoever the warrior dance honored.

"See, how happy is Queen Draga!" sang the voice.

Now a vast chorus joined in. Carried away by the effects of music and wine, somebody emitted a piercing yell. This too was taken up by the rest and re-echoed like the wild whooping of a Cossack band over the steppes. The men were growing hot. They threw off their shakos and embroidered tunics. Dancing in shirt-sleeves, they formed a dragon chain at the head of which, with arms folded behind his bovine neck, danced Dmitriyevitch himself.

The man beyond the garden gates stared stupidly upon the scene. Could he be dreaming? Apart from the guards and officers on duty at the palace, almost the entire Belgrade garrison seemed to have assembled here tonight. And every man, high and low, was dancing the Queen's *kolo!* Her Majesty had no idea of this. Her Majesty believed herself persecuted and in constant danger. Well, it was unfair to leave the Queen in such ignorance. He must prepare a report of what he had just seen, namely that the Army itself stayed up half the night to dance in honor of the sovereign. Conspiracies? If they existed, it would not be here that one uncovered them. Those chaps in the garden there were wild with enthusiasm. To pin charges of treason on a single one of them was sheer idiocy.

A glow of satisfaction spread over the face of the Queen's faithful detective. He had been sent to uncover villainy, but instead he had found something far more precious than the physical safety of his employer— he had found for Draga the throbbing pulse of her people. Tomorrow he would go to her and say:

"Even Voyan Masin, upon whom rests Your Majesty's darkest suspicion, must have been there. And everyone cast aside his dolman to join the royal *kolo!* There is no greater sign of allegiance. . . ."

The plain-clothes man crept cautiously down from a stone pillar on which he had perched and decided to go home. There was nothing more for him to do, after what he had just learned. Rather must he get some rest and prepare for a busy morrow. Who could tell? The Queen might reward him for the priceless service he had rendered. Perhaps he was in line for advancement at Court, some confidential job on the inside. After all, perspicacity was needed for this sort of thing. Well, once Her Majesty gave ear to his story something important was bound to happen.

Although the night was warm, the little man dashed briskly through the streets, unmindful of fatigue or heat. Behind him the chanting voices faded into a hum, then vanished altogether. Like a faint echo the words died on the lazy breeze:

"See, how happy is Queen Draga!"

From the distant *Kalimegdan* came the sound of carillon bells. It was one o'clock. As if in obedience to some prearranged command the music ceased. Hastily the gypsies packed their fiddles and filed out through the open gates of the *Takovo Café*. With furtive eyes they peered back at the panting and disheveled dancers who had stopped to wipe damp brows. Coats and helmets were being gathered up. In the light of a crescent moon the white gleam of sabers mingled with the dull blue of steel revolvers. The sight of these warlike implements did not please the Romany band leader.

"After all the drinking that's been done," he announced gloomily, "they're sure to end up in a brawl. We're making off just in time, before the police blame it on us!"

Raising his baton like a brandished lance, he drove the small troupe of musicians into the nearest side street. Reluctant, since their fear was equaled by their unquenchable curiosity, they obeyed him. But he was right, one-legged Tirano. If there was any trouble brewing, it would do no good for gypsy folk to hover around. With stealthy jungle steps the intimidated band fled through the night.

A tense silence had fallen upon the restaurant gardens. At the foot of the terrace men pressed closely together and fixed eager eyes upon one who stood towering above. It was Dragutin Dmitriyevitch, alone at the head of the stairs. A watch in his hand ticked off invisible minutes.

"Comrades," he said slowly, "we are ready."

A murmur ran through the group. Dmitriyevitch stemmed it with a gesture of his hand.

"The commanders of our five detachments," he ordered, "will come with me for a moment to review their instructions. What we are about to do must be done as thoroughly as possible. Everything is at stake!"

He turned and went into the building, followed by the slender Byronic figure of Voyan Masin, the stocky Tanko, Naumovic and two intelligence officers in charge of the Belgrade citadel. The door of a private suite closed behind them, but through its thin panels an indistinct rumble of voices could be heard.

The crowd outside stood motionless, listening, waiting. It was the hour of Serbia's liberation. Darkness before a crimson dawn.

CHAPTER XXXI

Two Spectators

SHORTLY after one o'clock that morning the Rumanian Minister to Serbia, Prince Edgard Mavro-Cordato, drove to the house of his Russian friend, Ivan Tcharikov. Earlier that evening the two men had engaged in repeated telephone conversations concerning the strange happenings within the *Konak* grounds. After the King's return from the concert, however, no further irregularities were apparent. His suspicions allayed, Tcharikov had gone to bed to sleep off a bad sinus congestion. He would leave worry to others.

Not so Mavro-Cordato. Related to Alexander Obrenovitch through the Kesko line, the Rumanian envoy lapsed into a state of uncomfortable apprehension. While pacing up and down the length of his study, he became suddenly aware of a rumbling noise akin to the shuffle of marching feet. Nervous and distraught, he again rang up the Russian Embassy but received no answer. The noise meanwhile came nearer. It swelled and died away once more within a block's distance, and now there could no longer be any doubt: a host of men moved through the night on some unknown and sinister errand.

Yet another time the Moldavian dignitary picked up the telephone receiver. Only now did he realize that there was no response from the central switchboard. Had someone tampered with the wires? He stepped to the window and looked out. Electric lights were burning as

315

usual. Then perhaps only his own telephone was out of order. An accident, of course. Plausible. But he, Mavro-Cordato, was cousin to the Serbian King. It looked like a queer coincidence. . . .

A moment later he had left his rooms and picked up a cab to drive him to the home of Tcharikov. While rolling through deserted avenues he sensed a tenseness in the warm June air. Here and there dark shutters opened softly and he could feel sleepy-eyed burghers peering out at him. Even in the quiet of their homesteads people seemed to be restless, proving to him that he had not been mistaken. Somewhere in the distance there was the echo of a strange commotion. He could still distinguish the rhythmic tattoo of relentless tramping feet.

Half-way between the Hotel London and the Russian Embassy the atmosphere was suddenly rent asunder by a dreadful screeching sound. High up among the ancient trees that lined the avenue a swarm of crows had been roused from slumber. Their flapping wings, followed by shrill screams of panic, could be heard many blocks away. Prince Mavro-Cordato experienced a palpable association of ideas. Long-forgotten grammar lessons with his German tutor. The poet Friedrich von Schiller. *"Die Kraniche des Ibykus . . ."* Quite unaccountably, small beads of perspiration broke out on his brow. *"Die Kraniche"*—the cranes of Greek tragedy?

"Accursed creatures," he whispered, annoyed by the chill that had gripped him at sight of the ill-omened birds. The distant tramping now grew muffled, furtive.

His steps quickened automatically when, after paying the drowsy driver, he at last reached his friend's door. The short journey had been a distinctly eerie one and

Mavro-Cordato had no intention of repeating it. Surely the Russian Embassy counted a capacious sofa among its possessions, where one might spend the remainder of a bad night.

He found Ivan Tcharikov, standing in the recess of an upstairs balcony, clad in a heavy dressing gown. The Russian's face looked peaked and white. With a pale hand that trembled slightly, Tcharikov pointed over the balustrade.

"Look, Edgard," he said, "the main gates—they are being opened."

Mavro-Cordato caught his breath. In the soft glow of the *Konak* lanterns a weird scene was being enacted. As if moved by some invisible arm the gigantic palace gates swung open and now, on swift and stealthy feet, a cordon of dark silhouettes crept along shaded pathways toward the porter's lodge. Before the oak portals of the royal abode they came to a standstill. But now, again in obedience to some blind force, the great carved panels moved slowly on their hinges.

"Good God," the Rumanian gasped, "they are pouring into the building, with no one to stop them—the sanctity of the *Konak* is being violated!"

"With the precision of a well-rehearsed plot," Tcharikov answered.

"But we must go to the King's aid. We must spread the alarm!"

The Russian's face took on a frozen look. "Too late. Our wires have been cut, as, I imagine, have those of the other embassies."

"That explains a thing or two——"

"Besides," Tcharikov continued, nodding toward a

shadow some distance up the street, "I'm being watched. My calls to the police station earlier this evening were unwelcome. Those fellows down there are organized to meet any emergency."

The other stared into the night with straining eyes. "They look like soldiers to me," he murmured, "there's not a man among them without uniform."

Tcharikov assented. "Mostly officers. I saw their epaulettes by the street light. That at least is reassuring."

"How so?"

"A bunch of anarchists or drunken troopers would lead me to expect the worst."

The other stroked his damp hair nervously. "And this way—you don't believe Sasha is in actual danger?"

There was a shrug of shoulders. "I can't say. But a monarch's own officers are bound by the highest pledge. You somehow don't visualize them laying hands on their master; it just isn't done. At the most——"

"At the most?"

"The King might be coerced into a renunciation. Old Milan's exit, you may recall, took place under circumstances not unlike the present. No time even for a curtain speech."

Mavro-Cordato heaved a generous sigh. "A bloodless abdication, then."

"Yes, I should call it that."

"Well, you've no idea, Ivan, of my relief. Frankly, I dashed over here with a case of plain funk. I was about to ask for your spare bed."

The Russian's gestures became instantly solicitous. "Make yourself at home; the place is yours."

Prince Edgard laughed. "Thanks, old man, but I'm over it now. I really should be trotting along."

"As you like. Cigarette?"

They smoked in silence, each absorbed in his own thoughts. Once Mavro-Cordato mused aloud:

"Has it ever occurred to you what trifles a major catastrophe sometimes hinges on?"

"For instance?"

"Oh, something so insignificant as Sasha's devotion to his commoner wife may change the map of Serbia."

Tcharikov's gaze was leveled on his friend. "There's a great deal of hysteria in history," he said slowly. "I'm afraid we shall never know how many of the world's calamities are linked with the dyspepsia of diplomats, the love-life of monarchs or the advanced arteriosclerosis of statesmen."

"You place patriotism pretty far down the line."

"I discount it altogether. Patriotism is a banner to be held in the wind where it floats picturesquely and never fails to win applause. It is seldom a motive."

The Rumanian had risen to his feet. He felt almost cheerful. He had given up the idea of the sofa altogether.

"Well, good-by," he said airily, "I'm on my way. We can read the rest in the morning papers."

He had barely finished when a salvo of gunfire crackled through the night. In the stillness that followed one could distinguish a stifled cry and the splintering of heavy wood. The two men on the balcony regarded each other with haggard faces. The Russian Ambassador was the first to speak.

"I don't think," he said, "that you had better go."

PART FOUR

A NIGHT IN THE KONAK

CHAPTER XXXII

Prelude

SCARCLY ten minutes before the two diplomats met on Tcharikov's balcony, Apis had stopped in the dimly lit vestibule of the *Konak* to check over the commands. With short clipped phrases he repeated his instructions. The men were to be divided into five groups under the *Knese* Masin, Captain Tanko, Lieutenant Naumovic, Commander Kostic and Commander Bruno, respectively. In accordance with a strictly defined plan they were to scout through the entire building. Servants, adjutants and all other members of the royal suite were to be overpowered and kept under temporary control. Drawn sabers were to be used in the event of police interference, but there must be no shooting, lest the alarm spread before the King and Queen had been found.

So far everything seemed to be working out according to schedule. The advance crew in black hoods had prepared the ground, taking up their positions at the most strategic points about the royal palace. Next, the procession of conspirators had started from the *Takovo* gardens without mishap, carefully threading their way through dark side streets and avoiding the wide *Slaviya* Square. Only Dragutin and a small contingent of officers strolled leisurely across the open space, passing the double guard before the police station. At sight of the military gentlemen the sleepy patrol came to a salute. Within, stretched out on a leather couch, lay the Prefect of Police,

323

mysteriously drugged with opium.   Dragutin grinned.
He returned the patrol's salute and headed for the short
Devoyacka drive which led directly toward the *Teraziye*
and the palace gardens.

Here, too, all calculations added up correctly.   The
gatekeeper, bribed since late afternoon, came scurrying
along a little side path, holding his keys in readiness.
Two sentries who demanded explanations were assured
with convincing glibness that the King had summoned
a special re-enforcement of the *Konak* guard.   Further
to insure their docility the pair were trampled underfoot
by the "re-enforcements" which had just rounded the
corner and were now rushing through the open gates.

With taut nerves suddenly released, the marching throng
stumbled across the palace grounds, seeking shelter under
the long avenue of trees.   From the guardhouse there
might emerge at any moment a furious squad of sharp-
shooters who, in that open terrain, would make short
shrift of the intruders.   But no.   Fat Panayatovic, the
Captain, had been knocked unconscious and locked in the
privy.   In the absence of their superior, the drowsy
night-watch milled stupidly about, retreating finally
to their bunks, where without much ado they were disarmed.

The gatekeeper had meanwhile unlocked the outer
palace doors.   Now, for the first time, there appeared
an obstacle.   The second door, at the far end of the lower
vestibule, had not been left open.   Since it was locked
from the inside, the gatekeeper did not have the keys.

Dragutin pressed hard against the oak panels and
tapped a short signal with the bronze knocker.   Had
Slavyanin failed him?   The exact time had been care-

fully computed. Was it possible that the man had misunderstood? Apis knocked again. There was no answer.
"Force the door," he ordered sharply.

A phalanx of men rammed the heavy structure. After
repeated efforts the lock crashed in its socket and the
portals burst open upon a dreadful sight. On the floor
just across the threshold, with his head in a pool of
blood, lay Sergei Slavyanin. He was still clutching a
slender key in his stiffened hand. Over the dead man
stood with brandished sword the defiant figure of General
Lazar, Adjutant to His Majesty, Alexander.

At sight of Apis, the elderly officer leaped forward. "I
killed him," he shouted hoarsely, "for treachery to his
King! And I shall do the same to you, Dragutin——"

"Dog!" snarled Apis, knocking the weapon from
Lazar's hand. "Only a dog could be loyal to such a master
as yours."

Without further hesitation the enraged Lazar reached
for his revolver, but as he did so a wave of blood gushed
suddenly from his mouth. A leering halberdier non-
chalantly wiped his blade on a piece of tapestry which
hung from the ceiling above the fallen officer.

Blindly the avengers moved on, kicking aside the lifeless form of General Lazar Petrovitch, hero of two wars
against Islam and now a martyr for his sovereign whom,
perchance, no martyrdom might save. . . .

It was during this savage onrush that a serious blunder
occurred. Pressed forward under its own momentum the
human avalanche was hurled against a far wall which
held, behind a glass door, the electric switchboard of
the *Konak*. (Only recently King Alexander had ordered
this innovation to be installed, providing for all-night

illumination of the halls and corridors.) There was a crashing sound, followed by the accidental discharge of a revolver and a shower of splintered glass. Then came a heartrending scream. In the quick darkness which ensued the heaving throng was spared a loathsome spectacle of two electrocuted musketeers burning to a crisp.

A long silence followed, broken at last by a plea: "Comrades, let us turn back before it is too late!"

With angry fingers Apis struck a match. In the faint flicker of light a senior officer turned suddenly ashen. His battle-scarred cheeks quivered as, with an agonized voice, he cried out:

"I cannot. I cannot, gentlemen—it is the King!" Covering his wrinkled face, Commander Bruno wept.

There was a tense pause, during which the others listened in consternation. The old man shook his head and continued to wail:

"Thrice I have fought for Serbia. But this—this is different. I cannot. I have sworn the King's oath!"

Dragutin stepped forward. "Traitor!" he snapped, shaking the man's shoulder. "You joined the Black Hand, didn't you?"

The old commander blinked miserably. "It was a terrible mistake. I never believed it would lead to—murder——"

"Murder!" Apis laughed fiercely as the match died between his fingers. "Nothing, not even tyrannicide, is murder in the holy Pan-Slav cause. You are a coward, Bruno, a chicken-hearted fool. . . ."

Darkness again. The old officer, overcome with horror, rushed toward the exit. He tripped over a sagging impediment and dropped the monocle which, it had been his lifelong boast, never deserted him. Groping his way about the floor, he found the ornamental disk floating, unbroken, on the gummy blood of Sergei Slavyanin. Necessity, not perkiness, caused him to polish the gory lens, for Bruno's single eye was almost without sight.

A warmish breeze was wafted in through the open portals. A cloud passed over the sickle of the moon, changing the delicate silver of the night into jet blackness. Gloom descended like a heavy blanket, spreading through the building which already harbored the smell of death.

With desperate effort Dragutin surveyed the situation. Darkness. And the search had not even begun. Worse than that, the short circuit must have alarmed the entire palace, so that *they*—upstairs—were now conscious of danger and might at this very moment make their escape. . . . That he must prevent, no matter at what cost. He must carry out this deed against all odds. Failure meant civil war. It brought the King's revenge upon the entire Officers' Corps and half the Serbian Army as well. Failure meant final defeat of the sacred Pan-Slav cause. It dealt a death blow to the dream of a Greater Serbia and a second Tsar Dushan whose power must stretch through Macedon and the Hellespont, from Danube and Drina to the shores of the Black Sea. . . .

He stood for a moment transfixed by that fanatic vision. Then, abruptly, his voice rose above the confusion:

"Brethren, if we give up now, we are lost! I entreat you to carry out your instructions to the letter——"

He paused, as if to recall some specific point. Without protest the men hovered about.

"Voyan," Apis cried out, "where is Voyan Masin?"

No one answered. Dragutin repeated the call. It was the voice of Naumovic which came back through the gloom:

"He is gone. He may have got upstairs already."

"How? Which way——"

"Through some window, or crawling into a cellar passage. Clear out of his mind, he's so afraid he won't have a hand in this business."

"Vladimir Tanko," Apis muttered in anger, "add Masin's men to yours and surround the building. We can't afford any more bungling. That maniac has done enough damage right now."

Somewhere in the dark Tanko answered, but his words were drowned by a startled exclamation.

"Listen! The gendarmes are out. This damnable shooting——"

For an instant everyone was paralyzed. In the distance the trot of galloping horses could be heard. Dragutin gave brief orders:

"Kostic, hold the gates. Inform the police that interference is useless. Lie to them, delay—anything to give us time to finish up in here."

Commander Kostic clicked heels and summoned his squad of men. An indistinguishable chain of shadows, they filed slowly out into the pallid grayness of the night. Behind them Apis closed the portals and turned to his remaining comrades.

"Now," he said fiercely, "the rest of you search. Force down all doors, make torches from broken furniture, and don't forget to collect candles. There should be tapers in chandeliers and wall sconces. Light up the place as soon as possible. And remember, there is no hope for anyone, if the deed miscarries. Go!"

They milled aimlessly about in the darkness, as if unable to make a forward move. Then, suddenly, the need for action set in. With outstretched arms which spread like tentacles they slipped quietly away. In small groups they filtered down the endless passages, groping along over carpeted stairs to upper regions. An ominous voiceless echo began to fill the ancient building. It was like a shuffling, creaking, hissing symphony produced by scraped floors, falling objects and the quick short gasp of untold panting lungs. Like some prehistoric monster of the sea, death besieged the palace, weaving huge coils in every direction. Like some blind infuriated Cyclops, horror stalked through the darkness, filling the air with a sinister presence.

CHAPTER XXXIII

Anticlimax

THE double doors to the Arabian Room on the second floor did not respond to the combined onslaught of a mere dozen men. With everyone scattered throughout the rambling building much time might be lost in waiting for reinforcements.

"Dynamite will do it," Apis declared, after lighting a match.

From his breast pocket he extracted a small cylinder with a fuse at one end. The match was applied and after a quick retreat to safety the spectators heard a loud detonation. In the glare of the explosion the door could be seen bulging forward, while from the ceiling a mass of crumbling stucco rained down upon bare heads. There was a mad scuffle as the men stormed over the burning débris into the room.

Just beyond the door-frame a damask portière caught fire. The glow illumined a life-sized portrait of King Milan dressed in Austrian parade uniform. At sight of this someone broke into hysterical laughter. That was the trouble with these Obrenos! They played politics with the Hofburg. They liked to see themselves in Hapsburg regalia, always catering to Teutonic tastes and customs whenever a chance was offered. Well, tonight the usefulness of Viennese trappings would be put to a test.

The oil in Milan's canvas would make an excellent flambeau. With a few saber thrusts the large painting was

torn from its gilt frame and rolled into a torch. Its sputtering end belched forth a dense cloud of malodorous
smoke. Through rising puffs of this foul incense the
forebears of the dynasty glared down in mute defiance.
Milosh Obilitch, who slew the Sultan. His descendant,
the *Voyvode* Milosh under whom *Knese* and *Gospodar,*
wealthy landowner and chieftain, were forced to unite
their interests. Milosh III, childless and unhappy with
his Hungarian bride, the Countess "Juppy" Hunyadi. It
was this Milosh who had been assassinated by the Black
Georges when, in 1868, they reopened the everlasting
feud. And now, Jefrenn Obrenovitch, the sickly brother
whose wife—Elena Maria Catargo—ran off to Bucharest
with her Moldavian lover, the dissolute Prince Cusa. At
Cusa's Court Jefrenn's small son, Milan, was schooled in
lechery and intrigue. By the time Serbia bestowed a
crown on Milan's head the hardy mountaineer stock had
been polluted. In this Obreno who was made a king in-
tegrity and leadership had died.

The torch burned high. In its radiance a group of
younger officers who had not entered a royal abode before
this gruesome night stood gaping at the rich scenes about
them. For some moments they were lost in admiring contemplation. The elegance of silk-covered chairs and
ivory-inlaid tabourets (graced with carafes of potent
wine) threatened to deflect their attention from the
macabre business ahead. Relentless in his purpose, Apis
drove them on.

"Faster, faster! The next chamber is the Queen's private salon, and after that comes the royal bedroom
suite. . . ."

Over the delicate teakwood pieces of Draga's sitting

room a leaping, tumbling horde now bounded against the white doors that took up most of the opposite wall. Here, as in the Arabian Room, the bolts were drawn. Apis reached for a new set of explosive shells. As the fuses were lighted the men drew back once more to a far corner. A raucous voice asked:

"Where is the bed? We must catch them in bed—together!"

A thundering crash drowned the scurrilous answer. As the cloud of powder and loose mortar cleared away, the door-frame disclosed blurred outlines of a draped canopy overhanging the royal couch. In a frenzy of murderous lust the men sprang through the flames and into the dark chamber beyond. Here a blind fury overtook them. With tremendous impact they hurled themselves against the footboards, firing at close range into the silken coverlets. In the roar of their fusillade no human outcry could be heard. When every gun had been emptied, swords were drawn and stabbed into the bedding with ghoulish thoroughness, until exhaustion checked the orgy.

"Faggots! Torches!" came the stridor of parched throats. "We want to see them——"

The burning scroll of King Milan's portrait was fetched from the anteroom where, during the explosion, it had been dropped by hands twitching for slaughter. Its suphurous glow now fell upon the ravaged bed, disclosing a mass of fluttering eiderdown and shreds of purple satin ("royal purple," which is not purple at all, but red). In the great ripped tatters of the canopy which hung from the ceiling the holy ikon and the embroidered coat of arms were slashed almost beyond recognition. But of Alexander and Draga there was not a trace.

Appalled, the crazed men stared blankly about. The King and Queen were gone. . . . They had escaped. . . . Ah, this was treachery—someone had betrayed the plot! Then, indeed, all was lost. For no man who had gone to murder his king could live.

Feverish minds were faced slowly with a bleak awakening. Each man returned now to thoughts of his own. Had they not all left well ordered, honorable homes behind? Would not their kinsfolk, their innocent wives and children, suffer for this folly which had led to naught? What else was there now to do but to blow up the whole *Konak* with whatever dynamite was left, and to perish with the Serbia that would never be? . . .

Among the older officers a low muttering was set up. Faithful Bruno had been right. He had defied Apis, the Bull—the demon in whose power they were all held spellbound like somnambulists. Bruno had harkened to conscience and refused to lift a hand against his king. Bruno alone was safe, while they were all caught in this infernal trap.

From the open window across the room there came a sudden gust of wind, followed by a choked whisper:

"Apis, we are lost!"

Dragutin emitted a gasp. He sped over the cluttered floor toward the speaker.

"Voyan! How did you get here? Where have they gone? Speak, man!"

A cowering figure crept through the latticed French doors and leaned against the wall.

The face was Voyan Masin's, but the voice sounded like that of a stranger. "I couldn't wait, Apis. I climbed along the outside, from balcony to balcony. But I missed their—the room—until I heard you in here and saw the bed was empty!"

His knees seemed to give under him, for he now bent over a chair and braced himself with both arms. Dragutin took another step. He gripped the other's shoulder in grim earnestness.

"Voyan," he insisted, "think! In all that time spent on these balconies—you must have seen something, anything. Give us a shadow of a clue, something to work on——"

Voyan shook his head. "Nothing, Apis," he said wearily, "all the windows were dark, and curtained besides. There's only one thing left for us to do— escape."

A wave of excitement stirred through the room. Escape! Could there be any hope of escape? With the King in safety, returning perhaps even now with a detachment of troops, who could talk of escape? Dragutin voiced the general sentiment as he scoffed:

"Impossible. If we fail, we shall know what to do. But before giving up we have yet a final search to make. The King may still be in the *Konak*. If so, we must find him."

The gleam cast by the burning door-frame disclosed two night tables, one on either side of the bed. Each held a candelabrum supplied with an assortment of wax tapers. Silently the men distributed these and, after lighting the wicks, set out upon another feverish hunt. Closets, cabinets, corners were ransacked and riddled with volleys from newly loaded revolvers. A lacquered door leading to the royal bathroom was shattered and torn down. Within, the details of a regal toilet offered themes for chill jocosity. A throne-like contrivance which at first mystified the prowlers turned out to be a weighing machine. It was adorned with coronet and royal arms, so that the King—even while in the nude—might at no time be deprived of his earthly badge of grandeur.

Piece by piece, each fixture was made the butt of salacious jesting. There followed a nervous discharge of pent-up bravado. Uppermost in this display of lugubrious humor loomed the consciousness that it was only a step to the brink over which they would all plunge into an abyss of fearful retribution. None of the men felt like laughing. But since none dared picture to himself the outcome of this night it was best to ignore saner promptings and to join in the orgy of obscenity.

From Sasha's commodious sitz-bath, which afforded ribald speculation on the subject of his girth, attention wandered to an adjoining cabinet filled with a multitude of childish playthings. Here was the nursery which Draga, the impostor, had fitted out while she deceived Belgrade and the capitals of western Europe with her false promise. There the scheming woman had disguised the fact of her sterility by piling up English swaddlings, French nostrums, a German doll house, and the innumerable properties necessary for her Comedy of Errors. At sight of the lace-covered cradle a roar of coarse merriment filled the room.

"Comrades," one hilarious subaltern cried out, "look where she planned to rock her darling Nikodem, or that rat—Paul!" He bowed in mock reverence. "Good evening, Prince!"

"Good evening, Prince!" the chorus howled, kicking the fragile infant's bed to bits.

From one apartment to the next the vandal rampage continued, leaving behind a trail so bleak and desolate that only madmen could have produced its like. Through open windows the moon cast a gray light upon the scene. Horror stalked in the wake of the wild hunters. Far away, the *Kalimegdan* bells caroled the passing hours and still the frantic search went on.

Now, to add to the general confusion, a loud barrage of gunfire started up outside the *Konak* gardens. Had Naumovic and Tanko been unable to hold off the police? Were re-enforcements pouring in from the barracks at the edge of town, perhaps in answer to the King's alarm? Quite possibly the wily Alexander himself was at this very moment out there among his followers, gloating over the capital trick he had played on his most fearsome enemy, the Black Hand. This meant that Apis and his men were caught in the slowly burning palace.

The shooting drew nearer. A heavy rumble of wheels indicated the arrival of artillery. Through broken windows the panic-stricken outposts retreated into the *Konak* where the Black Hand consolidated now into a single fighting unit. Behind torn damask curtains the men pointed blunt muzzles at their pursuers, holding the latter at bay. Only a straggling band of officers continued to retrace their steps in monotonous repetition of what was already a hopeless search. Now even Tanko and Naumovic had joined the rearguard of the hunt. With lighted tapers and improvised lanterns the thinning parade of specters scurried through the smoke-filled structure like phantoms running a hectic race.

Again the royal bedroom was pillaged. In Draga's little salon someone knocked over a stuffed polar bear. The

bulky shape lying prone in the semidarkness brought
screams of fright from the lips of men hardened in battle.

Early dawn, the color of lead, would soon stretch across
the sky. Yet the deed had not been done. With hollow eyes
Dragutin Dmitriyevitch glared from the *Konak* roof upon
the awful spectacle below. How long would it be possible
to hold the palace against those imbeciles who didn't
recognize freedom when they saw it? How long could his
own men brave the impact of artillery fire? But as yet
the artillery had not entered into action. Why? With the
Konak burning already, were the troops afraid to damage
the *Konak?* Or did it mean——?

A fiendish exultation suddenly swelled his heart. So
that was it! The King—the King must still be in the
palace! Then he was not out there with his troops, or the
cannon would have started their deadly work long ago.
The King was concealed somewhere in the building and
he, Apis, would come upon the hiding place, if it took
another day and night to do so. Swiftly he crept back
through the trap door that opened at his feet and hastened
once more along the second floor corridors. His teeth
were chattering, although he felt suffocated by the sultry
June heat. His lips moved incessantly as he ran.

"I've got it," he mumbled savagely, breaking into occasional snorts of triumph, "I've got it! And I'm a dunce of
the first rank, not to have thought of this before."

His brows joined in a determined frown. With giant
strides he traversed the flight of rooms, heading straight
for the royal bedchamber.

Somewhere along the placid valley of the Danube a
precocious cock began to crow. Its shrill and strangely
penetrating call seemed to come from another world.

CHAPTER XXXIV

ALCOVE SCENE

THE man awoke. His small black eyes pierced the darkness and he knew he was alone. There should have been a faint strip of light under the door, just at the foot of his bed, but he could not find it. His mother slept behind that door—or was it Lazar, trusty old *Beau* Lazar, as the Adjutant was called? At times it was very confusing.

The man shivered a little and a queer anxiety lodged in his heart. Why was there no light behind that door! Had Anya forgotten—but how could Anya forget; she was the Oracle of Provo, wasn't she? Or was she Mata, the dread soothsayer of Kremna? . . . Anyway, why must he hear their evil talk? They were always conspiring with their prophecies against the King.

Ah, that was it. Now he remembered. He, Sasha, was the King. And round about him, on duty through the night, were his brave officers—Slavyanin, Tanko, Naumovic, while beside him lay the one human being he loved beyond all things, the woman Draga. He reached across the bed to touch her form, and now the drowsiness of dreams fell from him with a wrench. She was gone. The rumpled bedclothes gave under his touch upon an awful emptiness.

God, what was that! Somewhere outside he heard a soft rumbling like the shuffle and stamp of many feet. Terrified, he jumped from the bed, clutching the carved footboards in unreasoning alarm. Under the long night-

338

shirt his flabby body shook violently while with dry lips he gasped one single word:

"Draga——"

Breathless, he listened for the answer which now drifted toward him across the spacious room.

"Yes, my Sasha—you must be quiet."

The knowledge of her presence caused his heart to lose a beat. Ah, thank heaven. . . .

"Where are you?" he whispered back. "What has happened?"

She seemed to hesitate before replying in what he sometimes called her "small smiling voice." He loved to hear Draga speak. She had a knack of making little words count.

"Nothing at all has happened," she said now. "The wind slammed this shutter, so I got up to close it." In proof of her statement she pushed an iron bolt into place.

Sasha was inordinately relieved. Somehow he had had a horrible premonition of danger; the kind of anguish he had suffered in nightmares throughout his earliest childhood. He must not let her know about it, though, for Draga laughed at such silliness. Draga was gallant and fearless. She had nerves of steel. It was just like her, for instance, to get up and move about in the darkness, bolting shutters and closing windows without seeking the assistance of her maid. The least he could do was to turn on the light for her. Groping his way about he reached the wall and turned on the switch.

For an instant the room was flooded in brightness. Cowering against the door with one ear pressed over the keyhole was Draga, her eyes staring fixedly into space.

And now there came the sudden report of a loud, distant crash. A piercing wail followed and the light went out.

Blindly the man stumbled across the room. With stiff clammy hands he reached for the woman's fingers.

"Draga, what was that?"

She squeezed his wrist between her warm little palms. "Nothing, my Sasha, only a short circuit downstairs. The wiring is so new—you know the servants haven't become used to it yet."

But he would not be reassured. "You were listening at the door. I saw you. What were you listening for?"

"I thought I heard Lazar ambling across the hall."

"At this time of night? That's absurd. Although if he does happen to be up we can ring for him and find out whatever is the matter."

There was a note of pleading in her voice as she protested: "No, Sasha—don't ring!"

But he had already found the bellpull and was tearing at it frantically. After several futile jerks the cord broke. There followed an eternity of silence and waiting, but no lackey or attendant came. Across the hall, in General Lazar's room, nothing stirred. On the other hand, despite closed doors and windows, Sasha grew conscious of the same noise he had heard upon first awakening. A beating, thumping sound. It had increased. Now it mingled with the subdued quaver of angry voices, and the unmistakable discharge of firearms.

With quivering jaws the King called the names of Tanko, Slavyanin and Naumovic, his royal bodyguard. But no one answered the timid outcry. He turned in despair to the woman beside him.

"They have betrayed us—they are coming to slaughter me in my own palace!"

She did not speak. She knew that her efforts to deceive him had failed. What had it availed that she, the light sleeper, peered behind window draperies upon the tumult in the gardens below?. . . She had herself hastened across the hall and roused poor Lazar who, half-clothed, rushed downstairs armed with his gun and saber. Returning, she had locked her little tea salon and the double doors to the bedroom, hoping thus to insure their safety until outside help arrived. For of this she was certain: whoever the desperadoes breaking into the palace might be, her brothers, the police and the guards in the barracks would hasten instantly to the King's aid. If only she could keep Sasha from waking.

But now he knew. That sixth sense with which, even as a child, he always anticipated calamity told him. His chill body had become soaked in perspiration. His tongue lay paralyzed in the dry oral cavity which was convulsed, now and then, in quick spasms of terror.

Taking pity on his utter helplessness, the woman's hand again clasped that of the man. Propelling him gently through the darkness, she opened a secret door that led into a wall closet. Here they waited, crouching amid her queenly finery and enveloped by the dank odor of mothballs and musk. Here they listened, with choking breath, to approaching footsteps, outcries, diabolic laughter and the random crack of pistols. The wilder the turmoil that reached this hidden alcove, the more poignant grew the solitude and agony of its forsaken occupants.

Presently there arose a din in the Arabian Room, followed by the splintering of doors and furniture in Draga's

salon. Through the keyhole of their cramped retreat the
glare of another explosion threw a bright flicker against
the gleaming satin of a gala robe. A dreadful detonation
seemed to tear the place apart. Sasha, shaken to the roots
of his being, buried his face in a cluster of garments.
Afraid that a clothes hanger might clatter down, the
Queen reached over him to steady its perilous sway.

The conspirators, meanwhile, sprang through the flaming doorway of the adjoining room and with insane fury
hurled themselves against the bed. The pitiful creatures
in the cupboard felt their bowels churn, as they became
eye-witnesses now to their own massacre. While a shower
of bullets pierced the soft bedding, a mortal man and
woman dared not breathe. In stony bewilderment they
saw and heard the avalanche of hate that was loosed
against their hapless persons. Incomprehensible, oh,
beyond all human conception—that anything they had
done should merit such punishment as this!

Now there was a pause. At sight of the empty bed the
avengers had been thrown into sudden panic. Somebody
spoke of blowing up the *Konak* and perishing in its ruins.
The Queen's nails dug into her husband's icy palm. At
least they would die together without being found! They
would die the same death as their henchmen.

Then, abruptly, Draga stiffened. She had heard a voice
through the thin partition. A low, still voice, familiar and
despised. The voice of Voyan Masin.

"Apis, we are lost!"

The King's myopic eyes, swollen without their accustomed spectacles, widened. Apis! So they were at last to
know the identity of this Apis, the arch-enemy of the
Obrenos, whose mysterious name had often come to their

ears. There, that was the voice of the leader! But wasn't that—how well Alexander knew it—wasn't that the voice of Dragutin Dmitriyevitch, virtually the head of the Serbian Army? The voice of his most trusted officer, of Sasha's friend. . . . The voice of Judas. . . .

Ah, the shame, the disgrace! A king betrayed by his own honor troops—this was more than any man could bear.

The commotion was set up again. Within arm's length of the hidden alcove stood the pair of candelabra. As greedy hands reached for the lighted tapers a bottle of heliotrope was knocked off one of the night tables. Its sickening aroma filled the smoking room. Through the frail closet door, which had already been pierced by stray bullets as death reached for his prey, the King and Queen could follow the renewed movements of the searchers. They saw the procession of flickering candles trail over broken furniture and carpets strewn with mortar. They heard the harrowing mirth that followed inspection of the King's private bath, they gave ear to the mocking cries that greeted the royal cradle.

"Good evening, Prince!"

The voice that aped these frivolous light-hearted words belonged to a youthful escort who had made merry at the Queen's supper table only a few hours before. Had everyone, *everyone,* turned against them? Did foolish words no less than foolish deeds exact so unmerciful a penalty?

How bitter this hostile echo to a happy evening—this cackling repetition of the fond little terms with which Draga addressed her brothers. As if she could help showing partiality to her kin! Everybody else had always been unkind. Everybody else had hated her. Only the Lunye-

vicas and the two men she had married, only Mihailo and
this poor boy, her Sasha—they had loved her. Why, then,
could she not shower upon these few the warmth that
poured frugally enough from her own frozen heart? Why
should she not bring Paul and Nikodem to Court, make
Voika a princess, bestow upon her mother the privileges
of a dowager grandame? From her own people she could
at least expect gratitude. Whereas these others, hirelings
and hypocrites that they were, rewarded even the King's
trust with their base treachery.

Her thoughts were weaving on in a vicious circle, when
the noise of footsteps gradually decreased. From distant
parts of the *Konak* came the occasional echo of a slamming door, indicating that the scene of the search had
momentarily shifted. Through the shuttered window at
one end of the wall closet pale dawn began to cast a first
faint gleam of light. With trembling hand Draga touched
her husband's face. The tips of her fingers knew his features in the dark. She stroked the cold cheeks gently and
with infinite compassion, for there was upon her a deep
sense of guilt. Twice she had married without love. Twice
she had brought unhappiness as her wedding portion. This
instant of self-recognition now released within her a foun-
tain of tenderness. She must comfort and soothe, for only
thus could she atone.

"Sasha, they have gone."

He tried to answer, but no sound came from his throat.

She repeated the words ever so softly. "Gone, Sasha,
quite gone!"

"They will come back," he managed at last to gasp in
dull despair.

"Before they return, my Sasha, help will have arrived."

He had begun to shake again. "No one will help us," he reiterated abjectly, "all have betrayed me."

She pressed his hand to her throbbing breast. "Hush, my darling, not so loud. But you must believe—we shall be saved."

"Queen of Serbia," he moaned obstinately, "who is to save us?"

"Don't be afraid," she begged, smoothing back the thick hair that hung over his brow, "my brothers will come to our rescue. Nikodem and Paul will not turn traitors."

"I can't believe it. They haven't got a chance to reach us." His voice was filled with all the desolation of childhood, the horror of lonely nights when of a sudden there had been no Anya coming to his aid. . . .

Draga was still casting about for words of solace. "Lazar and Naumovic must have gone to the barracks for help. Slavyanin will bring troops. But they all need time to get here, that's it—we must be patient!"

However, fear—elemental and prophetic—lodged firmly in his breast. "Nobody will come," he repeated in a dreadful monotone, "nobody will come."

She held him in her arms and gave utterance to the hard logic of her sex. "It's the women who are behind it all. I know. They are jealous! They believe I was your mistress even as far back as the Biarritz days, and so it has rankled them to kiss my hand."

"No, not the women," Sasha groaned, "my officers— my own officers have raised their swords against me." He could not get over it.

She tried to arouse his anger, to restore his fighting spirit. "Once we are safe, they must be punished. You

will destroy them like vermin. And after that you must
abolish the Constitution and make yourself dictator——"

He gulped at these words. "That's where I made my
mistake," he mumbled, as if to himself alone. "They knew
I planned to change the law—after we bought the
schooner. We should never have crossed the *Skupchina*
when they voted down that purchase."

"But you were absolutely right. You are the King!"
For a second she felt an impulse to taunt him with some
jocular twist, anything to cheer him. But she was incapable of performing such a *tour de force*. Quite suddenly she perceived that she had lost her sense of humor.
And Sasha had never had any. She watched him now as
his eyes stared bleakly ahead. His lips moved listlessly.

"They will set fire to the *Konak* and burn us alive," he
stammered.

Despite her admirable courage she shuddered at the
thought of such a death. Momentarily her assurance
threatened to collapse. But now she recognized the clump
of heavy feet straight overhead, somewhere atop the
building. In a wave of hope she rallied again.

"Listen! They've climbed the roof. They're ready to
give up the chase."

She hurried toward the window and peered out through
the crisscross of the latticework. He stalked after her on
awkward bare feet. There was a faint cracking of joints
as he raised himself on his toes to see. The sound, im-
perceptible under more ordinary circumstances, was
astonishingly audible. It shocked Sasha and made him
halt in his tracks. From the window came a soft staccato
reverberation that caused a stricture in his windpipe.

"There"—he pointed miserably—"someone is listening!"

Like a poised animal she watched, her senses keen and alert. A fine tapping against the glass pane, as of a myriad needles, gave the answer. Rain—slow and melancholy—began to fall upon a waking world.

With a sigh of relief the woman turned back. In the growing dawn her features became visible. Her nightdress with its pleated neck band and numerous canvas buttons looked grotesquely commonplace. Yet, for the first time since she had assumed the crown, there was something regal in her bearing. Always unconsciously the actress, she now rose to an heroic role. The wretched man beside her bowed humbly before this all-transcending fortitude. A grave realization took form in his confused brain. If they survived, he knew that Serbia's destiny would lie henceforth in the hands of a matriarch. If they survived.

He leaned against her, trusting, adoring. She was the Queen. But he was not a king, no, not in any sense. He was a pawn to be pushed across a complicated chess-board. He had been christened Alexander, after a great hero of the antique world. But he was no Alexander. He was that which he had always been: Sasha—looking for a strip of light.

CHAPTER XXXV

Voyan's Quest

AFTER meeting with Apis and his men in the royal bed-chamber, Voyan Masin had retreated once more through the open balcony. Under the misty veil of night he cowered in a small niche, watching the flickering candles disappear toward the interior of the palace. When they had gone he crept, with the utmost stealth, along the gallery connecting the broad front of windows known as the King's outlook. Each opening he passed led to some *chambre intime* of the royal suite, for it was from here that Alexander and his Court were accustomed to bow to the populace on feast days and official occasions.

Voyan knew himself to be in a precarious position since Apis, in an effort to forestall the King's escape, had given orders that anyone seen at a window was to be summarily shot down. Yet he must continue his hazardous quest. Crawling along on hands and knees, sometimes flat on his belly, he traveled the length of the balcony. From the far *Konak* gates a medley of voices reached his ears. Police and civilians were demanding explanations from one another. Above the confusion a single cry was hurled against the forbidding palace:

"The King's life is in danger!"

What sort of danger the people out there could not ascertain. Commander Kostic accompanied by several aides had gone into the streets to calm bewildered onlookers. He was instructed by Dmitriyevitch to prevent

possible riots with the assurance that help had already
arrived.

If this was so, skeptics demanded, why didn't the King
come forth surrounded by his helpers? Flames were licking their way through ground floor transoms; soon the
whole building would be ablaze. Where was the King?
Who were his saviors? Who, for that matter, was the
enemy?

Patiently Voyan Masin pursued his trail, ears sharpened to the sound of his own movements. Somewhere in
the distance a clanking bell resounded, followed by rolling
thunder. Firemen, no doubt, alarmed by the red glow in
the sky. An occasional gust of wind brought the distinct
clatter of horses' hoofs. Before long these unforeseen
public servants would crash upon the scene and force their
way through the gates. There was no argument against
city authorities intent upon extinguishing a conflagration.
In fact, to defy these was to reveal the true state of
affairs, for there could no longer be any pretense about
the King's safety. The next ten minutes, then, were of
the most vital importance.

His shadow moved more swiftly across the main balcony. The bedroom was now only a yard away when
Voyan, having retraced the same route for the third time,
became suddenly aware of a faint sound. He crouched
down to listen more intently. What he heard was no more
than the rustling of a leaf, but it had been accompanied
by something deeper, something strangely human, like a
low suppressed groan. One ear against the wall, he groped
with both hands through the gloom that was steadily lifting. Now his fingers were arrested by something just
below the coping. It seemed to be a cubby-hole set into

the masonry, forming a square opening. He slipped his hands across the space and felt the glass surface of a vent or window. From here it was that the sound came again, a trifle louder this time, a little more confident.

Unmindful of visibility from below, Voyan raised his head. A wild shudder ran through his body while the mechanism that was his heart refused to function. With shaking pulses, he clung to the wall and drank in each syllable of that desperate dialogue within. Maddened with lust for vengeance he witnessed the agony of that closet scene, gloating over each phase of its sheer torture. . . . There she squirmed, the she-devil who had wrecked his brother's life and Voyan's own! There she cowered in the darkness with her royal lover, the boy who had enhanced her fading charms with his poor callow youth. And now upon him, too, she brought disaster. Sasha was marked, even as Mihailo and Voyan had been marked, for love of a creature who could not love—a Circe who could only use the weakness of love for the feeding of her own strength. . . .

Presently, through the thin partition of shutter and glass, he heard the craven voice of the King. Something in its stark terror gripped him. Fear so unadulterated, so full-measured, drew from Voyan a primitive reaction. It was appalling to behold a grown man in such vast distress. . . . There ought to be an end of it, quickly. The judgment, if fall it must, should come now. This very instant. The longer it was postponed, the clearer Sasha's innocence would loom up in the mind of everyone. If he must pay for betraying his kingship to the greed of a scheming woman, the reckoning should be hastened before too many eyes were pinned upon that panic-stricken face.

In the blur of a graying dawn Voyan slipped against
the ledge of the window and noticed that it was wet. A
drizzle of rain had begun to fall. Well, that might thwart
the firemen who, at best, were a lazy lot. Through the
cool fog of morning the building belched forth sluggish
blankets of smoke; the flames were still struggling to get a
hold in the ancient stone and wood structure. To conquer
them remained an easy matter, once the hand pumps were
put into action. But the Danube ran tranquilly on beyond
the park, as yet untroubled by any effort on the part of
Belgrade's fire brigade. Now was the proper moment.
This was the time to strike.

He had stepped through the bedroom window and
brushed past swinging shutters when, across the débris of
furniture and bedding, he recognized the shape of Apis
standing in the doorway. In the glint of daybreak Dragutin's glittering gold braid (he had put on dress uniform
for this macabre occasion) shone brightly. The two men,
aware of each other, remained silent.

It was Voyan who, after a moment's hesitation, traversed the room. He was about to speak, revealing his
discovery of the hidden closet, when the sight of Dragutin's face checked him. It was hardly a face. Rather was
it a mask etched with such fury and hatred that the
younger man shrank back. Under dark bushy eyebrows
two eyes blazed like glowing coals, as Apis spoke:

"I was looking for you, Voyan. I was looking for the
traitor among us."

The other paled. "Dragutin, are you mad? You can't
know what you're saying——"

"That is for me to determine. I can still recognize a
bluff, Voyan, when I see one."

"What do you mean?"

"Just this. All our men have been on the job, searching every corner of this accursed place. You alone lagged behind. From the very start you've been guarding some ulterior purpose of your own."

"That's preposterous!" Voyan's voice rang thickly across the space that divided them.

Dragutin's lips spread into a brutal scowl. "Perhaps we've been mistaken in you all along, my boy. . . . Perhaps you came with us only to save your lady love, while we did you the favor of murdering her current bedfellow."

Voyan drew his gleaming poniard. "You've said quite enough," he cried savagely, "another word and it will be you instead of the King who is to feel this blade!"

"That proves it, I think," came the sneering reply. "The dirk was sharpened for Sasha, but not for your paramour! Very well, my friend, the lady will receive her due before your very eyes. . . ."

There was a sudden scuffle as Voyan leaped at the other's throat. But Dragutin met the attack with a vicious thrust of his arm. In the corridor outside a clamor was set up. In another second Tanko and Naumovic rushed into the room, followed by the drooping crew of searchers. Despair and fear lurked in their faces as they pleaded:

"Apis, dawn is here. Let us stop!"

Dragutin's jaws were set. "Before the sun is risen," he said hoarsely, "our task will be done."

"That's impossible," they protested, "the King has fled! He must have reached the fort long ago and may be marching on our backs this minute."

Apis remained firm. "The King is here. Our comrade, the *Knese* Masin, will lead us to the hiding place."

There was a violent commotion. Tanko seized Voyan's arm.

"Where? Where are they? Quick, before it's too late!"

Now it was Naumovic who pressed forward. Over his face fresh hope drew a bloodthirsty leer, while from the rabble behind him rose a hubbub of cheers.

Voyan became suddenly aware that a herd of madmen surrounded him. These were not officers of the King, resolved to visit justice upon a recalcitrant monarch. They were blood-crazed beasts of prey, bent upon slaughter for its own sake. To such as these no man could surrender that piteous pair trembling alone in the stillness of their walled retreat. The King, if Voyan now were to disclose his secret, would not be honorably executed, but would perish here amid the excesses of a ghastly carnage. And Draga—the woman Voyan hated because, even now, she was the only woman he would ever love—could he deliver her to these monsters? No, he could never do it! Even if it cost his own wretched life. . . .

Outside, the park was overrun with a growing crowd that milled about the building but balked at the natural barrier of flames. Voyan's brain labored frantically. In a flash the whole complex duality of his nature had become clear to him. All this, the maelstrom of his life, had its inception in that duality. Always he had loved her. Always he had fought her. That struggle, bred by his brother-love for Mihailo, had led him astray. He saw it now. He saw that from the very beginning he should have seized her, during that first wild infatuation, and carried her off with him. All's fair! Only this thing that he had done, this perversion of his own desire, this was not fair.

He must save her now. In half an hour full daylight would break and come to his aid. He must hold this pack of wolves at bay, procrastinating, sparring for time, until time itself won the victory. For, with the whole city aroused, the awful nightmare could not continue.

His mind was made up. "Follow me, comrades," he cried, "I'll show you the way!"

With urging gestures he pushed himself a path through their midst and ran down the corridor. But Apis, distrustful, roared after him:

"What! Downstairs again? I warn you, my friends, he is deceiving us——"

"The cellar," came Voyan's desperate call, "I saw them sneaking down a back stairway to the cellar."

In breathless haste he scurried on, drawing the puzzled avengers after him. They had reached the first landing and were stumbling down toward the ground floor. If only he could bait them long enough so that, before his ruse was discovered, the timid police might force their way up to the royal chamber—all would be well. After that, nothing mattered.

From the basement passages huge billows of smoke rose to meet them. In an instant, suspicion was turned upon Voyan. Apis was right, after all.

"If they had come down here the fire would have driven them out. He lies! He has betrayed us!"

Iron claws gripped Voyan's shoulders and he felt himself buffeted up the great stairs.

"Back to the bedroom," the pack howled angrily, "we

were on the right scent before. Beat him up if he tries any more tricks——"

Tossing and cuffing one another, the horde tore through the upper corridors again.

"See how he cringes! This is the floor—they're here, comrades, in this wing."

Dragutin drove them on through broken doors and vestibules.

"Vladimir, call the King. He is familiar with your voice and will not suspect you to be one of us."

The stocky Guardsman paused in his stride. "Your Majesty!" he bellowed. From empty walls a dreary echo repeated the call.

The chase went on, spreading from room to room. Everywhere they stopped for Tanko's cry. But there was no answer. The King, if he heard his aide-de-camp, either mistrusted the summons or obstinately refused to acknowledge it. That was the trouble with this Sasha. You never knew whether he was being childish and afraid, or just plain canny.

Again the action concentrated about the bedchamber. Voyan, a loaded pistol against his ribs, was pushed toward the ravaged couch and ordered to point the way. But he shook his head in silence, remaining impervious to all threats. While he endured Dragutin's vituperations, a squad of searchers went over the chamber inch by inch. If, up to now, a shelf or flower vase had chanced to remain unbroken, this final onslaught left complete devastation. From fireplace to shower curtain, sword thrusts aimed for hidden bodies, always with the same result. The King and Queen were nowhere to be found.

CHAPTER XXXVI

The Deed

SILENTLY, pausing now and then to rest on his haunches, a burly trooper crept along the baseboards. He had covered the length of the room and one of its sides when he jumped to his feet. With a short intake of breath he gasped out the information:

"Here, here! The boards don't meet—there's a crack through the wall paper!"

In a moment the spot was surrounded. A tattoo of eager fingers traveled along the rectangular outline. Somebody found a keyhole. Ah, a hidden chamber after all. . . .

"Break down the wall," Apis ordered, "here—the dynamite——"

With a last reckless effort Voyan plunged into their midst. "You are wrong," he gasped, "I tell you they have escaped! I give you my life in token——"

They jerked him aside. "He lies! Tanko, repeat the call. Tell the King to come out and stand up like a man."

A sudden pallor swept over the face of the royal aide, but he strode boldly forward, pressing his ear against the wall.

"Your Majesty," he purred softly, "it's Vladimir, Your Majesty's servant." He had meant to say "faithful servant," but the adjective stuck in his craw.

There was no answer. Voyan snatched at Dragutin's

356

sleeve. "You see, Apis, there is no one here. They have gone——"

Tanko was beating with both fists against the paneling. "Sire, help has arrived—we implore Your Majesty to open this door!"

Silence again. Only now, there was a shuffle of feet and the soft hiss of rapid breathing. Then, choked and remote came the shaking voice of the King:

"Vladimir, is it really you? You sound so strange, Vlado——"

"Yes, Your Majesty, upon my word, it is."

A pause. And then the King once more. "Remind my officers of their oath, Vlado. Tell them I shall forget these wrongs if they will remember their vows of allegiance."

Among the listeners a fierce whispering arose. Allegiance—bah! Who was this fallen Obreno to be giving them orders now? The trooper who had discovered the secret recess pounded his broad chest.

"We laugh at oaths," he snorted under his breath, "tell him he'd better hurry up, Tanko. Tell him to quit stalling."

The advice went unheeded, for at this moment a gentle voice could be heard through the partition. It was the voice of a woman; the voice of the Queen:

"Vlado, you broke bread with us at our last meeting. You drank wine from your master's cup. Give us the pledge of the King's officers that we shall be safe!"

A suppressed chuckle met this request. But the patience of the conspirators had reached breaking point. The chuckles thinned out into savage grunts.

"Laugh in her face, Tanko. Tell her we recognize

no pledge other than that of vengeance. Drag her out by the hair. We'll take care of the rest——"

The whispering had grown harsh and merciless. Vladimir Tanko's face spread into a liquid grin. With an evil gleam in his eyes he turned back toward the wall.

"Your Majesty," he cooed in dove-like accents, "I am told the officers agree to anything. . . ."

There was a long interval during which one could distinguish the metallic rattle of a key. With brandished dagger Tanko held his place squarely in front of the panel. He who had just sworn so shamelessly did not propose to miss the first triumphant blow.

The tiny keyhole gave a plaintive squeak and, as the door moved on its hinges, Vladimir's false arm rose to strike. But the knife dropped from his grip as a figure darted through the huddled group of men and leaped at the giant's throat.

"Blackguard!" cried the wild voice of Voyan Masin. With talon-like fingers he circled Tanko's neck, forcing the soldier to his knees.

This lighted the spark. A mad howl rose to the ceiling, and in the semi-darkness Naumovic's blade pierced Voyan's back. Vomiting a stream of blood, he sank to the floor. His eyes, turning glassy almost at once, did not see the open closet door. In its frame now stood, terror-stricken witnesses to his agony, the King and Queen of Serbia.

For a moment only they stood there. Alexander, blinking helplessly into the shadows, moved voiceless lips in a plea destined to remain forever unanswered. Beside him, spreading out her arms before the tragic man, was Draga, white as the gown that enveloped her. With one frail shoulder she endeavored to shield the husband who must suffer these things for love of her. With one last breath of life she shrieked, pointing to his pathetic figure:

"Forbear—he is your King!"

Then the orgasm broke. With foul and bawdy insult the pack of beasts fell upon her. At close range chamber upon chamber of cartridges was emptied into her small compact frame. She crumpled instantly into a heap of crimson flesh. Over her limp form the heavy corpse of Alexander fell with a loathsome thud, his blood-drenched nightshirt flapping against that of the Queen. A guffawing dragoon kicked the two bodies apart and buried his huge saber in the King's entrails. His example created a ghastly furore. Their cartridges spent, the executioners drew swords and hacked the bodies in an orgy of murderous lust. Heinous immolation was perpetrated on the ravished flesh.

Exhausted from their hideous labor some of the men now threw themselves across the royal bed, roaring with triumph. Others, nauseated by gun powder and the reeking vapors of that butchery, felt their stomachs turn. With weak quivering arms they clung to door-frames and portières spewing violently. Over all that dismal scene the rosy hue of dawn now crept heralding the birth of a new day.

Near the open window, where the trampled body of Voyan Masin had found a measure of immunity, stood tall and erect the shadow of Dragutin Dmitriyevitch. His pistol bulged untouched in its tooled holster, his polished sword hung dry in its bright sheath. Apis, the regicide, had murdered without taking part in his colossal crime.   He had inspired the deed without sullying his finger tips.   Symbolic and demoniacal, he towered above the gory tableau like the monster Moloch whose strength fed on the destruction of others.

He stepped out on the balcony now and leaned over the balustrade.   With a sepulchral voice he broadcast the message:

"*Ziveo!*   The tyrants are dead—long live Peter Karageorgevitch!"

From below an answering clamor rose.   Cries of doubt and panic mingled with elated "*Ziveos.*"   Jubilant officers embraced and cheered, while stolid patrolmen discredited the news with a contemptuous sneer.   Here and there half-hearted attempts were being made to storm the palace, but people were too confused for consolidated action.   From his high lookout Dragutin surveyed the scene.

"They refuse to believe," he muttered, turning back to the desolate room.   "We must show them the bodies. They must have proof."

In an instant greedy hands reached for the mauled torsos.   Through a rain-washed breeze the naked King tumbled downward to the stone-flagged ground.   Now the mutilated Draga was hurled, head foremost, to the spattered earth beside him.   Horribly disfigured, the two victims melted into a mass of pulp and gore.

A dreadful silence fell upon the spectators.   Cringing in awe, they shrank from the harrowing sight.   So it was true, after all.   That which had been predicted and grumbled about for years had come to pass.   The King whom no one wanted was dead.   The Queen whom all had hated and traduced no longer breathed. . . . A strange appalling emptiness hung over everything. A single glimpse of that which had been flung out of the upper windows left nothing more to hate, nothing to fight over. Sasha was dead. And of proud Draga nothing remained but a poor ravaged body—the slight body of a woman destroyed by satyrs in the guise of men.

The deed seemed somehow less heroic than its first conception. Even the murderers themselves were unable to explain the exact point at which their metamorphosis had taken place, changing them from a band of patriotic avengers into a horde of sadistic assassins. What was there about the reek of blood that drove men mad? Whatever its name, it lay at the root of war, gave stamina to all mass homicide. There was always less civil crime during times of martial strife. Could it be because license lives on the battlefield where the beast in man may indulge to the fullest in a legalized Saturnalia? Not lovers—killers are the true voluptuaries. Theirs is the Bacchanal, the crapulent delirium.

Slowly the curious mob withdrew, pouring through the *Konak* gates to the noisy street beyond. Befogged, yet impelled to some sort of action, the police began to make random arrests among the disheveled slayers who now came stumbling from the main portal, groping their way through dust and smoke. As though replenished by the white heat of human passions, the fire had gained impetus. With amazing speed the conflagration spread through the building, long tongues of flame licking their way across the entire façade.

Above the high arc of smoke the shape of Apis still dominated the picture. In his white dress uniform, burnished with gold and set off by a scarlet cape, the leader of the Black Hand stood motionless, remote, untouchable. His face revealed no sign of weakness as, with penetrating voice, he addressed the thinning mob:

"To the mountains, patriots! Hasten to welcome the sovereign of a greater Serbia——"

Here and there others took up the cry. "To the mountains! Hail King Peter of the brave line of Black Georges!"

That the candidate to Serbia's throne happened at the moment to be safely quartered in a distant Swiss resort in no way diminished the validity of such *Kudos.* The Alps were mountains too.

Through avenues and byways of a waking city the news of last night's happenings traveled on. Sleepy-eyed burghers blinked between half-open shutters, aghast at what they heard. Innkeepers and merchants barred their establishments and canceled their business for the day. The *Skupchina* was forced to open its doors to a roaring, galvanized throng intent upon launching another Utopian machine of government. As on that day, a score of years ago, when Cincar-Marko had extolled the merits of a boy king, so the present assembly rang out its eulogies of that which was to come—the Slav Millennium.

Meanwhile a detachment of armed men under the leadership of Captain Tanko marched to the Masin house along the Danube Quay. Before the astonished eyes of an obese and servile Anton the Lunyevica brothers were dragged from their beds. With military coats buttoned over their night clothes, Nikodem and Paul were shoved into a horse-drawn cart.

"Good morning, Prince!" Vladimir Tanko greeted his particular enemy.

The bewildered prisoners awoke to sudden understanding. Something must have happened at the palace! The crimson sky no longer showed the glow of dawn, it threw back an intense reflection of the blazing *Konak*.

"What have you done to the King?" Nikodem cried in terror. "Sasha has come to harm———"

Tanko grinned. "The King is out of danger," he announced complacently, "but to you, my noble friends, something is going to happen."

He placed a stubby finger on his gun while a cordon of guards tightened their hold upon the captives. Slowly the cart rumbled over cobblestone streets to the old *Topchider* battlefield at the outskirts of town.

Resigned to their fate, the brothers remained silent. In this hour of impending death they showed a singular fortitude, the deeply rooted serenity of peasants close to the soil. Only once, almost in unison, they turned to their captors and pleaded for the safety of their sisters. Tanko's roaring mirth was followed by a brutal question:

"How many sisters have you left?"

This told them what they needed to know. Draga— God, what must have been done to her———

With lips locked by despair, the brothers faced the firing squad. Without a whimper they collapsed, twelve bullets in their hearts. On reading the report Dragutin Dmitriyevitch was moved to say:

"At least, these Lunyevicas know how to die."

From the Danube came a chugging sound of hand pumps. Above the tumbling ruins of the *Konak* the fire brigade lapsed into ineffectual action. In the blackened rivulets of water which skirted the huge pyre two unclothed human forms tossed gently to and fro, while on a balcony across the *Teraziye* gardens a bearded man stared upon the dismal scene. Ivan Tcharikov, the Tsar's Envoy Extraordinary, had stood spellbound for hours—a dazed witness to the horrors of the night. Before his unbelieving eyes the palace had been stormed, the gaping windows burst into flame and, lastly, those two awful forms had been hurled through the air. With wide dilated pupils still mirroring that spectacle, the Russian murmured through lips that seemed paralyzed:

"*Beograd, Beograd*—thou art a White City no longer!"

Behind him emerged from the shadows the haggard face of Edgard Mavro-Cordato. He, too, regarded the *Konak* which was now a skeleton of crumbling stone. Then, pointing to the ground, he broke out:

"We can't leave them like that, Ivan—he was the King, and she his consort!"

Turning impulsively about, the Rumanian rushed toward the stairs. But Tcharikov was instantly beside him.

"Don't be insane, Edgard. You can't go out there now—you were known as a *pobratim,* a cousin to the King."

"But we must take them away," the other insisted, "we must hide their nakedness."

Tcharikov nodded, pushing his friend back into the room. In another moment he himself ran from the house. As he trudged through the deep mire of the palace gardens he encountered a cluster of morbid onlookers, peering greedily at the holocaust. In their eyes glistened a lewd, bestial curiosity.

Lifting his cloak so that it flared open in the breeze, Ivan Tcharikov covered the misery of Alexander and

Draga. As he did so a hand protruded from the black folds. It was a still, cramped hand. From the stiff clutch of its fingers oozed a lump of mud and grass. Sickened by the sight, Tcharikov did not pause to ascertain which of the piteous creatures had lived to claw the earth in final agony. A cold shudder ran down his spine as he retraced his steps through trampled flower-beds.

The crowd still moped about. Brutish faces stared at him in dull stupor. The Russian fell prey to a strange hallucination. As if in a trance, he suddenly saw before him the stolid—yet irascible—*moujiks* of his own country. He remembered quite distinctly that those who had visited revenge upon the Serbian King were little brothers of the Greater Slavs beyond the Volga.

Could Romanov heads lie safely, then, upon their pillows? Or, for that matter, Hapsburg brows?

Tcharikov shivered. Why did he shiver? Surely he could not have had a premonition of Sarajevo, Ekaterin-burg, or that other—as yet, too distant—Marseille. . . . Marseille: where a Karageorgevitch who made himself dictator would one day fare no better than the last Obreno. . . .

No, Tcharikov was no visionary. He merely felt that, for the moment, it was singularly unpleasant to look into the faces of the Belgrade *canaille*. Stalking gingerly past their front, the Russian Ambassador made for the shelter of his house.

PART FIVE

AFTERMATH

CHAPTER XXXVII

THE INQUEST

THE *Kalimegdan* bell rang out the vesper hour. It was twilight again, twilight of that same day which had been born in such an aurora of woe.

Fumes of carbolic acid filled the improvised morgue which had been set up in the guardhouse of the ruined *Konak*. Here, on narrow army cots, lay the cold bodies of Alexander Obrenovitch and his bride of less than three years. Over them, hands sheathed in surgical gloves, labored old Doctor Demosthen. For some inexplicable reason the former King's physician had been appointed coroner, an assignment which struck him as superfluous. Demosthen said as much to his friend and colleague, Doctor Michele, who assisted him. In the waning light that filtered in through shattered windows the two men performed a hasty autopsy.

Why an autopsy? Had not the details of last night's massacre been sent around the world on voracious cables? What purpose could be served by this belated farce?

The two physicians shook their heads quizzically. They knew well enough what was expected of them. The new Serbian Government, having swung into power by such bloody means, must now eradicate all trace of crime and formulate the account of Sasha's end in terms which left no blemish on the national escutcheon. "Out, damnéd spot. . . ." State records should be free of needlessly

369

descriptive ballast. The insane butchery of a king was at the most an execution. If possible, medical science was to determine that, congenitally, the victims in question had brought upon themselves an inescapable doom. It was up to Doctor Demosthen and his assistant to suggest that Alexander and Draga had figuratively placed the ax in the executioner's hand. Serbia had been given no choice. This, then, lay behind the order for an inquest before proceeding with the perfunctory interment of the royal remains.

Doctor Demosthen found it difficult to comply. There was no rhetoric with which one could disguise statistics. Try as he might to discount more grisly lacerations, the clinical report made ugly reading:

INQUEST, POST-MORTEM

—On the body of Alexander Obrenovitch, aged twenty-seven, only son of beloved King Milan and his wife Natalia Kesko—

Findings:

Bullet wounds (nineteen, two of these fatal—one below heart, one through abdomen)
Sword blows (five)
Loss of left eyeball
Spinal fracture (caused by fall from great elevation)

Remarks:

—With the exception of an unusual cephalic ossification (the skull, or brain pan, showing triple normal thickness), the said Alexander Obrenovitch was in a state of perfect health at the time of death—

It was Doctor Michele who on glancing over this document broke into mirthless laughter. "It's a wonder," he exclaimed, "that you don't put it all down to a deplorable accident!"

Demosthen's shoulders shrugged unhappily. "I might as well," he admitted.

"I notice," the other continued, "that you are giving them a peg on which to hang His Majesty's well-known stubbornness."

"Pronounced ossification of the cranium. It will permit them to go ahead and diagnose latent idiocy or whatever else is needed to provide the Karageorgevitch dynasty with a clean slate."

"That's ridiculous! These tough Obrenos were entitled to their heavy bones. If thick skulls had anything to do with it, all our mountaineers would be imbeciles——"

"Exactly," Doctor Demosthen agreed, picking up a scalpel, "but the urban gentlemen who will pass on this report have brittle tops that crack on almost no provocation." He tapped his temples with the instrument.

"I see," said Michele bluntly, "they would have liked you to detect an advanced case of paranoia, and since you didn't they will."

He paused to inspect a second paper which lay on the table before him. It bore the same caption as the first, but differed in its subsequent text.

INQUEST, POST-MORTEM

—On the body of Draga Obrenovitch, aged thirty-seven, born Lunyevica, widowed Masin—

Findings:

Bullet wounds (thirty-six)
Sword blows (approximately forty, the frequent inter-
sections rendering exact count impossible)
Severed parts (undetermined, due to above)

Remarks:

—With the exception of a weak left lung, as well as a
displacement of the womb (resulting in permanent sterility), the said Draga Obrenovitch was in a state of perfect health at the time of death—

The report slipped from Michele's hand. "They will
make much of her inability to provide an heir," he remarked.

The other nodded. "I was pressed particularly to
supply this proof of her shame, as though childlessness
carried a mandatory death sentence."

Both men fell silent, pursuing their own thoughts. Both
knew that the medical protocol must aid future historians
in recording the outrage of the past night as inoffensively
as possible. In order to belittle the savagery of the deed,
motive must be piled upon motive to form an adequate
balance. The judiciary department had already been called
upon to act, with the most gratifying results. It drew up
a series of counts against both the defunct King and
Queen. Sasha was guilty not alone of rejecting the two
requests made by the Black Hand—abdication or divorce.
He had defied the Constitution and was known to be contemplating its abolishment. An even stronger charge was
sustained against Draga. A shrewd magistrate had discovered that her attempts at infant substitution qualified

as a criminal offense, since traffic in human beings amounted to kidnapping. Her untimely end, therefore, actually saved the Queen from the ordeal of undergoing trial. The Black Hand had done her a favor, hadn't it?

In time, better and more fantastic accusations would crop up. After the French Commune had killed Marie Antoinette her judges really got down to the business of elaborating upon her depravity. This human urge to justify in retrospect a villainous act was perhaps the most candid manifestation of conscience.

As a buffer for the Belgrade conscience old Doctor Demosthen was something of a failure. Although willing to gloss over the more revolting minutiæ of his report, he would not perjure himself. A simple man, he had no words to suit those who would cover their deeds with the mantle of righteousness. The protocol, even as carefully as he had formulated it, would hardly convince future generations that an unseen divinity had acted in behalf of Serbia. But it was the best he could do. They could take it or leave it.

"A nice bit of understatement," Michele had commented dryly as his colleague rolled the papers into a neat scroll.

Demosthen did not mind. "A man can boil things down, can't he? The truth will still be there for anyone to see."

He was right. A sudden realization came over Michele. Old Demosthen with his two little slips of paper containing the scant outline of a double autopsy was probably the only biographer this last Obrenovitch and his queen would ever find. Sasha and Draga left no diaries, no letters, no documents of any sort. They were not people

of quality like Hapsburgs or Bourbons concerning whom
the world would read and write and speculate for centuries to come. They thought no imperishable thoughts,
performed no noteworthy deeds. Even their errors were
negligible. Only their Calvary was monstrous and out of
all proportion.

Still, it was their office, their elevation to a throne,
which in the old Greek sense made these two absurd and
shabby beings loom as protagonists in history's drama.
That, and the full measure of catastrophe which singled
them out—for seldom has individual fate been more
replete with pity and horror and catharsis.

Perhaps it was quite fitting that the only straight-
forward and unvarnished record of their lives should rest
in the files of a Belgrade police ledger. At least, Michele
thought so. For it came to him now that whoever might
care enough in future to draw a portrait from so sparing
and laconic a source would do so out of sheer compassion.
And this, a little compassion for his foolish and deluded
sovereigns, may have been all that the noncommittal
Doctor Demosthen had wanted.

"Well," Michele announced, immersing his hands in a
basin of water, "I guess our job's done. When is the
funeral?"

Demosthen rubbed a smudge of blood which clung to
the brim of his hat—a dismal souvenir.

"Tonight," he said, "after sundown."

"What's the big hurry?"

The other's eyebrows arched eloquently. "A delay
would only bring up the awkward problem of foreign
attendance; international pallbearers are sometimes embarrassing."

"True enough. I forgot about that," Michele mused. "You going my way, Doctor?"

Demosthen made a negative gesture. He held up the protocol. "I've got to stop at the Ministry by seven o'clock to deliver this. I'm late now. If you don't mind I'll run along."

They parted with brief nods while Michele finished his ablutions. Outside dusk deepened into darkness, driving a swarm of buzzing flies into the candlelit chamber. Michele paused to extinguish the flame when a fastidious impulse sent him across the room to the impromptu bier. He must adjust the length of canvas that scarcely reached over the two cots. In lifting the bloodstained cover he stared at the torn visages beneath. The black stubble of beard on the King's face seemed to have grown during the last hour, although the physician knew it was only the flesh shrinking in *rigor mortis*. From the hand which clutched a drying bit of grassy sod a finger was missing.

"Sasha," whispered the lone spectator, "poor King Sasha. . . ."

His eyes swerved for a second to Draga. Silent she lay. The vestiges of horror engraved upon that face were hewn away in grooves of barbarous immolation. Above the shattered temples a few strands of hair shone white, drenched of all pigment by the interminable hours of a ghastly vigil. Had she been brave or cringing in her stuffy hiding place behind the bedroom wall? The answer lay in those few strands of hair.

In death the sorry creatures rested. He, the boyish lover, whose father on seeing a photograph had deplored his son's dearth of masculine charm. She, the wedded spinster, who once had been the beauty of the Sava River

bank. Of him the rakish Milan had written to diverse
female acquaintances:

"My son Sasha is exceedingly plain. I don't think he
will get over among those who were so susceptible in
my day. . . ."

Of her the populace had muttered:

"Cry *Zivela Kralyitsa?* Never—she is not our Queen!"

In death they rested, linked for all eternity by the immense measure of their suffering, joined as one by the
enormity of their woe. Gently Michele replaced the cloth
and smoothed its mottled folds. He must forget, if life
henceforth was to be lived sanely, all this that he had seen.
Voyan Masin had not been able to forget. Rescued from
the burning *Konak,* he had perished at the near-by barracks still gasping out shreds of that dialogue between
two trapped mortal beings. It was this memory of what
he had overheard, rather than the wound, that had killed
him.

Michele must pull himself together and turn to other
thoughts. He must remember the little King who rode
upon a pony and hailed street children to the *Konak* gardens. He must remember the young matron who in days
long past, before she ever dreamed of wearing a royal
diadem, had come to him, Michele, longing for mother-
hood.

He would recall these two as perchance he alone among
men was able to recall them. And he must forget that
which to his dying day he knew he never would forget—their awful finish.

Snuffing the tallow light that flickered in its wall sconce,
Doctor Michele walked out into the starry night.

CHAPTER XXXVIII

The Trial

MIDSUMMER waned into brown autumn.

Serbia was Little Serbia still: browbeaten, cramped, openly despised by a contemptuous world. On her tragic throne sat lean King Peter I to whom success came after he had lost his appetite for it. Past middle-age, embittered by family discord, he was not able now to relish the crown and scepter bought for him at so cruel a price.

In his youth things would have been different. He had married Zorka, one of Montenegro's famous princesses. (Two other beautiful daughters of King Nikita and his wife Milena became Russian grand-duchesses, a third was Queen of Italy.) The lovely Zorka proved prolific. She bore five children in almost as many years and then quietly dead, taking two with her. In Peter's care remained a daughter Yelena whom he adored, and two sons who from earliest infancy nursed an inbred hatred for each other. These lads, another Black George Petrovitch and another Alexander, were the bane of their father's existence. On becoming king at the age of fifty-nine, Peter begged the *Skupchina* to make Yelena his heir.

"My sons are no good," he wrote from his Swiss tourist lodge, "and they ought not to succeed me. For this reason alone I would rather be president of a Serb republic than hereditary monarch."

The plea was refused and history wrote an epilogue which Peter had foreseen. Allegedly Sandro, the younger princeling, bribed servants to taunt and irritate his brother with daily insults until, in a fit of exasperation, the latter killed his valet. For this the heir to the throne was clapped into an insane asylum and forced (in 1909) to sign away his primogeniture. Sandro stepped into his brother's shoes. A quarter of a century later he called himself dictator and took a trip to Marseille. From there he was returned with coronachs and a *requiem*.

But it was in 1903 that a disillusioned King Peter faced the odium of all Europe. Serbia faced it with him, for the gloom that hung over the land would not lift. It would not lift, popular fancy agreed, until the murder of Sasha and the "Masinka" was avenged. Neither foreign trade nor prosperity would return unless the new government made some gesture of legal retribution. Failing this, the "Nation of Assassins" would remain barred from commerce with other lands.

As yet no vindicating move had occurred. The very anonymity which clothed the execution of Alexander and Draga still clouded justice. No one seemed willing to commit himself by identifying the *dramatis personæ* who had figured in the case. Belgrade annals for the year 1903 already chronicled at length that a change of dynasties had taken place, the Army was mentioned collectively as having "promoted" the mutation, and there the matter ended.

Time showed that there it could not end. Great Britain, for one, expressed disapproval by sending no representative to Peter's coronation. Other powers took the cue and held aloof until the Karageorgevitch monarch realized that something must be done. He must call upon the membership of the Black Hand, ferret out the actual culprits and hold a trial. To do this he must turn upon those who had made him king. He had no other choice since it was not his own but Serbia's reputation which hung in the balance. Also, and this eased somewhat the heavy burden of gratitude, he, Peter, had not asked for such a night of horrors as had been enacted for the benefit of his line.

It was a drizzly night in November when the secret Room of the Oath lighted up its tapers to receive another gathering of patriots summoned this time by a royal inquisitor. The waning wax fed feeble flames which failed to disperse the shadows from thickly draped walls. A silent conclave of men awaited the trial of Apis, arch-conspirator. Peter Karageorgevitch himself, his hawk-nosed profile half concealed by a cloak, presided over the hearing. The monarch whose ancestors had been gypsy herdsmen, as opposed to the more domesticated Obrenos, ran true to type. His straight hair was streaked with silver. His thin body looked wiry and strong. With shrewd eyes in which glowed a suppressed fire he gazed about the chamber, taking stock of those who had come to judge one of their own on a charge involving life and death.

He whom they would judge was not here. Dragutin Dmitriyevitch, the king-maker whose hands were blood-less, had not been seen since the hour of slaughter. Yet through its grapevine code the Black Hand had called upon him to speak in his defense and that of his desperate comrades. For everyone knew that it was the spirit of Apis, unfettered and magnified into a legion of grim avengers, which had dealt the fiendish blow that felled a dynasty. Everyone knew that Apis lived and breathed

only for Serbia and that the Black Georges, if they
proved unworthy, would be dethroned as ruthlessly as
their predecessors while Apis would go on, his hands
unsullied, building the Pan-Slav Empire.

King Peter understood. Vaguely he hoped that something might be disclosed during this trial which rendered
Apis vulnerable. If only a single person could be found
to turn evidence showing that Dragutin Dmitriyevitch
had fired a shot! It would be enough to justify a peremptory court-martial.

The sexagenarian monarch owed his new crown to the
Black Hand, but he did not intend to remain a creditor
for life. He longed to whitewash the circumstances attending his accession and to gain the respect of the civi-
lized neighbors who scorned him. By a bold punitive
gesture he hoped to clear his name of all implication in
the outrage visited upon King Alexander and Queen
Draga. What could be more effective than the annihila-
tion of the very demon who had inspired the deed?

But Apis was not here. Was he afraid to come? Had
he been warned that every legal trap was set against him?
Did he know that in the event of his acquittal by a military tribunal he would be taken into custody for a private
hearing at the palace? Perhaps he wasn't the hero they
all made him out to be. He had probably reached the
Straits by now and escaped to Turkey; for toward the
north, Russia and Hungary were already instructed to
watch his trail.

A short tapping interrupted these musings. In one
corner of the crowded room a door opened. Over its
threshold stepped the huge figure of a warrior. It was
Dragutin!

A hushed assembly stared in his direction and flinched. In one brief second it became apparent that not a single voice would be raised in testimony against him, nor one accusing finger. Sixteen commissioned officers already had admitted slaughtering the royal pair, while three dozen others vowed that they were thwarted only by the devious course of that endless nightlong search. Two score and twelve men eager to be branded as regicides, and not one of them prepared to betray the leader!

On the bench the magistrates put their heads together and whispered. "What are we to do against such odds?"

Shoulders were shrugged expressively. At last a wizened advocate made a proposal.

"Perhaps, gentlemen," he suggested, "the accused himself can be induced to volunteer a confession."

It was not much of an idea but for want of a better one the King's Council allowed it to prevail. Dragutin was invited to stand before the judges. He obeyed. A scornful smile played on his lips as he surveyed the faces of those present. By a twisted route the questioning began.

"Dragutin Dmitriyevitch, do you deny having declared yourself hostile to King Alexander when as a mere child he was first proclaimed as successor to his father's throne?"

The voice that spoke these words was strangely familiar. Apis looked up, as if startled. Instantly he recognized the aging features of Cincar-Marko with whom many years ago he had engaged in vehement altercation. The coincidence drew from him a mocking snort.

"You may have considered me hostile," he parried

carefully, "but in the light of subsequent events I think
that is hardly the word. My stand against the last
Obrenovitch seems to have been sheer loving kindness, since my frank advice might well have saved his
life."

Cincar blanched. "You are known to have been the
surliest and most unruly of His Majesty's subjects.
That alone is potential treason."

"I was consistent. I did not believe an Obrenovitch
capable of ruling Serbia. Such a conviction was bound
to affect my conduct."

"Precisely. So you go ahead and plot murder!" Cincar-Marko had risen to his feet and hurled the accusation
into Dragutin's face. The latter remained calm.

"If Serbia loved her King she should have protected
him."

"Ah!" came a note of triumph from the judges' bench.
"Then you admit your guilt. You, Apis, committed this
crime!"

"I did not kill."

"You planned the deed, yet you deny taking part in
its execution. Why? Are you a coward?"

The question lashed through the air like a whip.
Smoldering anger burned in Dragutin's eyes as he refused a retort. The voice of Cincar-Marko now grew
taunting:

"We are waiting, Apis. If you did not kill, could you
tell us just why you did not kill?"

A tense silence hung over the chamber before the
answer thundered forth. "Because a thousand men in
Belgrade were willing to do it for me! Does that mean
anything? If you were to execute all who took up arms

that night you would have to go out into the fields and recruit a new army."

There was a brief pause while the harassed inquisitor sought another approach. "Serbia's honor before the world is at stake unless we atone. The men you misled, Apis, will suffer punishment in heavy chains—but you have forfeited your life."

Dragutin's attitude was defiant. "I'm prepared to die— whenever it becomes possible for you to kill me. For the present I'm not worried, though. The new government can't afford the civil war my death would precipitate."

"Your conceit is colossal."

Apis bowed mockingly. "If I'm mistaken it will be an easy matter to lock me up or, better still, to hire a convenient assassin. Gentlemen, I live by the sword— by the sword I deserve to die. It happens to be my choice."

"We shall take note of your preference."

Again Apis bowed in derisive acknowledgment. "Too bad," he said slowly, "that the time is not yet ripe."

"Could you express yourself more plainly?"

"My work is not done."

Cincar-Marko raised eloquent eyebrows. "Very interesting. You seem to have further crimes in mind." He nodded significantly toward the center table where sat Serbia's new ruler.

Dragutin caught the nod. He turned and met the wavering eyes of Peter Karageorgevitch. "I have a duty," he said with emphasis, "like each one of us."

"What sort of a duty?"

For a moment Apis remained silent as if in contem-

plation of some distant vision. "It lies elsewhere," he
replied at last, making a vague gesture with his upraised
arm, "the Kingdom of the Yugoslavs is not at hand
while there are brethren who in Bosnia and Herzegovina
endure a foreign yoke."

A gasp of wonder filled the room. Bosnia, the lovely
banovina (province) in the Illyrian Alps, and Herzegovina, the mining center of the Balkans—both adminis-
tered by Austria since 1878—what about them? What
was this fanatical Apis up to now? That he meddled in
politics at home was bad enough, without letting him hurl
a firebrand abroad which would completely destroy national security.

Yet, oddly, even as he stood here on trial for his life,
this rampant patriot was able to stir their blood. All
who listened felt transported by his faith. The dignified
Cincar himself forgot judicial responsibility so far as to
inquire in an undertone:

"Have not the Austrians barred Serb nationals from
Sarajevo because they incite the native population? If
you escape justice today, Hapsburg gendarmes will be
less merciful."

Dragutin's face was clouded. "There are ways to
strike even at Hapsburg majesty."

He broke off while a low murmuring ran through the
assemblage. Ecstatic eyes were fixed on his countenance.
Here and there opinions began to be heard.

"Stand by him! He may need help for another deed."
And again: "He's right. If we choose wealth or a trade,
by these we die also. Whatever you live for won't keep
you alive, will it? Let's choose the sword with Apis!"

Extravagant pledges were being uttered. Men lost

sight of the original purpose for which the convocation
had been called. The spell of ancient dreams was upon
them, and they were as a race only too willing to be
mesmerized by such *abracadabra*.

Dragutin felt himself drifting a little apart. For the
first time he was able to view them objectively. Young
and old they were; but particularly young. That boy
there in the front row, Nedjelko Cabrinovic, was a mere
child. Beside him stood another, Tryphon Grabez, still
of school age. Apis knew them well. But what he did
not know was that these two came from the same village as that stripling Gavrilo Princip who a decade later
would write a flaming page in world history.

He saw their youth. It was this that made him think
of Voyan Masin. He remembered the *Konak* turning
into a furnace, and a man being carried from the blaze.
Voyan dying because he loved a woman better than his
oath. Yes, that was what Voyan had died for. Not the
liberation of Serbia or the esoteric ideals of the *Narodna
Obrana,* the Black Hand. But love. The prerogative of
youth.

What right had he, Apis, to sow this same conflict
in other young breasts? That he lashed older men's passions to a frenzy had never disconcerted him. It had
been his lifelong purpose to be a leader among his people.
Nor was he squeamish. The sacrifice of human life was
the price paid in the advancement of a cause, nothing
more. It went without saying that the cause he defended
was to his mind a noble and disinterested one. He had
dethroned the Obrenos not for his own gain but in order
that another Serbian house of classic lineage might prove
its worth. He would, if necessary, goad the Hapsburg

scepter into surrender of provinces he believed ethnolog-
ically to belong to his own Balkan race, even though these
provinces had prospered under Austrian rule. . . . But
those boys with their treble voices troubled him. That
they should consecrate their brief existence to that for
which Apis must have instruments, since Apis dared not
kill if he would finish his work for Serbia, this was too
much. If adult men threw in their lot with his they
knew what they were doing. But children who ought
still to be in school—that was different.

Never before had he realized so fully the extent of
his own power. Not only the symbolic Apis, but the
soldier Dragutin Dmitriyevitch had become almost a
legend. He was a creed rather than a person. Would
future generations believe that he had really lived? He
and his melodramatic band of conspirators were of the
stuff that made fiction, strange fiction that left men
doubting the facts behind it—incredible mummery that
changed the face of Europe.

He felt suddenly tired. The horrors of an unforgotten
night, a ghoulish funeral pyre, weeks of hiding that had
followed upon the cataclysm he, Apis, had brought to
pass—all this descended now upon his spirit with the
weight of evil dreams. His tongue felt thick and dry.
But there was something he must say before this inexplicable emotion passed, before he hardened again to
steel. Swinging about abruptly he faced the bench where
sat his dumfounded judges.

"Gentlemen," he said, carefully weighing each word,
"you want an admission of guilt. I am prepared to give
it. I, Dragutin Dmitriyevitch, murdered your King and
Queen!"

Furious protests rang through the building. "He lies! He is trying to shield us. We killed—we, the Army!"

The clamor rose about him like a surging sea. He stood silent, engulfed by the forces his own doctrines had set loose. Again his crime ceased to be crime, becoming blurred on the larger canvas of political destiny. Destiny then must finish this trial, for his countrymen would not.

He had awakened them at last to a national consciousness that discounted personal fate. The spark he had ignited would not die. It would be nursed and fed until some day its flames burned on the sacred altars of a kingdom for the Yugoslavs!

He would not live to see that day. He did not want to live to see it. He was afraid. Already he knew its advent would entail still further martyrdom. Martyrdom which, a sad clairvoyance told him, far outweighed the importance of boundaries laid out by an almost mythical Emperor Dushan. . . .

THE END

BIBLIOGRAPHY

For the historical background of *Royal Purple* the author is indebted to:

Heinrich Hueffner—*Diary of Queen Natalia,* Private Printing, Vienna.

Joseph Mallet—*La Servie Contemporaine,* Armand, Paris.

Princess Marthe Bibesco—*Royal Portraits,* Appleton-Century Company, New York.

Richard Linsert—*Kabale und Liebe,* Dafnis Verlag, Berlin.

Bruno Brehm—*Apis und Este,* R. Piper & Co., München.

Chedo Mijatovitch (Serbian Envoy to the Court of St. James)—*Memoirs,* London.

Karl Tschuppik—*Franz Joseph I,* Avalun Verlag, Berlin.

Louis Adamic—*The Native's Return,* Harper & Brothers, New York.

Vladimir, Baron Giesl—*Two Decades in the Near East,* Verlag Scherl, London Edition.

Malchal, J. K. Sabina—*Literatura Ceská XIX. Stoleti,* Prague.

Paul Limann—*Der politische Mord im Wandel der Geschichte.* Leipzig.

Police Archives, Belgrade—*Report for the Years 1900-1903, inclusive.*